PEARSON LANGUAGE CENTRAL
for MATH
Grades 3 – 5

Fitchburg Public Schools
Dr. Jim Cummins, Consulting Author

PEARSON

Glenview, Illinois • Boston, Massachusetts • Chandler, Arizona • Upper Saddle River, New Jersey

Language Central for Math
Fitchburg Public Schools Curriculum Project Team

Principal Author
Patricia Page Aube

Contributing Authors
Grades 3–5
Lee Cormier
Amy Dessureau
Helen Frerichs
Susan Hanno
Carmelita Hoffmann
Kelly Waples McLinden
Cynthia Rosancrans
Eileen Shireman

Project Director
Bonnie Baer-Simahk

Technical Assistance
Richard Lavers

Sponsor
Massachusetts Department of Elementary
and Secondary Education's (ESE) Office
of English Language Acquisition, 2009.

Cover Art: Lorena Alvarez

ISBN-13: 978-0-13-317434-2
ISBN-10: 0-13-317434-4

3 4 5 6 7 8 9 10   V057   15 14 13

CONTENTS

ABOUT THE AUTHORS AND REVIEWERS

Fitchburg Public Schools

The city of Fitchburg is a culturally diverse community of approximately 41,000 located in Central Massachusetts, 50 miles from Boston. It is noted for its old mills that line the Nashua River and its tightly knit neighborhood enclaves that retain their ethnic identity. Its former reliance on the paper industry has given way to healthier economic diversification.

The Fitchburg Public School System serves approximately 5,000 students in grades Pre K–12. Approximately 30% of students come from homes where a language other than English is spoken. Its percentage of students who are still in the process of acquiring English reflects the nation's average, approximately 12% of the total school population. FPS strives to provide learning experiences that engage all students so they achieve high academic standards while developing intellectual rigor, creative interest, and the social characteristics that prepare them for the challenges of living successfully and productively. The school system's mission is to provide coordinated curricular and extracurricular experiences that inspire students and support them as they work toward achieving high standards in literacy and numeracy.

All members of the school community—teachers, administrators, school committee, staff, and parents—support students in their pursuit of academic excellence through curricula that promote inquiry and stimulate curiosity as the foundation for lifelong learning. Bonnie Baer-Simahk serves as Fitchburg's Director for the Office of English Language Acquisition. Patricia Aube is the Math/ESL Curriculum Integration Specialist. Under their direction many contributors' expertise was synthesized to create the curriculum that provided the foundation of *Language Central for Math*.

Reviewers

Roula Dana Al Mouabbi
Bilingual Math Teacher
Dearborn, MI

Janine Balding
Curriculum Coordinator
Coolidge, AZ

Sheralee Connors
Curriculum Developer
Portland, OR

Ed D'Souza, Ph.D
Director of Secondary Instruction, K–12 Math/Science
Rialto, CA

Jamie Greene
ELL Consultant
Silver Spring, MD

Aile R. Gutierrez
ESL/Bilingual Teacher
Bergenfield, NJ

Hongying Shen
Senior Instructional Specialist/ESL
Brooklyn, NY

Brooke Stadler
ELL Program Coordinator
St. Paul, MN

Kristin Swanson
ELL Consultant
Portland, OR

TO THE TEACHER

English Language Learners In The Classroom

Teachers and schools across the United States are welcoming increasing numbers of English language learners (ELLs) into their classrooms. English language learners make up the fastest growing K–12 student population in the United States. In fact, the population of English language learners in U.S. public schools grew by nearly 60% from the 1995–1996 school year through 2005–2006 (NCELA 2008). And, it is expected that this student population will continue to grow over the next several decades (Collier and Thomas 2002; Leos 2004).

While English language learners share many characteristics with other students, they need support and scaffolding that are specific to them. Why? Because they represent a highly diverse population. They come from many home language backgrounds and cultures. They have a wide range of prior educational and literary experiences in their home languages. And, they come to school with varying levels of English language proficiency and experience with mainstream U.S. culture.

Clearly, English language learners are an increasingly large and important population of students. Helping these students learn, therefore, is becoming both a necessary and integral part of a typical American classroom.

But helping English language learners acquire content mastery is not enough. English language learners are also expected to participate in yearly high-stakes tests. Research has consistently shown that ELLs usually require at least five years, on average, to catch up to native-speaker norms in academic language proficiency (Cummins 1981). Nevertheless, many English language learners must take the tests whether or not they have developed academic language proficiency in English.

So, how do you, a math teacher, help your English language learners clear the hurdles of language acquisition while at the same time ensuring that they attain the same high-level content mastery as your other students? To start, this book has been designed to help you identify and respond appropriately to the varying needs of ELLs in your classrooms. It provides insight on how to help ELLs develop fluency as readers, writers, listeners, and speakers of academic English, while learning math concepts at the same time. In addition, it offers strategies and activities to help you scaffold and support ELL instruction so that all your students can learn in ways that are comprehensible and meaningful, and in ways that promote academic success and achievement.

Whether you have one English language learner in your classroom or many, the strategies and solutions offered in this book will hopefully help you feel more prepared to help your English language learners excel both today and in the future.

TEACHING ELL STUDENTS IN THE MATH CLASSROOM

DR. JIM CUMMINS
University of Toronto

Mathematics and Language

Mathematics can legitimately be considered to be a language in itself in that it employs symbols to represent concepts and operations that facilitate our thinking about aspects of reality. However, mathematics is also intimately related to the natural language that we begin to acquire as infants, the language that we use to communicate in a variety of everyday and academic contexts. Mathematics and language are interconnected at several levels:

- Teachers use natural language to explain mathematical concepts and perform mathematical operations. Students who have limited proficiency in English require additional support in order to understand mathematical concepts and operations taught in English. Among the supports that teachers can use to make instruction comprehensible for English learners are demonstrations using concrete, hands-on manipulatives; graphic organizers; simplification and paraphrasing of instructional language; and direct teaching of key vocabulary.

- As is the case in other academic disciplines, mathematics uses a specialized technical vocabulary to represent concepts and describe operations. Students are required to learn the meanings of such words as *congruence, ratio, integer,* and *quotient*, words that are likely to be found only in mathematics discourse. Furthermore, other terms have specific meanings in mathematics discourse that differ from their meanings in everyday usage and in other subject areas. Examples of these kinds of terms include words such as *table, product, even,* and *odd*. Homophones such as *sum* and *some* may also be confusing for ELL students. Grade 6 students are required to learn concepts such as least common multiple when ELL students may not know the broader meanings of the words *least* and *common*.

- In addition to the technical vocabulary of mathematics, language intersects with mathematics at the broader level of general vocabulary, syntax, semantics, and discourse. Most mathematical problems require students to understand propositions and logical relations that are expressed through language. Consider this problem at the Grade 4 level:

Wendy gave a total of 10 treats to her dogs. She gave her large dog 2 more treats than she gave her small dog. How many treats did she give to each dog?

Here students need to understand (or be able to figure out) the meanings of such words as total and treats. They need to understand the logical relation expressed by the more… than…construction. And they need to infer that Wendy has only two dogs, even though this fact is not explicitly included in the problem. Clearly, the language demands of the math curriculum increase as students progress through the grades, and these demands can cause particular difficulties for ELL students.

The Challenges of Academic Language

The intersection of language and content entails both challenges and opportunities in teaching English language learners. It is clearly challenging to teach complex math content to students whose knowledge of English academic language may be considerably below the level assumed by the curriculum and textbooks. In a typical math lesson, for example, several difficult words may be explained in the margins. However, there may be many more words in each lesson that are new to ELL students. These gaps in their knowledge of academic language are likely to seriously impede their understanding of the text.

Students may also be unfamiliar with grammatical constructions and typical conventions of academic writing that are present in the text. For example, academic texts frequently use passive voice, whereas we rarely use this construction in everyday conversation. Also, students are often given writing assignments to demonstrate their understanding. Without strong writing skills in English, ELL students will find it difficult to demonstrate content knowledge.

Obviously, teachers focus their instruction on explaining concepts to students, but ELL students may not yet have acquired the English proficiency to understand explanations that are accessible to native speakers of the language. Thus, a major challenge for teachers is to teach content effectively to *all* students, particularly those who are not yet fully proficient in English. Although this challenge is formidable, particularly at the intermediate level, teachers can draw on a knowledge base of recent research findings in order to implement instructional approaches that have proved highly effective in enabling ELL students to gain access to academic content.

Access Content

Activating and building students' background knowledge is an essential part of the process of helping students to participate academically and gain access to meaning. When we activate students' prior knowledge, we attempt to modify the "soil" so that the seeds of meaning can take root. However, we can also support or *scaffold* students' learning by modifying the input itself. We provide this scaffolding by embedding the content in a *richly redundant context* wherein there are multiple routes to the mathematical meaning at hand in addition to the language itself. The following list presents a variety of ways of modifying the presentation of mathematical content to ELL students so that they can more effectively get access to the meaning in any given lesson.

- **Use Demonstration** Teachers can take students through a word problem in math, demonstrating step-by-step procedures and strategies in a clear and explicit manner.

- **Use Manipulatives (and Tools and Technology)** In the early grades, manipulatives may include counters and blocks that enable students to carry out a mathematical operation, literally with their hands, and actually see the concrete results

of that operation. At the intermediate level, measuring tools, such as rulers and protractors, and technological aids, such as calculators and computers, will be used. The effectiveness of these tools will be enhanced if they are used within the context of a project that students are intrinsically motivated to initiate and complete.

- **Use Small-Group Interactions and Peer Questioning** Working either as a whole class or in heterogeneous groups or pairs, students can engage in real-life or simulated projects that require application of a variety of mathematical skills.

- **Use Pictures, Real Objects, and Graphic Organizers** We commonly hear the expression "A picture is worth a thousand words." There is a lot of truth to this when it comes to teaching academic content. Visuals enable students to "see" the basic concept we are trying to teach much more effectively than if we rely only on words. Once students grasp the concept, they are much more likely to be able to figure out the meanings of the words we use to talk about it. Among the visuals we can use in presenting math content are these: *pictures/ photographs, real objects, graphic organizers, drawings on overhead projectors, and blackline masters.* Graphic organizers are particularly useful because they can be used not only by teachers to present concepts but also by students to take notes, organize their ideas in logical categories, and summarize the results of group brainstorming on particular issues. Some graphic organizers that are useful for teaching math can be found on pages T37–T44.

- **Clarify Language (Paraphrase Ideas, Enunciate Clearly, Adjust Speech Rate, and Simplify Sentences)** This category includes a variety of strategies and language-oriented activities that clarify the meanings of new words and concepts. Teachers can modify their language to students by *paraphrasing ideas* and by *explaining new concepts and words*. They can explain new words by providing synonyms, antonyms, and definitions either in English or in the home language of students, if they know it. Important vocabulary can be repeated and recycled as part of the paraphrasing of ideas. Teachers should speak in a natural rhythm, but enunciate clearly and adjust their speech to a rate that ELL students will find easier to understand. Meaning can also be communicated and/or reinforced through gesture, body language, and demonstrations. Because of their common roots in Latin and Greek, much of the technical math vocabulary in English has cognates in Romance languages such as Spanish (e.g., *addition—adición*). Students who know these languages can be encouraged to make cross-linguistic linkages as a means of reinforcing the concept. Bilingual and English-only dictionaries can also be useful tools for language clarification.

- **Give Frequent Feedback and Expand Student Responses** *Giving frequent feedback* means responding positively and naturally to all forms of responses. Teachers can let their students know how they are doing by responding to both their words and their actions. Teachers can also assess their students' understanding by asking them to give examples, or by asking them how they would explain a concept or idea to someone else. *Expanding student responses* often means using polar (either/or) questions with students who are just beginning to produce oral English and 5 Ws (who, what, when, where, why) questions with students who are more fluent. Teachers can easily, and casually, expand their students' one- and two-word answers into complete sentences ("Yes, a triangle has one base") and respond to grammatically incorrect answers by recasting them using standard English syntax (Student: "I gotted 4 and 19 thousandths"; Teacher: "That's right, you have 4 and 19 thousandths").

Opportunities for Extending Language

Content teachers are usually acutely aware of the challenges of teaching ELL students within the subject-matter classroom. However, they may be less aware of the opportunities that exist for extending students' knowledge of academic English. Students who are learning math are also learning the language of math. They are learning that there are predictable patterns in the ways we form abstract nouns that describe mathematical processes. For example, many of these nouns are formed by adding the suffix *-tion* to the verb, as in *add/addition, estimate/ estimation*, etc.

Similarly, when students report back to the class on their observations of a problem-solving exercise or project, teachers have the opportunity to model the kinds of explicit formal language that is required to talk and write about mathematical operations. The feedback they provide to students on their oral or written assignments clarifies not only the mathematical concepts that students are learning but also the language forms, functions, and conventions that are required to discuss these concepts. Thus, math teachers are also language teachers and have significant opportunities to extend students' ability to understand and use academic language.

The Knowledge Base

There is considerable agreement among researchers about the general patterns of academic development among ELL students and the factors that support students in catching up academically. The following findings are well-established:

The language of academic success in school is very different from the language we use in everyday conversational interactions. Face-to-face conversational interactions are supported by facial expressions, eye contact, gestures, intonation, and the immediate concrete context. Conversational interactions among native-speakers draw on a core set of high-frequency words (approximately 2,000) and use a limited set of grammatical constructions and discourse conventions. Academic language, by contrast, draws on a much larger set of low-frequency words, including both general academic words and the specific technical vocabulary of a particular content area (e.g., *coordinate plane, triangular prism,* etc.). This language is found predominantly in two places—classrooms and texts (both printed and electronic).

ELL students typically require at least five years to catch up academically to native speakers; by contrast, basic conversational fluency is usually acquired within 1–2 years. These trajectories reflect both the increased linguistic complexity of academic language and the fact that ELL students are attempting to catch up to a moving target. Students whose first language is English are not standing still waiting for ELL students to catch up. Every year, they make gains in reading, writing, and vocabulary abilities. So, ELL students have to learn faster to bridge the gap. The fact that at least five years is typically required for ELL students to catch up academically highlights the urgency of providing academic and linguistic support to students *across the curriculum*. Ideally, ELL teachers and subject-matter teachers will work together to enable ELL students to develop the academic language skills they need to access subject-matter content and succeed academically.

All learning builds on a foundation of preexisting knowledge and skills. For ELL students in the early stages of learning English, this conceptual foundation is likely to be encoded predominantly in their home language (L1). This finding implies that students' L1 is potentially relevant to learning English academic skills and concepts. Students' L1 is the cognitive tool they have used to interact with the world and learn academic content. Thus, rather than ignoring students' L1, we should consider teaching for transfer across languages and encourage students to use their L1 as a stepping stone to higher performance in English academic tasks.

> "
> *The number of ELLs has grown rapidly in the last 15 years to about* **5 million** *students. Estimates project this number will increase 100%, to* **10 million,** *by 2015. (NEA 2008)*
> "

TEACHING ELL STUDENTS IN THE MATH CLASSROOM, *cont.*

The Pearson ELL Curriculum Framework

The core principles of teaching ELL students across the curriculum are outlined in The Pearson ELL Curriculum Framework. This framework was designed to assist content-area teachers in addressing the needs of the growing and diverse English language learner population. The five principles in the outer circle of the framework represent the ways in which the teacher plans and organizes the delivery of instruction. The three processes in the inner circle highlight what teachers attempt to do in direct interaction with their students. As depicted in the diagram, these principles and processes flow into each other and represent components or phases of a dynamic whole.

1 **Identify and Communicate Content and Language Objectives** In planning and organizing a lesson, teachers must first identify what content and language objectives they will attempt to communicate to students.

2 **Frontload the Lesson** Frontloading refers to the use of prereading or preinstructional strategies that prepare English language learners to understand new academic content. It involves strategies such as activating prior knowledge, building background, previewing text, preteaching vocabulary, and making connections.

3 **Provide Comprehensible Input** Language and content that students can understand is referred to as comprehensible input. Teachers make use of nonlinguistic supports to enable students to understand language and content that would otherwise have been beyond their comprehension. Typical supports or "scaffolds" include graphic organizers, photographs, illustrations, models, demonstrations, outlines, etc. Language clarification and use of paraphrasing also contribute to making the input comprehensible.

4 **Enable Language Production** Language production complements comprehensible input and is an essential element in developing expertise in academic language. Use of both oral and written language enables students to solve problems, generate insights, express their ideas and identities, and obtain feedback from teachers and peers.

5 **Assess for Content and Language Understanding** Finally, the instructional cycle flows into assessing what students have learned and then spiraling upwards into further development of students' content knowledge and language expertise.

Classroom Interactions

When we shift into the actual classroom interactions that this lesson cycle generates, a primary focus is on the extent to which teachers' interactions with students motivate them to engage academically. Promotion of motivation and engagement represents a process of negotiating identities between teachers and students. Students who feel their culture and personal identity validated in the classroom are much more likely to engage with academic content than those who perceive that their culture and identity are ignored or devalued. An excellent way of enabling ELL students to take pride in their academic accomplishments is to encourage (or require) them to undertake challenging project work while providing the support to enable them to complete the task successfully.

Differentiation of instruction is widely accepted as necessary to address the learning needs of a diverse school population. One-size-fits-all programs typically exclude ELL students from meaningful participation. When applied to ELL students, differentiation involves scaffolding of input to students and output from students. Activating prior knowledge and building background knowledge is one example of a differentiation/scaffolding strategy.

Assessment and intervention are fused into the cycle of motivating students and providing differentiated instruction that addresses the background knowledge and learning needs of individual students. It is essential that teachers regularly assess the extent to which ELL students understand the content presented through classroom instruction and in the textbook. If not, many students who are still in the process of learning academic English may grasp only a fraction of this content. This formative assessment represents an ongoing process in the classroom and, in comparison to most standardized tests, gives the teacher information that is immediately relevant to intervention and further scaffolding of instruction.

Conclusion

The knowledge base that research has generated about ELL students' academic trajectories shows clearly that ELL students must be understanding instruction and learning English across the curriculum if they are to catch up in time to meet graduation requirements. Teaching mathematics affords opportunities for extending ELL students' academic language proficiency. The Pearson ELL Curriculum Framework incorporates the essential elements that teachers need to implement effective instruction for all students—English-language and native English-speaking learners alike.

Dr. Jim Cummins

Dr. Jim Cummins is Professor and Canada Research Chair in the Curriculum, Teaching and Learning Department at the Ontario Institute for Studies in Education (OISE) at the University of Toronto. He holds a Canada Research Chair (Tier 1) and has been a recipient of the International Reading Association's Albert J. Harris Award (1979).

Dr. Cummins's research focuses on literacy development in multilingual school contexts as well as on the potential roles of technology in promoting language and literacy development. He has been a co-investigator on a large-scale project entitled "From Literacy to Multiliteracies: Designing Learning Environments for Knowledge Generation within the New Economy." He is currently involved in a project to validate the Ontario Ministry of Education's Steps to English Proficiency assessment tool. He is also conducting a research review on English Language Learners' academic trajectories.

LANGUAGE PROFICIENCY CHART

Use this chart to understand language proficiency levels in the four skill areas of listening, speaking, reading, and writing. Note that an English language learner will not necessarily be at the same proficiency level in all four skill areas.

		Level 1 Early Beginner **Entering/Starting**	Level 2 Beginner **Beginning/Emerging**
		BEGINNING	
CHARACTERISTICS OF THE ENGLISH LANGUAGE LEARNER	**Listening Skills**	• Minimal comprehension • One-step directions • Comprehends oral facts accompanied by pictures	• Limited comprehension • Two-step directions • Oral descriptions
	Speaking Skills	• Minimal speaking production • Individual words or two- to three-word phrases • Gestures and actions to communicate	• Two- or three-word phrases to some simple sentences • Simple information questions • Simple descriptions
	Reading Skills	• High-frequency words • Slowly, word-by-word • Concrete words represented by pictures • Environmental print • Sound/symbol/word relations • Picture dictionaries and glossaries	• Dependence on visuals and prior knowledge • Multi-step directions • Able to follow text that is being read aloud • Locate specific information • Bilingual dictionaries and glossaries
	Writing Skills	• Little or no ability • Express ideas through pictures and graphics • Label pictures using word bank	• List, label, and copy • Phrases and simple, short sentences • Present tense • Complete graphic organizers • Respond to questions

Level 3 Early Intermediate **Developing**	Level 4 Intermediate **Expanding**	Level 5 Advanced **Bridging**	Level 6 Transitioning **Reaching**
INTERMEDIATE		ADVANCED	
• Good comprehension • Simple sentences • Multi-step directions • Oral questions and descriptions	• Very good comprehension • Complex sentences • Understanding and application of oral information	• Comprehension of complex directions and discussions with processing time • Ability to draw conclusions and make connections from oral information	• Comprehension of elaborate directions and discussions • Nearly comparable to native English speakers
• Simple sentences • Simple content-based questions • Description of processes • Retell stories and events • Statement of opinion	• Complex sentences • Discussions of stories, events, and concepts • Speeches and reports • Statement of opinion and defense of point of view	• Nearly proficient • Academic discussions with minimal hesitation • Detailed explanations • Multimedia oral presentations	• Near native ability • Full participation in academic discussions and debates • Effective communication using abstract language
• Use of context clues to determine meaning of words • Sequence pictures, events, processes • Identify main idea • Interpret charts and graphs • Make predictions • English dictionaries and glossaries	• Use of reading strategies • Identify word families • Interpret information • Locate details to support main idea • Match cause to effect • Differentiate between fact and opinion	• A variety of grade-level academic texts with support • Able to use strategies and higher-order comprehension skills with support • Conduct research • Synthesize information from multiple sources	• A variety of grade-level academic texts, nearly comparable to native peers • Application of higher-order comprehension skills with minimal support • Able to critique material and support arguments
• Compound sentences • Paragraphs with main idea and details • Describe events, people, processes, procedures • Give opinions	• Multiple paragraphs • Summarize • Take notes using graphic organizers • Express original ideas • Explain problem-solving strategies • Able to edit/revise	• Expression of ideas at grade level with support • Grasp of basic grammar features • Content-related reports from multiple sources • Multiple genres • Ability to peer edit	• Expression of ideas at grade level with minimal support • Rare grammatical errors • Occasional difficulty with natural phrasing • Grade-level reports • Ability to peer edit with recommendations

FIVE ESSENTIAL PRINCIPLES FOR BUILDING ELL LESSONS

PRINCIPLE 1
Identify and Communicate Content and Language Objectives

Content Objectives

Effective educational practices, as well as state and federal mandates, require that English language learners meet grade-level standards. The first step in reaching these standards is clearly targeting and communicating the content objectives of a lesson. While the content objectives for English language learners are the same as for mainstream learners, the objectives must be presented in language that suits the students' levels of language proficiency. This involves using simpler sentence structures and vocabulary, paraphrasing, repeating, and avoiding idioms and slang.

Language Objectives

Language objectives focus on promoting English language development while learning content. They can be thought of as a scaffold to help students learn content objectives. Language objectives include: content vocabulary, academic vocabulary, and language form and function.

Content vocabulary These terms are the specialized vocabulary of a subject area. Content vocabulary can be particularly challenging for English language learners who come from a variety of school backgrounds. ELLs should receive explicit instruction of key vocabulary words. Studies show that with this instruction, students are more likely to understand new words encountered during reading.

Academic vocabulary These terms can be described as "school language," or the language that students encounter across all subjects—in discussions, in textbooks, and in tests—as opposed to the informal English words and structures used in conversation. Academic vocabulary includes words such as *summarize, similar, demonstrate, conclude,* and

survey. Research indicates that acquiring a strong grasp of academic vocabulary is perhaps the most vital factor distinguishing successful students from those who struggle in school. Becoming fluent in academic language will enable English language learners to understand and analyze texts, write clearly about their ideas, and comprehend subject-area material.

Language form and function Language forms include sentence structure and grammar, while language functions involve the purpose of language (such as classifying or comparing). The language forms and functions students need to complete academic tasks should be taught within the context of the lesson. To develop appropriate form and function objectives, teachers can use local and state standards developed for ELLs or coordinate with staff members who specialize in language development. For example, when teaching *greater than/less than,* the language objective might be the structures for comparison (*-er* and *less*) and the function of how to make comparisons.

Teaching Strategies and Support for Principle 1

There are a number of basic strategies teachers can implement to meet the needs of their English language learners. Many are commonsense, everyday strategies that teachers in all content areas already know and use. These strategies lay the foundation for a positive learning relationship between student and teacher.

- [ ] **Previous lesson objectives** Begin each lesson with a review of the previous lesson's objectives.

- [ ] **Content objectives** Present the content objectives using visual aids, graphic organizers, and paraphrasing. Write the objectives on the board.

- [ ] **Prior knowledge** Ask students to talk about the content based on their prior knowledge. Document the results of the discussion with a graphic organizer, such as a KWL chart.

- [ ] **Content and academic vocabulary** Present content and academic vocabulary.
  - Pronounce the word and have students repeat.
  - Provide examples, descriptions, visuals, and explanations.
  - Clarify the part of speech and discuss cognates, synonyms, and antonyms.
  - Ask students to provide examples, descriptions, visuals, and explanations of their own to determine comprehension.

- [ ] **Vocabulary notebooks** Have students keep a vocabulary notebook. Suggest that they use their own words to define the terms and incorporate visuals whenever possible.

- [ ] **Word-analysis strategies** Teach students word-analysis strategies so that new words can be attacked independently. For example, teach the prefix and the root of a vocabulary word. Write the meaning of the prefix and the root word on the board and have students do the same in their vocabulary notebooks.

- [ ] **Academic vocabulary practice** Provide flashcards or flashcard frames for key academic vocabulary. Have students use them for paired or independent practice, both during the week and for subsequent reviews. Encourage students to add personal notes and pictures to their flashcards.

- [ ] **Vocabulary practice** Design writing assignments so that students practice using the new words.

- [ ] **Language objectives** With the cooperation of an ELL teacher, provide language objectives at different proficiency levels.

- [ ] **Opportunities for language objectives** If the lesson's content includes idioms, colloquialisms, or slang, use these as opportunities to teach language objectives.

- [ ] **Lesson objectives review** End each lesson with a review of the lesson's content and language objectives and a preview of the next lesson's objectives.

PRINCIPLE 2
Frontload the Lesson

Frontloading is the use of prereading strategies that prepare English language learners to read new texts. The goal of frontloading is to reach all ELLs by lessening the cognitive and language loads, thereby allowing them to take control of their learning process.

Frontloading involves the use of the following strategies:

Activating prior knowledge Instruction is most effective when it links knowledge and experiences students already have to new concepts. Experiences can be academic, cultural, and personal. Teachers can help students see the relationships between their prior knowledge and the new lesson through direct questioning techniques, the use of visuals and graphic organizers, dramatization, and discussion. The more students know about the topic of a lesson, the more they will understand.

Building background knowledge In order to make a lesson's content accessible to ELLs, teachers may need to familiarize them with social, cultural, or historical facts and concepts of which mainstream learners are already aware. These facts and concepts may be brought out during the activating prior knowledge phase or through direct questioning and instruction.

Previewing text Previewing text serves the purpose of familiarizing students with what is to come in a lesson and putting them at ease. To preview text, teachers focus more closely on using visual supports such as taking a "picture walk" through a lesson. In addition, English language learners should be taught discrete skills that are required for successfully reading content-area texts, such as how to read and interpret charts, tables, graphs, and maps.

Setting a purpose for reading Teachers should help students realize that good readers focus on the message of the text. Teaching ELLs in the content areas also includes explicit instruction in the kinds of text structures they will encounter in content-area readings. In addition, it includes teaching reading strategies such as identifying the main idea and details, summarizing, and comparing and contrasting.

Making connections Teachers can extend the lesson by helping students see relationships between the lesson and other aspects of their lives. Connections can be made to other academic subjects, to current events, or to cultural traditions. By incorporating aspects of students' primary language and culture, teachers can ease the transition toward learning the content and language.

Integral to these frontloading strategies is the need for teachers to learn about the backgrounds of the English language learners. Learning about an ELL's experiences validates the student's sense of identity, increases the teacher's knowledge, and broadens the horizons of the English-speaking students in the class.

Teaching Strategies and Support for Principle 2

☐ **Prior knowledge** Determine English language learners' prior knowledge of a topic through a variety of activities. For example, have students

- use a KWL chart.

- brainstorm aspects of the topic.

- construct a concept map.

- relate the topic to their personal lives through the use of examples.

- discuss a series of true-or-false statements.

- put steps of a process in a sequence chart.

- complete information in a chart.

☐ **Cultural background** Because there may be cultural, historic, or societal factors with which English language learners are unfamiliar, teachers should learn about the background of these students. Teachers can then use this knowledge to determine what additional background knowledge (facts and concepts) need to be presented.

☐ **Lesson feature preview** Preview the lesson by calling attention to key features: titles, visuals, captions, charts, bold or italicized words, and any special features.

☐ **Self-questioning strategies** When previewing the text, students should be taught to ask themselves questions such as:

- What do I think this text is about?

- What do I already know about this topic?

- What do the features tell me?

☐ **Predicting strategies** Have students use predicting strategies. They can predict what a text is going to be about by looking at its title and the features. They can also read the first line of a paragraph and predict the theme. Students should always confirm any predictions after reading.

☐ **Note-taking organizers** Present a graphic organizer that students can use for taking notes. Show students how to use headings and subheadings to create an outline framework.

☐ **Set a purpose for reading** Have students set a purpose for reading so they take active control of their learning. After previewing a passage, students should ask themselves questions such as:

- What is this passage about?

- What is my purpose for reading the passage?

- How does this passage relate to the topic?

☐ **Make connections** At the end of a lesson, have students make a connection between what they have learned with (a) an aspect of their academic lives, and (b) an aspect of their personal lives. This activity can be done as a Think-Pair-Share exercise or in small groups.

FIVE ESSENTIAL PRINCIPLES FOR BUILDING ELL LESSONS, *cont.*

PRINCIPLE 3
Provide Comprehensible Input

Providing comprehensible input refers to making written and oral content accessible to English language learners, especially through the use of nonlinguistic supports.

Because English language learners are frequently overwhelmed by extraneous information and large blocks of text, they need help focusing on the most important concepts. With comprehensible input strategies, teachers make information and tasks clear by using step-by-step instructions, by making modifications to their speech, and by clearly defining objectives and expectations of the students.

Nonlinguistic supports teachers can use to accompany student reading include:

- photographs
- illustrations
- models
- cartoons
- graphs, charts, tables
- graphic organizers, such as flowcharts and KWL charts
- outlines

Graphic organizers and outlines provide essential visual aids by showing at a glance the hierarchy and relationship of concepts.

Nonlinguistic supports teachers can use during class presentations include:

- gestures
- facial expressions
- dramatization
- props
- tone of voice
- realia (real-life visuals and objects)
- models
- demonstrations

Another effective form of comprehensible input is the "think-aloud," especially as modeled by the teacher. In a think-aloud, the teacher stops periodically and shares how to make sense out of a text or problem by talking about his/her thought processes. The think-aloud shows how thinkers comprehend texts or solve difficult problems. ELLs can practice think-alouds, thereby learning to reflect and comprehend. Teachers can use the student's think-aloud to assess strengths and challenges.

A variety of comprehensible input techniques should be incorporated into lesson plans for English language learners as well as multiple exposures to new terms and concepts. Hands-on activities are particularly helpful to ELLs. The use of multimedia and other technologies will also enhance instruction.

Teaching Strategies and Support for Principle 3

☐ **Visuals** Provide meaningful visuals for English language learners. These may include pictures, images, diagrams, standard graphic organizers (e.g., Venn diagrams, charts, and concept maps), and outlines (filled-in or cloze).

☐ **Multimedia** Use a variety of media to reduce the reliance on language and place the information in a context that is more comprehensible.

- Bring realia (real-life objects) into the lessons. Have visual displays (graphs, charts, photos), objects, visitors, and authentic materials (newspaper and magazine clippings, etc.).

- Use video, audio, and CD/online interactive activities.

☐ **The five senses** Use teaching techniques that involve the other senses. For example:

- When teaching about ratios, have students taste salt water mixtures with varying ratios of salt to water.

- When teaching perimeter, have students trace the outlines of the objects being measured.

☐ **Hands-on learning** Provide hands-on experiences when appropriate to help students contextualize or personalize abstract concepts.

☐ **Demonstrations** Provide demonstrations of how something works, whether it is concrete (such as locating a point on a coordinate grid) or conceptual (absolute value).

☐ **Role-playing** Concepts can also be presented through role-playing or debates.

☐ **Think-alouds** Use think-alouds to model the kinds of question-asking strategies that students should use to construct meaning from text. Write the 5 Ws (Who? What? When? Where? Why?) on a wall chart, and remind students to use these questions as they read to help them understand the text.

☐ **Delivery of instruction** Providing comprehensible input also refers to the delivery of instruction. For example:

- Face students when speaking.

- Speak clearly and slowly.

- Pause frequently.

- Use gestures, tone of voice, facial expressions, and emphasis as appropriate.

- Avoid the use of idioms and slang.

- Say and write instructions.

PRINCIPLE 4
Enable Language Production

Enabling language production for English language learners encompasses the four skills of listening, speaking, reading, and writing.

Because the language used by teachers and in content-area textbooks and assessment is sufficiently different from everyday spoken language, English language learners find themselves at a disadvantage in the classroom. Acquiring academic language in all four skill areas is challenging and requires at least five years of exposure to academic English to catch up with native-speaker norms. Therefore, particular attention should be paid to expanding ELLs' academic language so that they can access the learning materials and achieve success.

Brain research has ascertained that people under stress have difficulty learning and retaining new concepts. Students with limited language are naturally highly stressed. By promoting interaction among students where all contribute to a group effort, practice language, and develop relationships with one another, anxieties are reduced, thereby enabling more effective learning. See ideas for peer learning strategies beginning on page T28.

While the four language skills are intertwined, English language learners will likely not be at the same proficiency level in all four skills. Teachers will need to modify their instruction in response to students' strengths and needs in each area, keeping in mind the following concepts:

- When providing listening input to ELLs, the language must be understandable and should contain grammatical structures and vocabulary that are just beyond the current level of English language development.

- Teachers should provide appropriate "wait time" for students to respond to questions. ELLs need time to process the question and formulate an answer.

- For cultural reasons and/or due to lack of oral language skills, ELLs may not express themselves openly or may consider it disrespectful to disagree with authority figures.

- Teachers should encourage students to verbalize their understanding of the content.

- Think-alouds and recordings of oral reading increase oral language production.

- In addition to frontloading and comprehensible input from the teacher, ELLs need to practice effective reading strategies, such as asking questions, taking notes, predicting, and summarizing.

- There is a direct correlation between speaking and writing; by increasing oral language production, writing skills can be increased. For example, teachers can have ELLs say and write vocabulary to connect oral and written language.

- Opportunities for students to write in English in a variety of writing activities should be built into the lessons. For example, reading-response logs and journaling are activities that increase written language production.

Teaching Strategies and Support for Principle 4

☐ **Listening skills** Use audio recordings to develop English language learners' listening skills as well as fluency and accuracy.

☐ **Idioms, colloquialisms, and slang** Give explanations of any idioms, colloquialisms, or slang that arise in content.

☐ **Oral communication activities** Present specific oral communication activities. For example:
- telling or retelling stories
- role-playing
- giving instructions
- giving oral reports
- debating
- brainstorming

☐ **Speaking skills** Model summarizing information and reporting on projects or experiences. Then have students summarize and report.

☐ **Reading comprehension skills** Provide explicit teaching of reading comprehension skills. These are particularly important for expository reading. For example, teach or review summarizing, sequencing, inferring, comparing and contrasting, asking questions, drawing conclusions, distinguishing between fact and opinion, or finding main idea and details.

☐ **Reading strategies practice** Have students practice using reading strategies. For example, ask them to
- record the main ideas and details for certain paragraphs.
- develop their own questions.
- write the facts and opinions for certain paragraphs.

☐ **Paraphrase** Provide ELL-appropriate paraphrases of text questions.

☐ **Writing skills** Suggest dialogue journals for note taking and responses to writing prompts.

☐ **Writing process** Review or teach the steps of the writing process (prewrite/draft/revise/edit/publish).

☐ **Note-taking support** Provide note-taking supports, such as writing templates, fill-in-the-blank guides, or other graphic organizers.

☐ **Self-monitoring** Provide students with checklists for monitoring their own writing, such as checklists for revising, editing, and peer editing.

☐ **Partner writing** Pair ELLs with writing partners for peer feedback.

☐ **Scoring rubrics** Provide scoring rubrics for oral and written assignments and assessments. For example, students' writing can be evaluated for focus, ideas, order, writer's voice, word choice, and sentence structure. Students should be evaluated according to their proficiency levels.

FIVE ESSENTIAL PRINCIPLES FOR BUILDING ELL LESSONS, *cont.*

PRINCIPLE 5
Assess for Content and Language Understanding

An ever-increasing emphasis on assessment requires that all students—including English language learners—achieve the same high standards. Yet below-level language proficiency can have a negative impact on an ELL's success in the content areas. It is, therefore, essential to use assessment results as a way to identify an ELL's strengths and challenges.

Three types of assessments are key to instruction for all students, including ELLs: diagnostic assessment, formative assessment, and summative assessment.

Diagnostic assessment Diagnostic assessment is used for placing English language learners into the appropriate class, as well as for providing a diagnosis of strengths and challenges.

Formative assessment Formative assessment is part of the instructional process. It includes ongoing informal and formal assessment, reviews, and classroom observations. Informal assessments include class discussions, teacher observations, self- and peer-assessment, and teacher-student conversations. Formal assessments include essays, quizzes, tests, and presentations.

Formative assessment is used to improve the teaching and learning process—which is particularly important in regards to English language learners. By using formative assessments, teachers can target an ELL's specific problem areas, adapt instruction, and intervene earlier rather than later.

Summative assessment Summative assessment occurs at the end of a specific period and evaluates student competency and the effectiveness of instruction. Examples are mid-year and final exams, state tests, and national tests.

Federal and state law requires that all students, including English language learners, be assessed in reading, math, and science.

Assessment accommodations Assessment accommodations for ELLs can minimize the negative impact of the lack of language proficiency when assessing in the content areas. These accommodations can be used for formal and informal assessments.

Possible assessment accommodations include: time extensions, use of bilingual dictionaries and glossaries, repeated readings of listening passages, use of dual-language assessments, allowing written responses in the native language, and separate testing locations.

Teaching Strategies and Support for Principle 5

☐ **Informal assessment** Use a variety of informal assessments for ELLs including acting, singing, retelling, demonstrating, and illustrating.

☐ **Content area log** Have students keep a "content area log." Use a two-column format with the headings What I Understand and What I Don't Understand. Follow up with students on the What I Don't Understand items so that they can move those items into the other column.

☐ **Portfolios** Portfolios are a practical way to assess student progress. Provide specific examples of what to include in a portfolio, including examples of speaking and writing. Some portfolio items might be:
- written assignments
- recordings of speaking samples, oral presentations, or role-playing
- exercise sheets
- scoring rubrics and written evaluations by the teacher
- tests and quizzes

☐ **Formal assessments** Use a variety of formal assessments such as practice tests, real tests, and oral and written assessments.

☐ **Assessment format** Create tests with a variety of assessment formats, including dictation, multiple choice, cloze, and open-response formats.

☐ **Standardized tests** Have students practice taking standardized tests by using released test items. These are often available online from your state department of education or district website.

☐ **Academic vocabulary** Explicitly teach the academic English words, phrases, and constructions that often appear in standardized test items. This might include *best, both, except,* and *probably.*

☐ **Restate directions** When giving directions, restate the directions in simplified English, repeat the directions, and emphasize key words.

☐ **Repeat directions** Verify a student's understanding of the directions by having the student repeat the directions in his/her own words.

☐ **Bilingual glossaries** Provide students with bilingual glossaries of academic vocabulary.

☐ **Written assessments** Writing portions of assessments are generally the most difficult for English language learners. Therefore, the writing process should be practiced. Teachers should carefully guide students through the prewriting step with examples of brainstorming, outlining, using a graphic organizer, etc.

STRATEGIES FOR TEACHING ENGLISH LANGUAGE LEARNERS

Teaching Strategies

The following list of teaching strategies can help you differentiate the content for your English language learners. While the Teacher's Edition has identified places where these strategies may be particularly useful, you will likely find many other opportunities to apply them in your class.

There are five basic types of strategies:

- **Reading Support Strategies** provide support for students as they interact with the text and lesson concepts.

- **Vocabulary Strategies** help students who are struggling to learn and comprehend lesson vocabulary terms.

- **Peer Learning Strategies** promote cooperative learning. Beginning and intermediate speakers are able to hear and see concepts presented in different ways, while more advanced speakers benefit by teaching lesson concepts.

- **Organizing Information Strategies** provide students with a scaffolded way to organize lesson information. Often the strategies involve using a graphic organizer.

- **Comprehension Check Strategies** allow teachers to monitor student understanding in an ongoing manner. At a glance teachers can see how many students understand and how many do not.

Reading Support Strategies

Anticipation/Reaction Guide

Before starting a lesson, ask the class questions that focus on lesson topics. While the questions can address topics that have not yet been covered, make sure they require students to access some prior knowledge. After the lesson, have students re-answer the questions and compare how their answers have changed.

Language Proficiency Adaptation Accept relevant terms or short phrases from beginning speakers. Require intermediate and advanced speakers to write full-sentence responses. Encourage all ELLs to read their answers aloud so that they can practice speaking in English.

Cloze Prompts

Provide the class with sentences in which key words or phrases have been replaced with blanks. As students work through the lesson, they should fill in the blanks with the correct terms or phrases.

Language Proficiency Adaptation Provide beginning speakers with word banks to help them complete the cloze prompts. Challenge advanced speakers to create their own cloze prompt sentences and then trade with a partner to help them review lesson concepts.

Directed Reading-Thinking Activity (DR-TA)

This strategy teaches students to make predictions, read to acquire lesson concepts, and then follow up with a review. Have students follow these steps:

- Skim the headings, images, and vocabulary in the text.

- Make a prediction of what the reading is about.

- Read the text.

- At teacher-defined stopping points, compare predictions with concepts and information learned in the lesson.

- Revise predictions.

Language Proficiency Adaptation For beginning speakers, stop more frequently to compare predictions with what students have learned. Give them additional time to respond to what they have read.

Know/Want to know/Learned

KWL charts help students activate prior knowledge, gather information, and check for understanding.

To fill in a KWL chart:

- Before the lesson, have students fill in the K and W columns.

- K column: Students write what they **Know** about the topic.

- W column: Students write what they **Want** to know about the topic.

- After the lesson, have students fill in the L column.

- L column: Students write what they **Learned** about the topic.

KWL charts can be modified to include a **Background** section at the beginning—these are BKWL charts. Use a BKWL chart when you provide students with background information about the lesson. Students can take notes in this column. You may also wish to add an R column after the L column for students to list topics for future **Research.**

Know	Want to know	Learned

Language Proficiency Adaptation Accept drawings and relevant terms or phrases from beginning speakers. For intermediate speakers, encourage them to write in full sentences. Require advanced speakers to write in full sentences. Check their questions for correct sentence structure.

STRATEGIES FOR TEACHING ENGLISH LANGUAGE LEARNERS, *cont.*

Lesson Preview

Have students preview the lesson by skimming topic headings, diagrams, pictures, vocabulary, and key concepts. Then, have students write down or discuss what they think the lesson will be about.

Language Proficiency Adaptation Give English language learners additional time to discuss their predictions with one another. If desired, pair beginning and intermediate speakers with advanced or native English speakers.

Question-Answer Relationships (QAR)

Students learn to recognize four different types of questions so that they can better answer them. After working through a lesson, have students answer and/or write questions of each type.

- *Right There:* Answers are found directly in the text.

- *Think and Search:* Answers come from finding information in different parts of the text and fitting these ideas together.

- *Author and You:* Answers are inferred—they are a mix of students' own knowledge and the author's writing.

- *On My Own:* Answers are composed of students' own knowledge.

Language Proficiency Adaptation Have beginning and intermediate speakers work together to answer questions of each type. Suggest they break the activity into steps. First, have them read the question and confirm what it is asking. Then, have them label the question with its type. Finally, suggest they write the answer. For advanced speakers, have them both answer and write questions of each type.

Quick Write

Give students a short period of time (one, five, or ten minutes) to write everything they know about a topic. Encourage them to write continuously about the topic for the entire time, even if they have to repeat a fact several times.

Language Proficiency Adaptation Accept drawings and/or lists from beginning speakers.

Stop and Answer

Write a list of sequential questions on the board. Next to the question, indicate when each question should be answered. As students read the lesson or discuss a concept, stop them at the specified points and have them answer the questions.

Language Proficiency Adaptation Encourage all English language learners to discuss the questions with one another. These discussions will give them extra opportunities to practice their speaking and listening skills.

Vocabulary Strategies

Frayer Model

The Frayer model helps students understand a vocabulary term by having them examine its definition, characteristics, examples, and nonexamples.

To fill in a Frayer model:

- Write the vocabulary term in the center oval.

- Write the definition, brainstorm characteristics, and provide examples of the term in the appropriate boxes.

- In the nonexample box, list things that are not examples of the term, but are similar in some way.

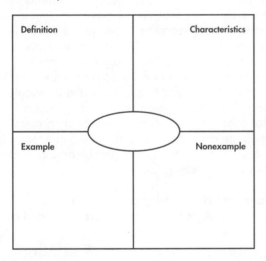

Language Proficiency Adaptation For English language learners who are proficient in writing in their native language, have them use the bottom right box (nonexamples) to define the term in their native language. You may also choose to permit drawings in the "characteristics" box.

Vocabulary Word Map

This graphic organizer helps students learn vocabulary by associating the terms with related words and images.

To fill in a vocabulary word map:

- Write the vocabulary term in the top box.

- Fill in the bottom boxes with terms, phrases, or images that are associated with the vocabulary term.

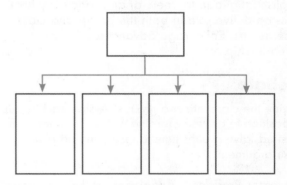

Language Proficiency Adaptation If possible, pair beginning speakers with intermediate and advanced speakers that have the same native language. Suggest that the more-proficient English speakers describe the vocabulary terms in the students' native language, then work with the beginning speakers to complete the word map.

Word Wall

Designate a wall in your classroom to be used as a word wall. Add key vocabulary and difficult words, along with their definitions, for the entire class to reference. Encourage students to contribute to the word wall.

Language Proficiency Adaptation Support beginning and intermediate speakers by suggesting they write down words for you to define and post. Encourage students to add definitions in their native languages.

STRATEGIES FOR TEACHING ENGLISH LANGUAGE LEARNERS, *cont.*

Peer Learning Strategies

Key Concept Discussion

Divide the class into small groups. Have each student identify a key concept—a main idea or lesson topic—to discuss within his or her group. After small-group discussions, have the class talk about at least one key concept from each group.

Language Proficiency Adaptation Make sure English language learners at all proficiency levels take an active role in both the group and class discussions. Encourage advanced speakers to take a leadership role.

Debate

Divide the class into two groups. Assign each group a position to argue regarding a discussion topic. If desired, give groups time to research and plan their arguments.

Language Proficiency Adaptation Make sure groups contain a mix of students at different language proficiency levels. Encourage all English language learners to take an active role in the debate.

Gallery Walk

In a gallery walk, small groups of students work together to respond to posted prompts and review the responses of other groups.

- Post chart-paper stations around the classroom, each displaying a concept or question for groups to respond to.

- Divide the class into groups and assign each group a different color to write with. The number of groups should equal the number of stations.

- Have each group walk to a station and respond to the posted question or prompt.

- Groups should then circulate through the stations, or "gallery." At each station, have them evaluate the previous groups' answers, making any necessary corrections or comments, and adding any relevant information.

- When groups return to their original stations, have them work together to summarize the information on their charts.

Language Proficiency Adaptation Arrange students so that each group contains a mix of students at different language proficiency levels. Encourage beginning speakers to contribute both orally and, if appropriate, in writing.

Jigsaw Review

In a jigsaw review, each student is responsible for teaching a concept to a small group of students. Divide the class into learning circles. The number of students in each learning circle should equal the number of concepts you will assign students to review. Assign each student in a learning circle a number. Have students with the same number join to form a study group. For example, all the 2s should work together. Then, assign each study group a different concept or topic to review. Study groups should create a lesson plan to teach the concept. Have students return to their original learning circles and take turns teaching their lessons.

Language Proficiency Adaptation Encourage beginning speakers to create and present visual aids to their learning circles.

Problem and Solution

Present students with a problem. Have small groups discuss the problem and propose a solution. Each group should share their solution with the class. Have the class compare and contrast the different solutions.

Language Proficiency Adaptation Make sure groups contain a mix of students at different language proficiency levels. Encourage all English language learners to take an active role in both group and class discussions.

Reader-Writer-Speaker Response

In this strategy, students discuss a question or topic in groups of three. Each group member plays a different role. The *Reader* reads about the topic, the *Writer* records the discussion, and the *Speaker* shares the group's comments with the class.

Language Proficiency Adaptation Make sure groups contain a mix of students at different language proficiency levels. Suggest advanced speakers assume the role that will challenge them most. For example, if a student is a more proficient English writer than speaker, encourage him or her to be the group *Speaker*.

Think-Pair-Share

Give students a question or topic to think about individually. Next, have pairs of students discuss the topic. Pairs should then share their comments with the class or with another pair.

Language Proficiency Adaptation If possible, pair beginning and intermediate speakers with more advanced or native English speakers.

Topic Circles

Arrange the class in small-group circles. Introduce a topic or idea. Then, have one member of each circle give a fact or detail about the topic being discussed. The student to their right should then provide a different fact or detail. The cycle should continue until there is no more new information to share.

Language Proficiency Adaptation Allow beginning and intermediate speakers extra time to share their facts and details. You may also wish to permit beginning speakers to refer to their books or notes during the discussion.

Organizing Information Strategies

Timeline

Have students create a timeline to display events that have occurred in a sequential order. Suggest they show the passage of time as a straight line with important events and discoveries marked along the way.

Language Proficiency Adaptation For the timeline descriptions, accept relevant terms or short phrases from beginning speakers.

Cause-and-Effect Diagram

To visually represent cause-and-effect relationships, suggest students make and fill out cause-and-effect diagrams. Reinforce that a single cause can have multiple effects, just as several causes can contribute to a single effect.

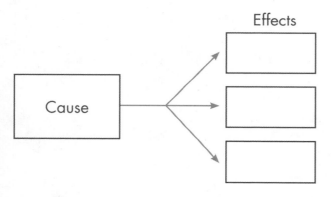

Language Proficiency Adaptation Provide support for beginning speakers by supplying word/phrase banks.

Cluster Diagram

Have students show how concepts are related by making a cluster diagram.

To create a cluster diagram:

• Write the main idea or topic on a sheet of paper. Circle it.

• Draw lines branching off the main idea, connected to circles that contain concepts or characteristics related to the main topic.

• Continue adding facts and details in a branching pattern, connecting related ideas and facts.

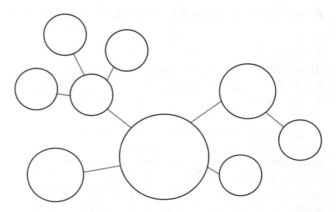

Language Proficiency Adaptation If possible, pair beginning and advanced speakers with the same native language. Allow them to brainstorm in their native language and then work together on their diagrams.

Compare-and-Contrast Table

A compare-and-contrast table helps students organize the similarities and differences between two or more concepts, objects, or processes.

To create a compare-and-contrast table:

- Draw a table.

- Label the columns with the items being compared.

- Label the rows with the characteristics being examined.

- Fill in the boxes with the characteristics of each item.

	Item 1	Item 2	Item 3
Characteristic 1			
Characteristic 2			

Language Proficiency Adaptation Provide beginning speakers with a partially filled-in table and/or a word bank to help them complete their tables.

Concept Map

A concept map helps students organize concepts using visual relationships and linking words. Mapping out these connections helps students think about how information fits together.

To create a concept map:

- Draw a box and write the main concept inside it.

- Draw arrows to additional boxes. Use linking words along the arrow lines to describe the relationships between connected boxes.

- In the second set of boxes, write details that support the main concept.

- Continue to add boxes and linking words as necessary to further organize details and facts.

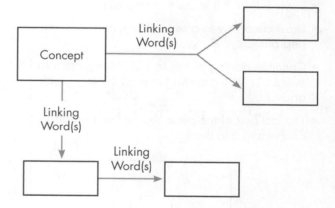

Language Proficiency Adaptation If possible, pair beginning and advanced speakers with the same native language. Allow them to brainstorm in their native language and then work together on their concept maps.

STRATEGIES FOR TEACHING ENGLISH LANGUAGE LEARNERS, *cont.*

Cornell Notes

Cornell notes is a note taking-strategy for outlining lesson concepts. The Cornell notes strategy helps students identify and list key words. Additionally, it requires students to summarize lesson concepts.

Language Proficiency Adaptation Encourage English language learners to list any terms that they are unfamiliar with in one column. Suggest they write a definition for each listed term in another column.

Cycle Diagram

Have students use a cycle diagram to show the steps involved in a repeating process.

To create a cycle diagram:

- Draw a box. Fill in the first step of the cycle.
- Draw an arrow to a second box and fill in the next step of the cycle.
- Continue adding boxes in a circular pattern for every step of the cycle. Connect the steps with arrows.
- The last box of the cycle should have an arrow connecting it to the first.

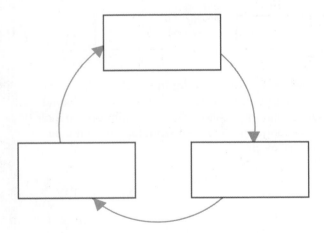

Language Proficiency Adaptation Allow beginning speakers to use drawings and other visual aids in their cycle diagrams.

Fishbone Map

A fishbone map helps students organize complex topics into main ideas and supporting details.

To create a fishbone map:

- Draw a "backbone," or set of horizontal lines, and fill them in with a topic.
- Draw diagonal lines that extend off of this backbone. Label each of these diagonals with a main idea related to the topic.
- Draw several lines branching off each diagonal. Write details that support each main idea on these lines.

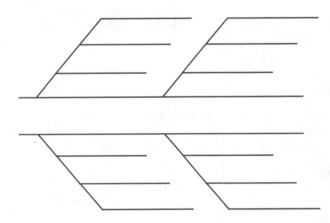

Language Proficiency Adaptation Allow beginning speakers to work in pairs. Encourage intermediate speakers to work independently at first, and then share their work with another student, revising their fishbone map as necessary.

Flowchart

Students can use a flowchart to show a sequence of steps or events in a process. Make sure students understand that a flowchart can have one or more paths.

To create a flowchart:

- Write the first step of a process inside a box.

- Use an arrow to connect this first box with a second box that contains the next step in the process.

- Continue connecting boxes until all steps of the process are represented.

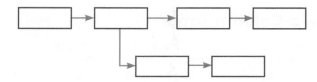

Language Proficiency Adaptation Encourage beginning speakers to use drawings and other visual aids in their flowcharts.

Main Ideas and Details Chart

Students can use this chart to organize lesson concepts by main ideas and supporting details. Advise them to use clues from the text such as headings and topic sentences to determine main ideas.

To create a main ideas and details chart:

- Draw a line down the center of a sheet of paper to divide it into two columns.

- In the left column, write the main ideas of the topic or reading.

- In the right column, write the supporting details for each main idea.

Main Ideas	Details

Language Proficiency Adaptation Accept short phrases or drawings for main ideas and details from beginning speakers. Encourage intermediate speakers, and require advanced speakers, to write in full sentences.

STRATEGIES FOR TEACHING ENGLISH LANGUAGE LEARNERS, *cont.*

Spider Map

A spider map is a way to review and organize information that stems from a central topic.

To create a spider map:

- Write the main topic in a circle.
- Draw diagonal lines branching off the topic and label these with the topic's key concepts.
- From the branches, draw horizontal lines that group facts, details, and examples to support each key concept.

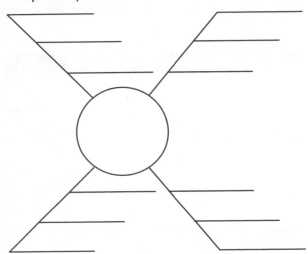

Language Proficiency Adaptation Allow beginning speakers to work in small groups to complete their spider maps. Encourage intermediate speakers to work independently at first, and then share their work with another student, completing and revising their maps as necessary.

T-Chart

A T-chart helps students organize lesson information including concepts, vocabulary, questions, and facts.

To create a T-chart:

- Divide a sheet of paper into two columns. Write a heading for each column based on the information being organized. For example, you might use the headings Key Term and Definition.
- List information.

Language Proficiency Adaptation Provide beginning speakers with a partially completed chart. Make sure advanced speakers write in complete sentences.

Two-Column Table

A two-column table is similar to a T-chart in that it organizes lesson information. It can also be modified to include additional columns as necessary.

Language Proficiency Adaptation Accept short phrases or drawings from beginning speakers. You may also wish to provide partially completed tables to beginning speakers. Encourage intermediate speakers, and require advanced speakers, to write in full sentences.

Venn Diagram

Students can use a Venn diagram to help them compare and contrast items.

To make a Venn diagram:

- Draw two (or more) overlapping circles.
- Write the unique characteristics for each topic in its own circle.
- In the center overlap, write characteristics that the topics share.

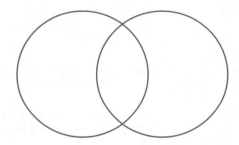

Language Proficiency Adaptation Provide banks of short phrases for beginning speakers to place in the diagram.

Comprehension Check Strategies

It is critical to check for student understanding as you proceed with a lesson. If you move forward and most of the class is not with you, you will lose the students. Each of the following strategies allows teachers to poll a class and see at a glance who is understanding a concept and who is not.

Card Responses

Have each student prepare a set of cards, each card with one answer. Ask questions and have students hold up the appropriate card to indicate their answer to the question. For example, when studying angles, students could create four cards, each with one of the following words: *acute, obtuse, right, straight.* Show examples of each of these 4 angles, and have students hold up the card that classifies the angles.

Signals

Create a set of true-or-false statements or multiple-choice questions with numbered answers to check student understanding of the material being taught.

- True or False: Make a statement and have students indicate with a thumbs up gesture if they agree or a thumbs down if they don't agree. Have students indicate their gestures in front of their chests to minimize others imitating their answers.
- Multiple Choice: Provide answers written on the board that are numbered 1–4. Ask questions for which one of the answers is appropriate. Ask students to hold up one, two, three, or four fingers to indicate which of the four answers is the correct one after each question.

Slates

Have each student create an erasable slate by stapling a clear transparency to sturdy cardboard (staple a sheet of white paper between the two if a clearer writing surface is required). Provide students with erasable markers. Ask questions for which short answers are sufficient and have students provide answers by writing on their erasable slates and holding up their slates in front of them (three or four words should be the maximum length). Slates can be wiped clean with tissues to be used for subsequent questions.

REFERENCES

Anthony, A. R. B. 2008. Output strategies for English language learners: Theory to practice. *The Reading Teacher*, 61(6): 472–482.

August, D. & Shanahan, T. (Eds.). 2006. *Developing literacy in second-language learners: Report of the National Literacy Panel on language-minority children and youth.* Executive Summary.

Barrera, R. B. & Jiménez, R.T. 2000. *Literacy instruction for bilingual Latino students: Teachers' experiences and knowledge.* Office for Bilingual Education and Minority Language Affairs, Washington, DC.

Beilenberg, B. & Fillmore, L.W. 2004–2005. The English they need for the test. *Educational Leadership*, 63 (4).

Collier, V. & Thomas, W. 2002. *A national study of school effectiveness for language minority students' long-term academic achievement.* Santa Cruz, CA, and Washington, DC: Center for Research on Education, Diversity & Excellence.

Cummins, J. 2005. Affirming identity in multilingual classrooms. *Educational Leadership*, (63)1: 38–43.

Cummins, J. 2005. A proposal for action: Strategies for recognizing heritage language competence as a learning resource within the mainstream classroom. *The Modern Language Journal*, 89: 585–592.

Cummins, J. 1999. BICS and CALP: Clarifying the distinction. *Working Papers on Bilingualism*, no. 20.

Cummins, J. 1981. The role of primary language development in promoting educational success for language minority students. In *Schooling and Language Minority Students: A Theoretical Framework.* Sacramento, CA: California Department of Education.

Fillmore, L. W. 2007. English learners and mathematics learning: Language issues to consider. In *Assessing Mathematical Proficiency.* MSRI Publications, 53.

Fillmore, L. W. & Snow, C. E. 2000. What teachers need to know about language. ERIC Special Report.

Garcia, G. E. 1992. The literacy assessment of second-language learners. Center for the Study of Reading.

Garcia, G. E. 1994. "Supporting Second Language Literacy: Enhancing the English Literacy Development of Students Who Are Learning English-as-a-second-language." *Illinois Reading Council Journal, 22* (1) Special Supplement.

Garcia, G. E. & Bauer, E. B. 2002. Lessons from a classroom teacher's use of alternative literacy assessment. *Research in the Teaching of English, 36.*

Garcia, G. E. & Godina, E. 1994. Bilingual preschool children's participation in classroom literacy activities: 'Once upon a time' and its alternatives. Paper presented at the annual meeting of the National Reading Conference.

Garcia, G. E. & McCarthey, S. J. 2005. English language learners' writing practices and attitudes. *Written Communication*, 22 (1).

Garcia, G. E. & Pearson, P. D. 1990. Modifying reading instruction to maximize its effectiveness for all students. Technical Report #489, Urbana Center for the Study of Reading, Illinois University.

Jiménez, R. T. 2002. Key research, policy, and practice issues for fostering the literacy development of Latino students. *Focus on Exceptional Children,* 34 (6): 1–10.

Jiménez, R.T., Garcia, G. E. & Pearson, P. D. 1996. The reading strategies of bilingual Latino/a students who are successful English readers: Opportunities and obstacles. *Reading Research Quarterly,* 31(1): 90–106.

Kieffer, M. J. & Lesaux, N. K. 2007. Breaking down words to build meaning: Morphology, vocabulary, and reading comprehension in the urban classroom. *The Reading Teacher*, 61: 134–144.

Leos, K. 2004. *No Child Left Behind.* Paper presented at the annual conference of the National Association for Bilingual Education, Albuquerque, NM.

National Clearinghouse for English Language Acquisition (NCELA). 2008. *Educating English language learners: Building teacher capacity.* Washington, DC.

National Clearinghouse for English Language Acquisition (NCELA). 2008. *How many school-aged limited English proficient (LEP) students are there in the U.S.?* Washington, DC.

National Education Association (NEA) 2008. *NEA 2008 Campaign Briefing Book.* Washington, DC.

NCTE position paper on the role of English teachers in educating English language learners (ELLs).

Schleppegrell, M. J., Achugar, M. & Oteiza, T. 2004. The grammar of history: Enhancing content-based instruction through a functional focus on language. *TESOL Quarterly,* 38 (1): 67–93.

Short, D., Crandall J., and Christian D. 1989. *How to Integrate Language and Content Instruction: A Training Manual.* The Center for Applied Linguistics.

Short, D. & Echevarria, J. 2004–5. Teacher skills to support English language learners. *Educational Leadership* 62 (4).

Name _____ Date _____

Frayer Model

Definition (in your own words)   Characteristics

Example (in your life)   Non-Example

Vocabulary Word Map

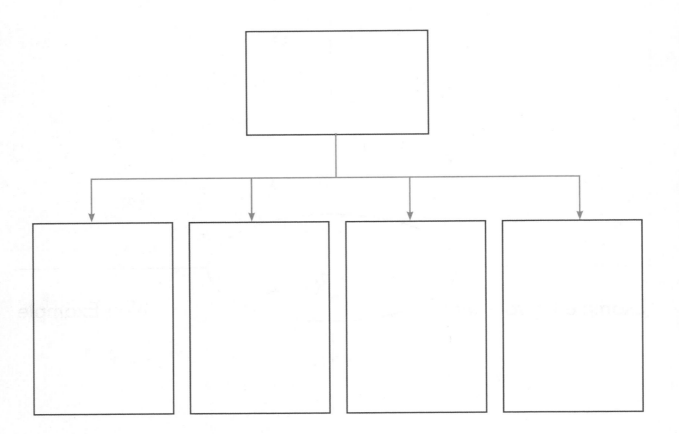

Terms with Multiple Meanings

Math	Everyday

Math	Everyday

Vocabulary Term Table

Term	Explanation	Drawing	Example

Vocabulary Study Sheet

Vocabulary Term Nest

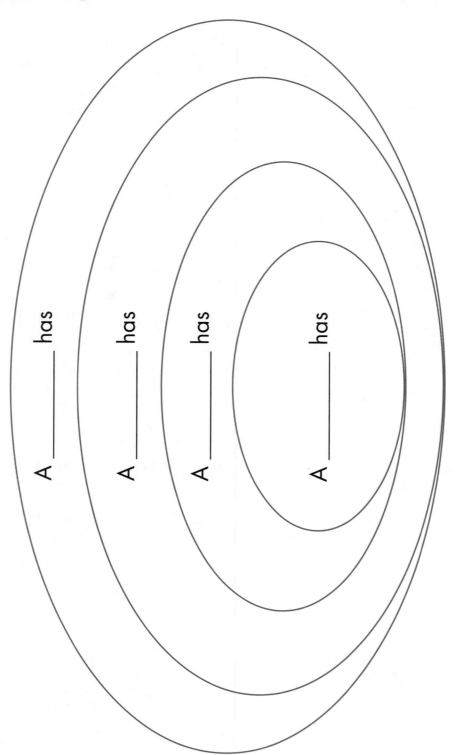

A _____ has

A _____ has

A _____ has

A _____ has

Know/Want to know/ Learned Chart

Learned				
Want to know				
Know				

Partner Problem Sheet

Partner A	Partner B

IMPLEMENTING THE PROGRAM

Features and Components

- Modules organized according to the vocabulary and language associated with specific math strands

- Lessons that can be used in conjunction with any math curriculum

- Lessons that develop students' academic language through visual support, hands-on activities, and opportunities for talking and writing.

- Systematic and predictable instruction in language development across the grades

Teacher's Edition Grades 3–5

Grade-Level Student Editions

Flexible Implementation Options

DAY 1
60-minute class

OR

DAYS 1, 2, 3, and 4
15-minute classes

SCOPE AND SEQUENCE

	Grade		
	3	4	5
Number and Operations			
Comparing Numbers	•		
Meaning of Multiplication	•		
Multiplication and Division Facts	•		
Understanding Story Problems	•		
Fractions	•		
Fractions on a Number Line	•		
Addition and Subtraction	•	•	
Place Value	•	•	•
Estimation	•	•	•
Comparing and Ordering Numbers		•	
Multiplication		•	
Division		•	
Factors and Multiples		•	
Decimal Notation		•	
Fractions and Decimals		•	
Whole-Number Operations		•	•
Prime and Composite Numbers			•
Greatest Common Factor and Least Common Multiple			•
Simplifying Fractions			•
Fraction Operations			•
Comparing and Ordering Fractions and Decimals			•
Decimal Operations			•
Fractions, Decimals, and Percents			•
Ratios			•
Algebra			
Number Sentences	•		
Patterns	•	•	
Patterns in Tables		•	
Variables and Equations		•	
Variables			•
The Coordinate Plane			•
Graphs of Equations			•

		Grade	
	3	4	5
Geometry and Measurement			
Figures in Our World	•		
Lines	•		
Angles	•		
Triangles and Quadrilaterals	•		
Shapes	•	•	
Lines and Angles		•	
Transformations and Symmetry		•	
Points, Lines, and Angles			•
Measuring Angles			•
Properties of Shapes			•
Units of Measure	•		
Measurement Tools	•		
Time	•	•	
Perimeter and Area	•	•	•
Measurement		•	
Converting Units of Measure		•	•
Surface Area and Volume			•
Data Analysis and Probability			
Collecting and Organizing Data	•	•	
Representing Data	•	•	
Mean, Median, and Mode			•
Graphs			•

TEACHER'S EDITION FEATURES

Math Background

Communicate and clarify math concepts.

Frontload the Lesson

Activities build background and connect to students' prior knowledge.

Content and Language

Modeling and discussion support content and language objectives.

Lesson 11

Patterns

Vocabulary Patterns, repeating patterns, repeat, addition pattern, subtraction pattern, rule, multiplication pattern, division pattern

Materials Index cards, color counters (optional), colored pencils or markers

Math Background

- *Repeating patterns* are commonly found in decorative art and music. Sometimes the set of repeating elements is referred to as a *pattern unit*.
- Changing patterns include addition, subtraction, multiplication, and division patterns, though they are not limited to these. Changing patterns are defined by their first element and a *rule*.

↻ Frontload the Lesson

What words will help you explain patterns?

Talk About It

Build Background As students sort the cards, read the terms aloud. Have students tell what they know about the terms they placed in the first two piles.

↻ Content and Language

You Will

Model Read the objectives aloud and explain them in your own words. Use visual examples to support your explanations.

Your Turn

Guide Discussion Have students read the objectives and tell what the objectives mean to them.

Patterns

Essential Question What words will help you explain patterns?

You Will
- Understand repeating patterns.
- Understand addition, subtraction, multiplication, and division patterns.
- Use math vocabulary to describe and continue patterns.

Talk About It

Make an index card for each vocabulary term below. Place each card in one of three piles.

Pile 1: I know what this terms means.
Pile 2: I have heard of this term, but I am not sure how it is used in math.
Pile 3: I have not heard of this term.

pattern   division pattern   rule
repeating pattern   repeat   multiplication pattern
addition pattern   subtraction pattern

What do you know about each term? Explain, using the sentence starters for support.

I know … means …
I think … means …
I do not know what … means.

Your Turn

Look at the objectives under You Will at the top of the page. Working with a partner, predict what you are going to learn. Use the sentence starter for support.

I am going to learn about …

Patterns 41

Leveled Instruction

Early Beginner Early beginners may not use many words in their responses. Encourage them to use pictures, manipulatives, and gestures to communicate, or answer yes/no questions.

Beginner Have students partner with students of higher English language proficiency to complete activities. Expect oral responses of short phrases and simple sentences.

Early Intermediate Encourage students to use sentence starters for support. Model using the sentence starters as needed.

Intermediate Encourage students to express their ideas without sentence starters, if possible, using full sentences. Expect some grammatical mistakes.

Advanced/Transitioning Expect students to form written and spoken sentences of greater complexity. Have them use a more varied English vocabulary and try varied sentence structures.

Leveled Instruction

Teaching strategies accommodate all levels of English language proficiency.

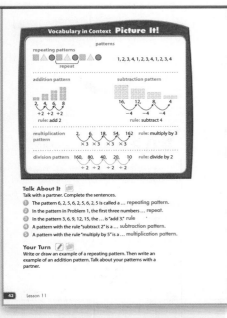

Academic Vocabulary

- Discuss patterns students find in daily life: sewing patterns used to cut fabric to make clothing; rhythmic patterns in music; or a repeating design on wrapping paper or fabric.

- Clarify that in this context, a *rule* describes how to go from one number to another in a pattern. It explains how the pattern works, as soccer rules explain and govern that game.

- Note that *repeat* is used as a verb, noun, and adjective (*repeating*) in this lesson. Help students become familiar with all three usages.

Additional resources for building and reinforcing vocabulary are provided on pages T37–T41.

Cultural Consideration

Visual patterns are familiar elements in the art and design of many cultures. African and Asian fabric designs and Arabic mosaic tiles are some examples.

↻ Comprehensible Input

Guide students to understanding

Vocabulary in Context Picture It!

1. **Say the Term** Have students repeat, stressing each syllable. Then combine syllables and have students repeat.

2. **Introduce Meaning** Connect the term to the visual that illustrates it.

3. **Demonstrate** Use counters or number lines to model different kinds of patterns. For example, use a number line with curved arrows to show a skip-counting pattern such as 3, 6, 9, 12. Help students express the rule.

4. **Apply** Have students demonstrate understanding with Talk About It.

Repeat the routine for each vocabulary term.

Remind students that they can review vocabulary terms for the four operations on pages 89 and 90 and record more terms as they learn them.

Talk About It

Guide Discussion Have students discuss the responses with a partner. Then provide this additional sentence completion, if time permits:

A pattern with the rule "divide by 4" is a … division pattern.

Intervention

If students have trouble naming addition, subtraction, multiplication, and division patterns …

Then write examples of patterns on the board and point to each. Emphasize the connection between the rule and the first word of each type of pattern.

Your Turn

Guide Discussion Ask volunteers to share their patterns and describe them for Your Turn.

Comprehensible Input

Visuals, demonstrations, and hands-on experiences improve understanding.

Intervention

"If/Then" statements help monitor progress and provide reteaching suggestions.

Academic Vocabulary

Provides clarification to help ELL students understand teachers, lessons, and math language.

Language Production

Pair and group work provide ample opportunities to use language in conversations.

Comprehension Support

Modeling and hands-on activities target potential problem areas.

Patterns

↻ Language Production

Comprehension Support Help students understand the words *necklace* and *beads*. Show students that there are 3 different types of beads on the necklace: red, blue, and yellow. Some students might need help with the names of colors. Review the words *circle* and *square* to help students talk about the patterns in Problems 2 and 3. Draw examples of each.

Model Ask students to look for a pattern in the necklace. *The first beads are red. There are 2 red beads.* Write 2 on the board. Continue counting the next group of blue beads, and so on, until a repeating number pattern emerges. For Problems 2 and 3 show students how the visuals match the numbers. Then discuss how they change. *Each number of circles is two fewer than the one before. So, the rule is to subtract 2.* In Problems 4 and 5, encourage students to think about what can be added, subtracted, multiplied, or divided to get from any number to the next.

Talk About It

Guide Discussion Have students complete the Talk About It sentences with a partner. Remind them that if they need help with the terms, they can look back at Vocabulary in Context Picture It!

Your Turn

Guide Discussion Give students a few minutes to write about the letter pattern. Then have them share their ideas with a partner.

Do You Understand?

① What is the pattern in the necklace? Start with the red beads. Count how many of each color. Write the pattern with numbers.

2, 3, 1, 2, 3, 1, 2, 3, 1

Find the rule for these patterns. Then find the next number in the pattern.

② 10, 8, 6, 4, __2__   Rule: __subtract 2__

③ 4, 7, 10, 13, __16__   Rule: __add 3__

④ 55, 50, 45, 40, __35__   Rule: __subtract 5__

⑤ 10, 20, 40, 80, __160__   Rule: __multiply by 2__

Talk About It
Complete the sentences about patterns.

① The pattern made by the necklace is a … repeating pattern.
② The pattern in Problem 2 is a … subtraction pattern.
③ The pattern in Problem 5 is a … multiplication pattern.
④ To find the next number in the pattern in Problem 4, I first find the … rule.

Your Turn
Look at this pattern of letters.

A A B C A A B C A A B C A A B C

Write a few sentences about the pattern. Tell what kind of pattern it is. Describe the pattern to your partner.

Patterns   43

Leveled Language Proficiency

Students at each proficiency level should be able to perform the following tasks.

Listening/Speaking

Early Beginner Recognize a few vocabulary terms and follow very simple conversations with support. Repeat simple phrases, and use vocabulary terms to answer questions.

Beginner Follow simple directions. Recognize and use some vocabulary terms. Say individual terms and simple phrases, and repeat longer phrases and short sentences.

Early Intermediate/Intermediate Begin to follow and take part in more abstract discussion about vocabulary terms in spoken phrases and sentences. Show an ability to express abstract ideas about target vocabulary.

Advanced/Transitioning Understand complex sentence structures; follow abstract conversations involving lesson vocabulary. Speak on abstract topics, including those that involve lesson vocabulary, with few if any grammatical and syntactical errors.

Listening/Speaking Levels

Target goals for listening and speaking are provided for each proficiency level.

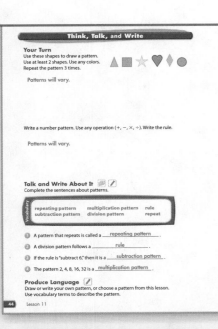

Assess Understanding

Your Turn

Model Name the shapes that can be used to create a pattern. Help students understand the task. *I have to make up a pattern using shapes. I have to use at least two different shapes. That means I can use two shapes, or I can use more than two. I can use any colors.* Then have students do the activity independently.

Talk and Write About It

On Their Own Have students work with a partner to complete the sentences.

Produce Language

On Their Own Remind students that they can look back at Vocabulary in Context Picture it! for examples of the patterns discussed in the lesson.

Wrap Up

Table Talk Have students look back at the lesson's objectives. Allow time for them to reflect on what they have learned and then answer the essential question.

☑ **Learned** and applied vocabulary related to patterns

☑ **Spoken** statements about patterns

☑ **Written** statements about patterns

Assess Understanding

Informal assessments and written responses build fluency with language.

Writing Support

Activities promote understanding through writing and conversations.

Leveled Language Proficiency

Students at each proficiency level should be able to perform the following tasks.

Reading/Writing

Early Beginner Read some short, common words and easier vocabulary terms, if given visual support or help from a partner or adult. Copy terms and phrases from the board; write 1–2 vocabulary terms independently.

Beginner Read a growing number of everyday words and some lesson vocabulary terms. Use sentence starters and visual supports to write individual terms and phrases.

Early Intermediate/Intermediate Read most lesson vocabulary in isolation and in context; read sentences composed of phonetically regular words and sight words, including directions. Write full sentences with support to describe ideas and explain vocabulary with some spelling and grammatical errors. Read and understand some abstract ideas.

Advanced/Transitioning With minimal support, read and write full sentences, with few errors, that contain concrete and abstract ideas related to lesson vocabulary. Use sentence starters only as necessary.

Reading/Writing Levels

Target goals for reading and writing are provided for each proficiency level.

CONTENTS
Grade 3

Place Value

Vocabulary Digits, numbers, place value, thousands, hundreds, tens, ones, place, value, standard form, expanded form, word form

Materials One balloon (not inflated), measuring sticks that indicate feet and meters

 Math Background

- In the number 2,536, the *place value* of the 5 is hundreds; the *value* of the 5 is 500.

- Numbers can be written in expanded form: $2,536 = 2,000 + 500 + 30 + 6$.

- Numbers can also be written in word form: "two thousand, five hundred thirty-six."

Place Value

Essential Question What do you need to know to understand and discuss place value in math class?

You Will
- Identify place value in numbers through 9,999.
- Represent numbers using standard form, expanded form, and word form.
- Use key terms to talk about numbers.

Talk About It

Rate these mathematical terms according to the following scale:
1. I have never heard of this term before.
2. I have heard this term, but I do not know how to use it in math.
3. I understand this term and know how to use it in math.

_____ digits	_____ tens
_____ numbers	_____ hundreds
_____ place value	_____ thousands
_____ ones	_____ standard form
_____ place	_____ expanded form
_____ value	_____ word form

Explain what you know about these terms, using the sentence starters.
I do not know what … means.
I think … means …
I know … means … in math.

Your Turn
Look at the objectives listed under You Will at the top of the page. Working with a partner, predict what you will learn. Use the sentence starter for help.
I will learn about …

↻ Frontload the Lesson

 Essential Question What do you need to know to understand and discuss place value in math class?

Talk About It

Build Background Have students rate the terms. Encourage them to tell what they know about familiar terms.

↻ Content and Language

You Will

Model Read the objectives aloud and explain them in your own words. Use diagrams to support your explanations.

Your Turn

Guide Discussion Have students read the objectives. Discuss what they mean to them. Ask students to tell how they think the lesson might help them in math class.

Leveled Instruction

Early Beginner Beginners should partner with students at higher language proficiency to complete the activities. Single words and gestures should be expected as answers.

Beginner Beginners can answer in short phrases, especially when sentence starters are provided.

Early Intermediate Expect phrases and simple sentences from these students as answers to the activities.

Intermediate Students should produce complete sentences and tackle the activities with little assistance.

Advanced/Transitioning Students should produce detailed answers with minimal assistance and partner with students at lower language proficiency levels to offer them assistance.

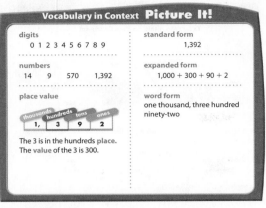

Vocabulary in Context Picture It!

digits	standard form
0 1 2 3 4 5 6 7 8 9	1,392
numbers	**expanded form**
14 9 570 1,392	1,000 + 300 + 90 + 2
place value	**word form**
	one thousand, three hundred ninety-two

thousands hundreds tens ones
| 1, | 3 | 9 | 2 |

The 3 is in the hundreds place.
The value of the 3 is 300.

Talk About It
Talk with a partner. Complete the sentences.
1 The number 4,876 is written in … **standard form.**
2 In the number 4,876, the 4, 8, 7, and 6 are all … **digits.**
3 In the number 2,598, the 5 is in the … **hundreds place.**
4 5,000 + 100 + 20 + 6 is written in … **expanded form.**
5 In the number 8,764, the … of the 8 is 8,000. **value**

Your Turn
Write a four-digit number. Tell how to read the number. Then use the vocabulary terms to describe the number in different ways to a partner.

Academic Vocabulary

- Use the familiar context of *place* (where something is; a location) to help students understand that the location of a digit in a number means the same thing as *place*. Point to your desk and say, *This is my place.* Point to a digit in a number and say, *This is the (tens) place. So this is the (tens) digit.*

- When reading numbers, students might be confused by the singular vs. plural forms of *thousands* and *hundreds*. Explain that in English, whenever we refer to a specific amount (3,000 or 200), we use the singular form (*three thousand* and *two hundred*). We usually use the plural form to talk about *thousands of people* or *hundreds of choices*.

- For Do You Understand, remind students that the type of *table* used in the activity is not a piece of furniture. It shows facts in an easy-to-read way.

Additional resources for building and reinforcing vocabulary are provided on pages T37–T41.

Cultural Consideration

In some countries, decimal points are used the way we use commas in the United States. One thousand would be written 1.000 rather than 1,000. Clarify this for students as needed.

↻ Comprehensible Input
Guide students to understanding

Vocabulary in Context Picture It!

1. **Say the Term** Have students repeat, stressing each syllable. Then combine syllables and have students repeat.

2. **Introduce Meaning** Connect the term to the visual that illustrates it.

3. **Demonstrate** Use visuals to demonstrate. Blow up a balloon to demonstrate *expanded*. Ask students to talk about the change in size. Summarize: *This is an expanded balloon. The expanded balloon is bigger, but it is still a balloon.* Present the vocabulary term, *expanded form,* and say, *The expanded form of a number looks bigger, but it's still the same number.*

4. **Apply** Have students demonstrate understanding with Talk About It.

Repeat the routine for each vocabulary term.

Talk About It

Guide Discussion Ask students to state the word form of each four-digit number in the sentence starters. Then provide this additional sentence completion, if time permits:

In the number 6,079, the 6 is in the … place. **thousands**

Intervention

If students have difficulty reading large numbers …

Then provide a chart with the word names and numerals for the numbers one through nineteen, *twenty, thirty, forty, fifty, sixty, seventy, eighty, ninety, hundred,* and *thousand.* Have students refer to the chart to help them read various numbers.

Your Turn

Guide Discussion Have pairs of students share the numbers they chose and the descriptions they used in Your Turn.

Place Value

↻ Language Production

Comprehension Support Tell students that this diagram shows the heights of some of the world's tallest mountains. Show students a meter stick and discuss *meter*. Read the data with students. Students will write the heights in different forms to complete the table on the page.

Model Point out that the information for the first mountain has been filled in. *Let's read this first number together as I write the words on the board. Eight thousand, eight hundred fifty. Now let's read the expanded notation. Eight thousand plus eight hundred plus fifty. The next row in the table is for the second mountain. Let's fill in that row.* Continue guiding students as they fill in the table.

Talk About It

Guide Discussion Have students work in pairs and refer to the table for examples of each type of number representation. Encourage them to discuss when they might use each type of notation.

Your Turn

Guide Discussion Some students may wish to plan their responses by writing their answers. Then have them work in pairs to complete Your Turn.

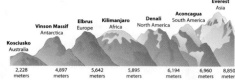

Tallest Mountain on Each Continent

Kosciusko Australia	Vinson Massif Antarctica	Elbrus Europe	Kilimanjaro Africa	Denali North America	Aconcagua South America	Everest Asia
2,228 meters	4,897 meters	5,642 meters	5,895 meters	6,194 meters	6,960 meters	8,850 meters

Write the numbers for the heights in the table below. Use standard and expanded form.

Mountain Heights		
Mountain	**Standard Form**	**Expanded Form**
Everest	8,850	8,000 + 800 + 50
Aconcagua	6,960	6,000 + 900 + 60
Denali	6,194	6,000 + 100 + 90 + 4
Kilimanjaro	5,895	5,000 + 800 + 90 + 5
Elbrus	5,642	5,000 + 600 + 40 + 2
Vinson Massif	4,897	4,000 + 800 + 90 + 7
Kosciusko	2,228	2,000 + 200 + 20 + 8

Talk About It 💬
How can you represent numbers? Complete the sentences to explain.

1. In standard notation, you write the number using … digits.
2. In expanded notation, you show the … of each digit. value

Your Turn 💬
Look at this number: 4,312. Describe this number to a partner using vocabulary terms.

Place Value **3**

Leveled Language Proficiency

Students at each proficiency level should be able to perform the following tasks.

Listening/Speaking

Early Beginner Follow oral directions that are supported by visual clues. Repeat simple phrases, and use single vocabulary terms to answer questions.

Beginner Follow simple directions; recognize some vocabulary terms. Say individual terms and simple phrases, and repeat longer phrases and short sentences.

Early Intermediate Show understanding of vocabulary terms through actions. Respond briefly to questions, showing an increasing understanding of lesson vocabulary.

Intermediate Recognize vocabulary as individual terms and in the context of spoken sentences. Participate in limited discussion using words and phrases.

Advanced/Transitioning Clarify meanings of terms as needed by asking questions or using resources. Support responses with additional details and explanations.

Your Turn

Look at the table.

Some of the World's Tallest Buildings	
Building	**Height (in feet)**
Taipei 101 Tower	1,667
Petronas Towers	1,483
Willis Tower	1,450
CITIC Plaza	1,283
Empire State Building	1,250

Choose one building. Describe its height in three different ways.

Building: _____

Height in standard form: _____

Height in expanded form: _____

Height in word form: _____

Talk and Write About It 💬 ✏️

Complete the sentences about the building you chose.

Vocabulary				
digits	thousands	ones	standard form	
numbers	hundreds	value	expanded form	
place value	tens	place	word form	

① The height of the building is a number with four ___digits___ .

② The digit 1 is in the ___thousands___ place.

③ The heights in the table are in ___standard form___ .

Produce Language ✏️

Write about the different forms for representing numbers. Try using all the terms you rated with a 1 or 2 on the first page of the lesson.

4   Lesson 1

Leveled Language Proficiency

Students at each proficiency level should be able to perform the following tasks.

Reading/Writing

Early Beginner Show willingness to read for meaning when visual support or the assistance of others is provided. Copy lists of words; write 1–2 vocabulary terms independently.

Beginner/Early Intermediate Read simple sentences with the help of a partner or an adult and visual support; read some vocabulary terms independently. Use sentence starters and other organizers to write individual words and phrases that use vocabulary terms.

Intermediate Show understanding of written material by the ability to follow directions or summarize text. Write full sentences and complex phrases about lesson concepts, using vocabulary terms; sentences may contain some grammatical and spelling errors.

Advanced/Transitioning Read and carry out simple and complex written instructions; read sentences about lesson ideas that use lesson vocabulary. Write complete sentences with very few errors.

↻ Assess Understanding

Your Turn

Model Introduce the table. Explain that these measurements are in feet rather than meters. Display a ruler or yardstick and discuss *foot/ feet*. Read the table with students. Then choose a building and describe its height. *The Taipei 101 Tower is 1,667 feet tall.* Write 1,667 on the board. *Now I'll write it in expanded form: 1,000 + 600 + 60 + 7. Next, I'll write it in word form: One thousand, six hundred sixty-seven.* Have students choose another building and describe its height.

Talk and Write About It

On Their Own Have students work alone for 10 minutes. Then have them compare the building they chose with a partner and share their sentence completions.

Produce Language

On Their Own Have students review how they rated the terms on page 1. Have students use the terms they have learned in this lesson in their writing.

Wrap Up

Table Talk Have students look back at the lesson's objectives. Allow time for them to reflect on what they have learned and then answer the essential question.

☑ **Learned** and applied vocabulary related to place value and the different forms for representing numbers

☑ **Spoken** statements about place value and the different forms for numbers

☑ **Written** statements about place value and the different forms for numbers

Comparing Numbers

Vocabulary Compare, equals, is equal to (=), greater, is greater than (>), less, is less than (<), symbols

Materials Comparing Schools Four Corner Activity (pages 91–93), scissors, glue

Math Background

• Any two numbers can be compared using the words (and symbols) *is equal to* (=), *is greater than* (>), or *is less than* (<).

Frontload the Lesson

Essential Question How do you use words and symbols (<, >, =) to compare numbers?

Talk About It

Build Background Read aloud the steps in the Four Corner Comparing Schools Activity. Place the following information in each corner of the room: (1) Jefferson School: 185 students, (2) Monroe School: 207 students, (3) Lawson School: 322 students, and (4) Cortez School: 430 students. Have students work in pairs to complete the activity. Ask for volunteers to say what they might know about the terms shown in red on the Four Corner cards (*is equal to, is greater than, is less than*).

Content and Language

You Will

Model Read the objectives aloud and model restating them in your own words.

Your Turn

Guide Discussion Have students read the objectives. Discuss what these objectives mean to them.

Comparing Numbers

Essential Question How do you use words and symbols (<, >, =) to compare numbers?

You Will
• Use the symbols <, >, and = to compare numbers.
• Use math vocabulary to compare numbers.

Talk About It

Tear out the Comparing Schools Four Corners Activity sheet on pages 91–92. Then cut out the activity cards on page 93.

Work with a partner.

Each corner of the room shows a school and the number of students at that school.

Step 1 Go to a corner of the room. On the activity sheet, write the name of the school and the number of students in one of the boxes.

Step 2 Follow the directions in the box. Paste the correct card in the box.

Repeat Steps 1 and 2 for each corner of the room.

Look at the red terms in each box. What do you know about these terms? Use the sentence starters for support.

I know … means …
I think … means …
I do not know what … means.

Your Turn
Look at the objectives listed under You Will at the top of the page. Working with a partner, predict what you will learn. Use the sentence starter below.

I am going to learn about …

Comparing Numbers **5**

Leveled Instruction

Early Beginner These students should partner with students of higher language proficiency to complete activities. Use gestures, drawings, and simple phrases to help students understand the concepts of the lesson.

Beginner Use gestures, drawings, and simple phrases to help students understand the concepts of the lesson. Expect short and simple words or phrases to answer questions.

Early Intermediate Encourage students to use sentence starters as support. Expect short and simple sentences to answer questions.

Intermediate Students should be able to complete activities with minimal assistance. Help students include details in their written and oral language.

Advanced/Transitioning Students should be able to produce detailed answers with minimal assistance and should partner with students of lower level language proficiency to support them in completing activities.

compare Tell how things are the same or different.	greater Bigger

15 is greater than 13.

| 15 | > | 13 |

equals The same amount as

12 + 4	equals	16.
12 + 4	is equal to	16.
12 + 4	=	16

less Smaller

24 is less than 31.

| 24 | < | 31 |

symbols

| = | > | < |

Talk About It

Talk with a partner to complete these sentences.

1. 29 ... 25. is greater than
2. 40 plus 40 ... 80. is equal to (or equals)
3. 20 < 60 means twenty ... sixty. is less than
4. 171 > 112 means one hundred seventy-one ... one hundred twelve.
   is greater than

Your Turn

Share your Four Corners activity sheet with a partner. Talk about how you compared the numbers. Use the terms on this page.

Academic Vocabulary

- Discuss words similar in meaning to *greater*, such as *bigger*, *more*, or *larger*. Also, discuss words similar in meaning to *less*, such as *smaller*, *fewer*, or *littler*.

Additional resources for building and reinforcing vocabulary are provided on pages T37–T41.

↻ Comprehensible Input

Guide students to understanding

Vocabulary in Context Picture It!

1. **Say the Term** Have students repeat, stressing each syllable. Then combine syllables and have students repeat.

2. **Introduce Word Meaning** Connect the term to the visual that illustrates it.

3. **Demonstrate** Use gestures and visuals to demonstrate. As *greater* and *less* are discussed, you might want to verify the relative sizes of the two numbers by using counters, place-value blocks, or a number line.

4. **Apply** Have students demonstrate understanding with Talk About It.

Repeat the routine for each vocabulary term.

Talk About It

Guide Discussion Have students discuss the sentences with a partner. Provide this additional sentence completion, if time permits:

When you tell how two things are the same or different, you ... them. **compare**

Intervention

If students have trouble remembering the symbols of inequality, > and < ...

Then show students that the smaller part of the "arrow" points to the smaller number.

Your Turn

Guide Discussion Have pairs of students discuss their Four Corners activity sheet. Remind students to use vocabulary to explain how they compared the numbers on their cards.

↻ Language Production

Comprehension Support Direct students' attention to the data shown under the picture of a school.

Model Discuss the comparison at the top of the page. Help students use the data to find the number of students in Grades 3 and 5. *Are the numbers the same? Which one is bigger? Which one is smaller? So, we say that 94 is less than 121.* Have students complete the remaining comparisons. Be sure students understand that they should compare the numbers in the same order as the order in which the grades are mentioned in the problem.

Talk About It

Guide Discussion Have students complete the Talk About It questions on their own. Then have students work in pairs or small groups to discuss their answers. Encourage students to check one another by referring to definitions in Vocabulary in Context Picture It!

Your Turn

Guide Discussion Have students discuss their comparisons in pairs or small groups. Have volunteers tell how their numbers compare and then ask them to write the comparison on the board using a symbol.

Do You Understand?

You can use words and symbols to compare the number of students in Grade 5 to the number of students in Grade 3.

Words: 94 is less than 121.

Symbols: $94 < 121$

Grade 3: 121 students
Grade 4: 109 students
Grade 5: 94 students
Grade 6: 109 students

1. Compare the number of students in Grade 6 to the number of students in Grade 3.
   Words: 109 __is less than__ 121.
   Symbols: 109 $<$ 121

2. Compare the number of students in Grade 4 to the number of students in Grade 6.
   Words: 109 __is equal to (or equals)__ 109.
   Symbols: 109 $=$ 109

3. Compare the number of students in Grade 6 to the number of students in Grade 5.
   Words: 109 __is greater than__ 94.
   Symbols: 109 $>$ 94

Talk About It
What words and symbols can you use to compare numbers? Complete the sentences to explain.

4. The symbol > means … is greater than.
5. The symbol < means … is less than.
6. The symbol = means … is equal to (or equals).

Your Turn
Pick any two numbers in the box at the right. Tell your partner how the two numbers compare.

41	193
68	400
193	255

Leveled Language Proficiency

Students at each proficiency level should be able to perform the following tasks.

Listening/Speaking

Early Beginner Recognize a few vocabulary terms and follow very simple conversations with support. Repeat simple phrases, and use vocabulary terms to answer questions.

Beginner Follow simple directions; recognize some vocabulary terms. Say individual terms and simple phrases, and repeat longer phrases and short sentences.

Early Intermediate Begin to follow more abstract discussion about vocabulary terms. Speak in phrases and simple sentences, showing an increasing understanding of lesson vocabulary.

Intermediate Understand abstract ideas; recognize vocabulary as individual terms and in the context of spoken sentences. Show an ability to express abstract ideas about vocabulary.

Advanced/Transitioning Understand complex sentence structures; follow abstract conversation involving lesson vocabulary. Speak on abstract topics, including those that involve lesson vocabulary, with few if any grammatical and syntactical errors.

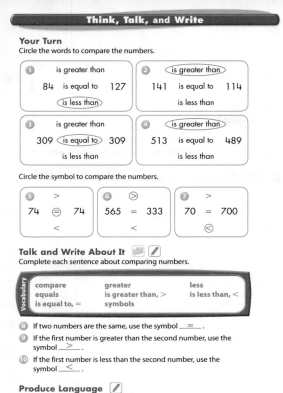

Your Turn

Circle the words to compare the numbers.

① is greater than
84 is equal to 127
(is less than)

② (is greater than)
141 is equal to 114
is less than

③ is greater than
309 (is equal to) 309
is less than

④ (is greater than)
513 is equal to 489
is less than

Circle the symbol to compare the numbers.

⑤ >
74 (=) 74
<

⑥ (>)
565 = 333
<

⑦ >
70 = 700
(<)

Talk and Write About It 💬 ✏️

Complete each sentence about comparing numbers.

Vocabulary		
compare	greater	less
equals	is greater than, >	is less than, <
is equal to, =	symbols	

⑧ If two numbers are the same, use the symbol __=__ .

⑨ If the first number is greater than the second number, use the symbol __>__ .

⑩ If the first number is less than the second number, use the symbol __<__ .

Produce Language ✏️

Write about what you have learned about comparing numbers. You may include examples. Use as many vocabulary terms and symbols as you can.

8   Lesson 2

Leveled Language Proficiency

Students at each proficiency level should be able to perform the following tasks.

Reading/Writing

Early Beginner Read some vocabulary terms with support, along with a few common words. Write short terms independently; copy terms and phrases.

Beginner Read a growing number of everyday words and some lesson vocabulary terms. Use sentence starters and visual supports to write individual terms and phrases.

Early Intermediate Read most vocabulary terms in isolation or in context; read sentences made up of simple, phonetically regular words and sight words. Write simple sentences with support to describe ideas and explain knowledge of vocabulary, with some errors.

Intermediate Read lesson vocabulary in context; read and follow simple directions; read and understand some abstract ideas. Write in full sentences with some grammatical errors, using sentence starters as needed and including vocabulary as appropriate.

Advanced/Transitioning Read and write full sentences containing concrete and abstract ideas related to lesson vocabulary with minimal support.

↻ Assess Understanding

Your Turn

Model Work through the first comparison with students. Ask if the numbers are the same. Then ask which is the bigger number and which is the smaller number. Discuss the correct phrase that describes how the numbers compare. Have students work in pairs to complete the rest of the comparisons.

Talk and Write About It

On Their Own Have students work independently or with a partner to complete the sentences.

Produce Language

On Their Own Have students work independently to write what they have learned about comparing numbers. Remind them to refer to Vocabulary in Context Picture It! for help. You may wish to have students share their sentences with the class.

Wrap Up

Table Talk Have students look back at the lesson's objectives. Allow time for them to reflect on what they have learned and then answer the essential question.

☑ **Learned** and applied vocabulary related to comparing numbers

☑ **Spoken** statements about comparing numbers

☑ **Written** statements about comparing numbers

Addition and Subtraction

Vocabulary Add, addition, equals, plus, addends, sum, subtract, subtraction, minus, difference, place value, hundreds, tens, ones, symbols, regroup

Materials Index cards

Math Background

- The answer to an addition problem is called the *sum*, and the answer to a subtraction problem is called the *difference*.

- When adding or subtracting large numbers, begin with the ones, then the tens, then the hundreds, regrouping as needed.

Addition and Subtraction

Essential Question What words and symbols do you need to know in order to learn about addition and subtraction?

You Will
- Add 2-digit and 3-digit numbers.
- Subtract 2-digit and 3-digit numbers.
- Use key terms to describe addition and subtraction.

Talk About It

Copy each term from Vocabulary in Context on a card. Listen to your teacher read each term. Create three piles of cards.

1. Place terms that you know in **Pile 1.**
2. Place terms you have heard but are not sure what they mean in **Pile 2.**
3. Place terms you do not know in **Pile 3.**

What do you know about each term? Explain. Use the sentence starters for support.

I know ... means ...
I think ... means ...
I do not know what ... means.

plus

difference

regroup

Your Turn
Look at the objectives listed under You Will at the top of the page. Working with a partner, predict what you will learn. Use the sentence starter below.

I am going to learn about ...

Frontload the Lesson

Essential Question

What words and symbols do you need to know in order to learn about addition and subtraction?

Talk About It

Build Background Read each term and ask students to make a vocabulary card. Encourage students to tell what they know about the terms they place in piles 1 and 2.

Content and Language

You Will

Model Read the objectives aloud and explain them in your own words. Display and discuss the symbols + and −.

Your Turn

Guide Discussion Have students read and discuss each objective. Ask students to tell what the objectives mean to them.

Leveled Instruction

Early Beginner Pair early beginners with students who have higher language proficiency. Have the early beginner point to parts of an example as the more advanced student models the appropriate vocabulary.

Beginner/Early Intermediate Beginners can answer in short phrases, especially when sentence starters are provided.

Intermediate Encourage students to work independently and to use complete sentences when asking and answering questions with the teacher and classmates.

Advanced/Transitioning Provide minimal assistance and encourage students to give detailed answers in complete sentences. Have them use their language skills to help students at lower language proficiency levels.

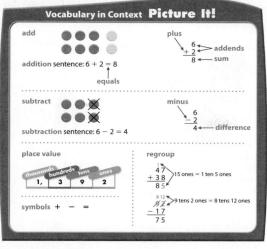

Vocabulary in Context Picture It!

add

addition sentence: 6 + 2 = 8
equals

plus
$$\begin{array}{r} 6 \\ +\ 2 \\ \hline 8 \end{array}$$ addends, sum

subtract

subtraction sentence: 6 − 2 = 4

minus
$$\begin{array}{r} 6 \\ -\ 2 \\ \hline 4 \end{array}$$ difference

place value

thousands	hundreds	tens	ones
1,	3	9	2

symbols + − =

regroup
$$\begin{array}{r} 4\ 7 \\ +\ 3\ 8 \\ \hline 8\ 5 \end{array}$$ 15 ones = 1 ten 5 ones

$$\begin{array}{r} 8\ 12 \\ \cancel{9}\cancel{2} \\ -\ 1\ 7 \\ \hline 7\ 5 \end{array}$$ 9 tens 2 ones = 8 tens 12 ones

Talk About It
Talk with a partner. Complete the sentences.
1. Use + to do … **addition.**
2. Use − to do … **subtraction.**
3. Add numbers to find the … **sum.**
4. Subtract numbers to find the … **difference.**
5. When subtracting, sometimes you cannot subtract the ones, so you need to … **regroup.**

Your Turn
Write an addition sentence. Write a subtraction sentence. Talk about the parts of each sentence with a partner. Use all the vocabulary terms you can.

10   Lesson 3

Academic Vocabulary

- Students might have difficulty with the homophones *sum* and *some*. Consider writing and/or illustrating both words on the board, and pointing to the particular word when it is spoken to prevent confusion.

- Point out that while *difference* or *different* in everyday language means *not the same* or *not similar,* in math *difference* has a very specific meaning.

- Identify the prefix *re–* in *regroup*. Explain that *re–* means *again,* as in *rewrite, review,* and *remake*. So, *regroup* means to group again.

Additional resources for building and reinforcing vocabulary are provided on pages T37–T41.

Cultural Consideration

In languages such as Hebrew and Arabic, which are read from right to left, numbers are still read from left to right, as in English. Be sure all students understand that our numbers are read from left to right; however, you do addition and subtraction in vertical form from right to left.

 # Comprehensible Input
Guide students to understanding

Vocabulary in Context Picture It!

1. **Say the Term** Have students repeat, stressing each syllable. Then combine syllables and have students repeat.

2. **Introduce Meaning** Connect each term to the visual that illustrates it.

3. **Demonstrate** When you discuss *regroup*, walk through the problems at the board, connecting each step you take to the visuals. *Seven plus eight equals fifteen. I regroup fifteen into 5 ones, here in the ones place, and 1 ten, up here in the tens place.*

4. **Apply** Have students demonstrate understanding with Talk About It.

Repeat the routine for each vocabulary term.

Remind students that they can review vocabulary terms for addition and subtraction on page 89 and record more terms as they learn them.

Talk About It

Guide Discussion Have student pairs complete and discuss each sentence. Then provide this additional sentence completion, if time permits:

Numbers that are added are called … **addends.**

Intervention

If students have difficulty saying number sentences …

Then write an addition problem and a subtraction problem on the board. Underneath each, write the same problem using words for each number and symbol. Diagram each problem by connecting the words to the numbers and symbol.

Your Turn

Guide Discussion Have pairs of students share the number sentences they used for their discussion in Your Turn. Encourage them to point to each part of the sentence and say the related vocabulary term. According to proficiency levels, they might also talk about how they found each sum or difference.

↻ Language Production

Comprehension Support Explain that the words on the cards tell about the visuals and present a problem. Students will use addition or subtraction to solve the problem and answer the question.

Model Before discussing the problems on the cards, review 3-digit addition and subtraction with problems such as 218 + 127 and 375 − 138. Emphasize lesson vocabulary and carefully discuss regrouping. For example, in the subtraction problem, explain: *I can't subtract 5 ones minus 8 ones. So I regroup the 7 tens and 5 ones as 6 tens and 15 ones.* Show students how to record the steps in the subtraction process.

Link the written information about Bridal Veil Falls to the visual. *This waterfall is called Bridal Veil Falls. It's part of Niagara Falls in New York. The picture shows that water drops 78 feet from the top to the rocks, and flows 103 feet over rocks to the pool of water below. The problem is to figure out the total height of Bridal Veil Falls. So, I will use addition to add the two numbers.* Guide students as needed through the Statue of Liberty card as well.

Talk About It

Guide Discussion Have students work in pairs. Encourage them to point to and name the different symbols and numbers in their problems. Provide time for students to plan their responses to the questions.

Your Turn

Guide Discussion Have students work in pairs. One partner writes and talks about a problem. Then they switch roles. Some students may benefit from planning what to say about their problem by first writing out a few sentences describing it. Partners can record their work on copies of T44.

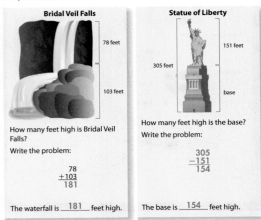

Do You Understand?

Complete the cards.

Bridal Veil Falls

78 feet
103 feet

How many feet high is Bridal Veil Falls?
Write the problem:

$$\begin{array}{r} 78 \\ +103 \\ \hline 181 \end{array}$$

The waterfall is __181__ feet high.

Statue of Liberty

151 feet
305 feet
base

How many feet high is the base?
Write the problem:

$$\begin{array}{r} 305 \\ -151 \\ \hline 154 \end{array}$$

The base is __154__ feet high.

Talk About It 💬
How did you solve the problems? Complete the sentences to explain.
1. For the Bridal Veil Falls problem, I used … addition.
2. For the Statue of Liberty problem, I used … subtraction.
3. To add the numbers, I started with the … digit. ones
4. When subtracting, I had to … regroup.

Your Turn ✏️
Choose two numbers and one symbol from the box at the right. Write and solve a problem. Tell your partner about the problem.

+	−	567
94		830

Leveled Language Proficiency

Students at each proficiency level should be able to perform the following tasks.

Listening/Speaking

Early Beginner Follow oral directions that are supported by visual clues. Use single vocabulary terms to answer questions.

Beginner Follow simple directions; recognize some vocabulary terms. Make simple requests and respond to questions with simple phrases.

Early Intermediate Show understanding of directions and vocabulary terms through actions. Voluntarily participate in class activities by using words, phrases, and expressions.

Intermediate Demonstrate comprehension of vocabulary terms used in context. Participate in limited discussion using words and phrases.

Advanced/Transitioning Comprehend oral interactions that include both simple and complex sentence structures. Use vocabulary terms appropriately during academic discourse and participate fully in discussions.

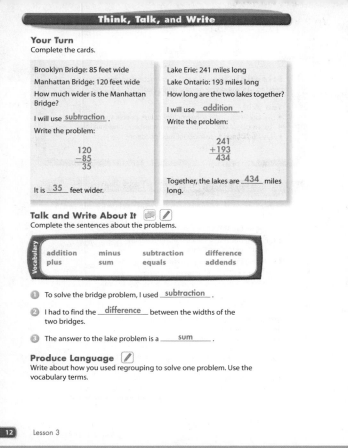

Your Turn

Complete the cards.

Brooklyn Bridge: 85 feet wide
Manhattan Bridge: 120 feet wide
How much wider is the Manhattan Bridge?

I will use __subtraction__ .

Write the problem:

$$\begin{array}{r} 120 \\ -85 \\ \hline 35 \end{array}$$

It is __35__ feet wider.

Lake Erie: 241 miles long
Lake Ontario: 193 miles long
How long are the two lakes together?

I will use __addition__ .

Write the problem:

$$\begin{array}{r} 241 \\ +193 \\ \hline 434 \end{array}$$

Together, the lakes are __434__ miles long.

Talk and Write About It

Complete the sentences about the problems.

Vocabulary

| addition | minus | subtraction | difference |
| plus | sum | equals | addends |

1. To solve the bridge problem, I used __subtraction__ .

2. I had to find the __difference__ between the widths of the two bridges.

3. The answer to the lake problem is a __sum__ .

Produce Language

Write about how you used regrouping to solve one problem. Use the vocabulary terms.

12　Lesson 3

Leveled Language Proficiency

Students at each proficiency level should be able to perform the following tasks.

Reading/Writing

Early Beginner Show understanding of written material by following directions or stating what is learned. Copy lists of words; write 1–2 vocabulary terms independently.

Beginner/Early Intermediate Connect graphic features with text to enable independent reading. Use vocabulary terms to complete sentence starters.

Intermediate Show understanding of written material by ability to follow directions or state what is learned. Write full sentences, with some errors, that feature vocabulary terms.

Advanced/Transitioning Independently read instructions and academic text. Write complete sentences with very few errors.

↻ Assess Understanding

Your Turn

Model Explain that these cards present information about two bridges and two lakes. Read the top of each card with students. It might be helpful to discuss the comparative form of *wide* used in the first problem. The ending *–er* indicates that two things are being compared. Also discuss the noun form, *width,* as that word appears in the second sentence under Talk About It. Explain to students that they will decide whether to use addition or subtraction, write and solve the problems, and complete the final sentence on each card with the answer.

Talk and Write About It

On Their Own Have students work alone for 10 minutes. Then have them compare their problems in pairs and share their responses to the questions.

Produce Language

On Their Own Have students use the terms they have learned in this lesson in their writing. Encourage them to review Vocabulary in Context Picture It! as needed.

Wrap Up

Table Talk Have students look back at the lesson's objectives. Allow time for them to reflect on what they have learned and then answer the essential question.

☑ **Learned** and applied symbols and vocabulary related to addition and subtraction

☑ **Spoken** statements to describe addition and subtraction

☑ **Written** statements about how to add and subtract numbers

Meaning of Multiplication

Vocabulary Multiply, times, factors, product, multiplication, multiples, array, row, column, even numbers, odd numbers

Materials Index cards, pictures of rows of seats and a column (as in a pillar)

Math Background

- Multiplication can be used to solve repeated addition problems. For example,

$$3 + 3 + 3 + 3 + 3 + 3 = 18$$
$$3 \times 6 = 18$$

- An *array* is frequently used to model a multiplication sentence. The number of rows and the number of columns represent the *factors,* and the total number of elements is the *product.*

⟳ Frontload the Lesson

Essential Question

What vocabulary terms do you need to use when you discuss multiplication?

Talk About It

Build Background Have students sort the terms. Encourage them to tell what they know about familiar terms.

⟳ Content and Language

You Will

Model Read the objectives aloud and explain them in your own words. Use diagrams and drawings to support your explanations.

Your Turn

Guide Discussion Have students read the objectives. Discuss what these objectives mean to them. Ask students to tell which ideas are most interesting to them.

Meaning of Multiplication

Essential Question What vocabulary terms do you need to use when you discuss multiplication?

You Will
- Model, write, and solve multiplication problems.
- Learn about odd numbers, even numbers, and multiples.
- Use key terms to talk about multiplication.

Talk About It

Make an index card for each vocabulary term below. Place each card in one of three piles.

1. Place terms that you know in **Pile 1.**
2. Place terms you have heard but are not sure what they mean in **Pile 2.**
3. Place terms you do not know in **Pile 3.**

factors	product	array
multiples	even numbers	column
multiplication	odd numbers	row
multiply	times	

multiples

What do you know about each term? Explain, using the sentence starters for support.

I know … means …
I think … means …
I do not know what … means.

Your Turn
Look at the objectives listed under You Will at the top of the page. Working with a partner, predict what you will learn. Use the sentence starter below.

I am going to learn about …

Meaning of Multiplication   13

Leveled Instruction

Early Beginner Partner students with those at higher language proficiency level, so they might have assistance at hand. Expect single words and gestures as answers.

Beginner Structured assistance is helpful for beginners. They can answer in short phrases, especially when sentence starters are provided.

Early Intermediate Expect phrases and simple sentences from students as answers to the questions. Provide immediate feedback so students can self-correct.

Intermediate Students should be able to produce complete sentences as answers. They should require minimal assistance in understanding information and questions.

Advanced/Transitioning Students should produce answers that include some details and elaboration. Partner them with students at lower language proficiency levels so they might offer them assistance.

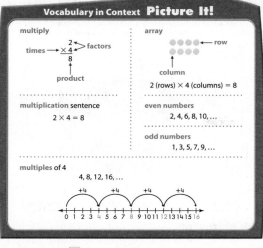

Vocabulary in Context **Picture It!**

multiply

$$\begin{array}{r} 2 \\ \times\,4 \\ \hline 8 \end{array}$$

times → $\times 4$ → factors

product

array

● ● ● ● ← row
● ● ● ●

column

2 (rows) × 4 (columns) = 8

multiplication sentence

2 × 4 = 8

even numbers

2, 4, 6, 8, 10, …

odd numbers

1, 3, 5, 7, 9, …

multiples of 4

4, 8, 12, 16, …

+4   +4   +4   +4

0 1 2 3 4 5 6 7 8 9 10 11 12 13 14 15 16

Talk About It

Talk with a partner. Complete the sentences.

1. The numbers you multiply are called … **factors.**
2. The answer to a multiplication problem is the … **product.**
3. 1, 3, and 5 are … **odd numbers.**
4. All multiples of 2 are also … **even numbers.**
5. 6 × 4 = 24 is a … sentence. **multiplication**

Your Turn

Look at the array in the chart above. How can you describe it?
Use as many vocabulary terms as possible. Tell a partner.

Academic Vocabulary

- As you discuss multiplication sentences, point out that *times* means "multiplied by," and does not refer to the time on a clock. Also, discuss the similarities and differences between *sentences* in English or another language and *sentences* in math.

- Make clear the differences between *array* and auditory similarities, such as *a ray* (narrow beam of light; part of a line with exactly one endpoint), and the name *Ray*.

- Reviewing the architectural use of the terms *row* and *column* might help students remember which is which in an array. Provide pictures if possible, of a row of seats going across a sports arena and a column standing vertically.

- Help students differentiate between the labels of *odd* and *even* numbers and the non-mathematical uses of the terms. *Odd* is used to describe something strange or unusual, but an odd number is not unusual—half of all numbers are odd! *Even* is most commonly used to describe something that stays steady ("an even speed"), a level surface, or a tie in a sporting situation.

Additional resources for building and reinforcing vocabulary are provided on pages T37–T41.

↻ Comprehensible Input

Guide students to understanding

Vocabulary in Context Picture It!

1. **Say the Term** Have students repeat, stressing each syllable. Then combine syllables and have students repeat.

2. **Introduce Meaning** Connect the term to the visual that illustrates it.

3. **Demonstrate** Use gestures and drawings to demonstrate. For example, when teaching the term *array*, draw 2 rows of triangles with 8 triangles per row on the board. Point to the rows and say, *There are 2 rows in this array.* Point to the columns and say, *There are 8 columns in this array.*

4. **Apply** Have students demonstrate understanding with Talk About It.

Repeat the routine for each vocabulary term.

Remind students that they can review vocabulary terms for multiplication on page 90 and record more terms as they learn them.

Talk About It

Guide Discussion Have students discuss the responses with a partner. Then provide this additional sentence completion, if time permits:

Things in an array are arranged in rows and … **columns.**

Intervention

If students have difficulty discriminating between the terms *multiply* and *multiple* …

Then review the words, focusing on the endings. Clearly articulate each word and have students echo it several times. Point out that you multiply to *get* a product, but a multiple *is* a product.

Your Turn

Guide Discussion Have pairs of students keep track of the number of vocabulary terms they used during their discussion in Your Turn. Then have pairs share their results.

↻ Language Production

Comprehension Support Tell students that multiplication can be used in their daily lives. For example, the tiles on a floor are probably an array. You can multiply the number of rows by the number of columns to find how many tiles cover a floor. If your classroom has a tiled floor, draw attention to it, or display a picture of a tiled floor. Then discuss the different "rooms" pictured on page 15.

Model Describe the tiles in the hallway. *There are 2 rows and 10 columns of tiles. 2 and 10 are the factors in the multiplication sentence for this array.* Have students determine the product. *The product, 20, tells me that there are 20 tiles in the hallway.* Have students complete the other tile problems.

Talk About It

Guide Discussion Have students work in pairs to complete the sentences. Have them refer to the arrays they formed and the corresponding multiplication sentences. Provide time for them to plan their responses.

Your Turn

Guide Discussion Have students work in pairs to complete Your Turn. Remind them that they can refer to Vocabulary in Context Picture It! to review vocabulary terms.

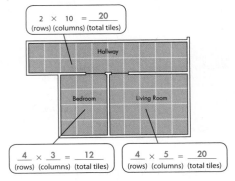

Do You Understand?

The tiled floors of three rooms are pictured below. Complete the multiplication sentences to find the number of tiles in each room.

$$2 \times 10 = \underline{20}$$
(rows) (columns) (total tiles)

Hallway

Bedroom   Living Room

$$\underline{4} \times \underline{3} = \underline{12}$$
(rows) (columns) (total tiles)

$$\underline{4} \times \underline{5} = \underline{20}$$
(rows) (columns) (total tiles)

Talk About It 💬
How does multiplication work? Complete the sentences to explain.

1. One way to picture multiplication is with an ... **array.**
2. The number of rows and the number of columns in the array are the ... **factors.**
3. The total number in the array is the ... **product.**

Your Turn ✏️
Write a multiplication sentence. Explain it to a partner. Use the sentence starters for support.

The factors are ...

The product is ...

Meaning of Multiplication   **15**

Leveled Language Proficiency

Students at each proficiency level should be able to perform the following tasks.

Listening/Speaking

Early Beginner Recognize a few vocabulary terms and follow very simple conversations with support. Make and respond to requests, using single words or short phrases.

Beginner Follow simple directions; recognize some vocabulary terms. Say individual terms and simple phrases, and repeat longer phrases and short sentences.

Early Intermediate Show understanding of key ideas, especially when visual support is provided. Retell the steps required to complete an activity, using vocabulary terms properly.

Intermediate Show comprehension of vocabulary terms and words that have multiple meanings. Participate in limited discussion using words and phrases.

Advanced/Transitioning Demonstrate understanding of explanations without requiring concrete references. Participate fully in discussions, including those on abstract topics, using a variety of sentence structures.

Your Turn

Draw different arrays that each have 6 columns. Write the multiplication sentence for each array. The first two are done for you.

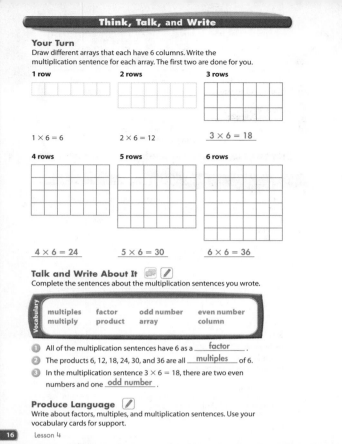

1 row

$1 \times 6 = 6$

2 rows

$2 \times 6 = 12$

3 rows

$3 \times 6 = 18$

4 rows

$4 \times 6 = 24$

5 rows

$5 \times 6 = 30$

6 rows

$6 \times 6 = 36$

Talk and Write About It 🗨 ✏

Complete the sentences about the multiplication sentences you wrote.

Vocabulary
multiples factor odd number even number
multiply product array column

1. All of the multiplication sentences have 6 as a ___factor___ .
2. The products 6, 12, 18, 24, 30, and 36 are all ___multiples___ of 6.
3. In the multiplication sentence $3 \times 6 = 18$, there are two even numbers and one ___odd number___ .

Produce Language ✏

Write about factors, multiples, and multiplication sentences. Use your vocabulary cards for support.

Leveled Language Proficiency

Students at each proficiency level should be able to perform the following tasks.

Reading/Writing

Early Beginner Participate in some independent reading when strong visual support is provided. Copy vocabulary terms, and write one or two of them independently.

Beginner/Early Intermediate Read simple sentences and vocabulary terms with the help of someone at a higher level of language proficiency. Use sentence starters to write individual words and phrases, including vocabulary terms.

Intermediate Follow written directions and retell what was read independently. Write simple sentences that use vocabulary terms properly, although with some grammatical errors.

Advanced/Transitioning Read and carry out written instructions and independently read lessons with ease of comprehension. Write a variety of sentences, including those that explain vocabulary terms, with few errors.

↻ Assess Understanding

Your Turn

Model Use sticky notes or draw on the board to show the 1×6 array. *This array has 1 row and 6 columns. So, the multiplication sentence for this array is $1 \times 6 = 6$.* Similarly, discuss the 2×6 array. Have students draw other 6-column arrays having 3, 4, 5, and 6 rows and record the correct multiplication sentences.

Talk and Write About It

On Their Own Have students work independently to complete the sentences.

Produce Language

On Their Own Have students use the terms they have learned in this lesson in their writing. Encourage them to review the terms from Vocabulary in Context Picture It! on page 14, as needed.

Wrap Up

Table Talk Have students look back at the lesson's objectives. Allow time for them to reflect on what they have learned and then answer the essential question.

☑ **Learned** and applied symbols and vocabulary related to multiplication

☑ **Spoken** statements to describe multiplication and the components of a multiplication sentence

☑ **Written** statements about multiplication and the numbers involved

Multiplication and Division Facts

Vocabulary Multiply, factors, times, product, divide, divided by, dividend, divisor, quotient, array, row, column, fact family, multiplication facts, division facts

Materials Picture of a marching band (optional)

Math Background

- Facts are number sentences that can be committed to memory, such as $5 \times 6 = 30$ and $24 \div 3 = 8$.

- A fact family contains related facts. Most fact families involve four facts. Some fact families (such as $6 \times 6 = 36$ and $36 \div 6 = 6$) involve just two facts.

Multiplication and Division Facts

Essential Question What words and symbols should you use when you learn about multiplication and division facts?

You Will
- Write multiplication and division facts.
- Learn about multiplication and division fact families.
- Use key terms to talk about multiplication and division.

Talk About It

Look at the list of terms below. In the first two columns of the chart, write terms you **know** or **want** to know more about.

array	division fact	multiply
column	divisor	product
divide	fact family	quotient
divided by	factor	row
dividend	multiplication fact	times

Know	Want	Learned

What do you know about each term you wrote in the chart? Explain, using the sentence starters for support.

I know … means …
I want to know more about …

Your Turn 💬
Look at the objectives under You Will at the top of the page. Working with a partner, predict what you are going to learn. Use the sentence starter for support.

I am going to learn about …

Multiplication and Division Facts **17**

Frontload the Lesson

Essential Question

What words and symbols should you use when you learn about multiplication and division facts?

Talk About It

Build Background Read the list of words aloud to the class. Model how to use the Know-Want-Learn chart. (See page T43 for additional copies.) Ask for volunteers to say what they might already know about various terms.

Content and Language

You Will

Model Read the objectives aloud and explain them in your own words. Use diagrams and drawings to support your explanations.

Your Turn

Guide Discussion Have students read the objectives. Discuss what these objectives mean to them.

Leveled Instruction

Early Beginner Partner students with those at higher language proficiency levels, so they might have assistance at hand. Expect gestures, or single words and simple phrases as answers.

Beginner Beginners can answer in short phrases, especially when sentence starters are provided.

Early Intermediate Expect phrases and simple sentences from these students in answering questions and joining discussions. Provide immediate feedback so students can self-correct.

Intermediate Students should produce complete sentences that show their comprehension of activity information and questions.

Advanced/Transitioning Students should produce a variety of sentence types when answering questions or making comments. They can offer support and assistance to students at lower proficiency levels.

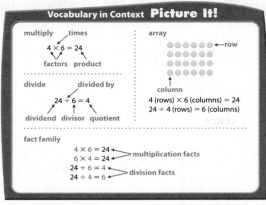

Academic Vocabulary

- Students may associate the term *product* as something they buy. Point out that in math *product* has a very specific meaning—the answer in a multiplication sentence.

- Distinguish the mathematical meaning of *times* from its various everyday meanings, such as the parts of a day—i.e., hours, minutes.

- Make clear the differences between *array* and auditory similarities, such as *a ray* (narrow beam of light; part of a line with exactly one endpoint), and the name *Ray*.

- Discuss the term *family*. Point out that members of a family are related. Then write a fact family on the board and explain that the facts in a fact family are related.

Additional resources for building and reinforcing vocabulary are provided on pages T37–T41.

Cultural Consideration

In some countries, a middle dot is more commonly used than the *times* or × symbol to indicate multiplication:

$$4 \cdot 6 = 24$$

↻ Comprehensible Input

Guide students to understanding

Vocabulary in Context Picture It!

1. **Say the Term** Have students repeat, stressing each syllable. Then combine syllables and have students repeat.

2. **Introduce Meaning** Connect the term to the visual that illustrates it.

3. **Demonstrate** Draw the following triangle on the board to model how a fact family relates to multiplication and division.

Say: *If I cover the top number, I can multiply the bottom numbers to find the product. If I cover one of the bottom numbers, I can use the other two numbers to divide.*

4. **Apply** Have students demonstrate understanding with Talk About It.

Repeat the routine for each vocabulary term.

Remind students that they can review vocabulary terms for multiplication and division on page 90 and record more terms as they learn them.

Talk About It

Guide Discussion Have students discuss the sentences with a partner. Then provide this additional sentence completion if time permits:

In the division fact $40 \div 8 = 5$, the number 40 is the … **dividend.**

Intervention

If students have difficulty pronouncing the division terms stemming from the base word *divide* (*division, dividend, divisor, divided by*) …

Then review the words, focusing on the short *i* and long *i* sounds in the words. Clearly articulate each word and have students echo it several times.

Your Turn

Guide Discussion Have pairs of students keep track of the number of vocabulary terms they used during their discussion in Your Turn. Then have pairs share their results.

↻ Language Production

Comprehension Support Tell students that the arrays show two different ways that a marching band could be arranged. (If possible, show a picture of a marching band.) Explain that when people stand in rows and columns, they form an array. Students will use the arrays to write fact families.

While most fact families contain four facts, some students might observe that some arrays yield fact families with only two facts. For example, a 4 × 4 array corresponds to the fact family of 4 × 4 = 16 and 16 ÷ 4 = 4.

Model Focus on the top array. What numbers are in the fact family? *I will count the rows and the columns. Then I will find how many in all.* Model counting the rows and columns and write the numbers on the board. *Now that I have the numbers, I can write the multiplication and division facts. I will start with multiplication.* Say the first multiplication fact, and ask a volunteer to say the second one. Repeat for the division facts.

Talk About It

Guide Discussion Have students work in pairs to complete the sentences. Provide time for them to plan their responses.

Your Turn

Guide Discussion Have students share their division fact with a partner. Note that two different division facts are possible (27 ÷ 3 = 9 and 27 ÷ 9 = 3), so their answers might not be the same.

Do You Understand?

Look at two ways a marching band can line up. Complete the fact family for each array.

Fact Family

4	×	3	=	12
3	×	4	=	12
12	÷	4	=	3
12	÷	3	=	4

Fact Family

5	×	6	=	30
6	×	5	=	30
30	÷	5	=	6
30	÷	6	=	5

Talk About It 💬
What terms help you to understand multiplication and division facts? Complete the sentences to explain.

1 There are usually four facts in a … fact family.

2 In a division fact, the number you are dividing by is the … divisor.

3 In a multiplication fact, the numbers being multiplied are the … factors.

Your Turn 🖊
Write a division fact that belongs in the fact family for 9 × 3 = 27. Write how the facts are related. Share with a partner.

Leveled Language Proficiency

Students at each proficiency level should be able to perform the following tasks.

Listening/Speaking

Early Beginner Recognize a few vocabulary terms and follow very simple conversations with support. Make and respond to requests, using single words, short phrases, or gestures.

Beginner Recognize some vocabulary terms, especially when visual support is provided. Say individual terms and respond to requests with simple phrases.

Early Intermediate Show understanding of oral questions that use key terms. Reply to questions with short answers or requests for clarification.

Intermediate Show comprehension of vocabulary terms used during discussions. Participate in limited discussions using words and phrases.

Advanced/Transitioning Demonstrate understanding of discussions that use a variety of sentence structures. Use key terms and other grade-level vocabulary during discussions.

Your Turn

Draw an array with 9 rows and 4 columns.
Then write the fact family that goes with the array.

Array	Fact Family
	$9 \times 4 = 36$
	$4 \times 9 = 36$
	$36 \div 4 = 9$
	$36 \div 9 = 4$

Talk and Write About It

Complete the sentences about the array and the fact family.

Vocabulary			
dividend	factors	quotient	fact families
product	times	divisor	array

1. In each division fact, 36 is the ___dividend___ .

2. In each multiplication fact, 36 is the ___product___ .

3. The number of rows and the number of columns in my array are
   the ___factors___ in the multiplication facts.

Produce Language

Write the terms you learned about in this lesson in the third column
of the chart on page 17. Write what you know about these terms.
Use sentence starters from throughout the lesson for support.

Leveled Language Proficiency

Students at each proficiency level should be able to
perform the following tasks.

Reading/Writing

Early Beginner Read a few, short common words and
some vocabulary terms, with help from a partner and when
strong visual support is provided. Copy words and phrases
from the board. Write individual vocabulary terms once the
meanings are understood.

Beginner/Early Intermediate Read simple sentences
with the help of someone at a higher level of language
proficiency. Use sentence starters to write individual words
and phrases, including vocabulary terms.

Intermediate Follow written directions and demonstrate
comprehension of reading done independently. Write
simple sentences that use vocabulary terms properly,
though with some grammatical errors.

Advanced/Transitioning Carry out written
instructions and independently read lessons with ease of
comprehension. Write a variety of sentences, and use
correct mechanics when editing them.

⟳ Assess Understanding

Your Turn

Model Draw an array. Model counting out
the rows and columns and using the numbers
to create a multiplication fact. Have students
volunteer the remaining facts in the fact family.
Then have students work on their own arrays.

Talk and Write About It

On Their Own Have students work
independently or with a partner to complete
the sentences.

Produce Language

On Their Own Have students complete the
Know-Want-Learn chart from the beginning of
the lesson. Have students write what they have
learned about these terms and share their ideas
with the class. If students have no new terms
to add to column 3, ask them to write about
several of the other terms in the lesson.

Wrap Up

Table Talk Have students look back at the
lesson's objectives. Allow time for them to reflect
on what they have learned and then answer the
essential question.

☑ **Learned** about multiplication and division
fact families and applied symbols and
vocabulary related to multiplication and
division

☑ **Spoken** statements to describe related
multiplication and division facts

☑ **Written** statements about multiplication and
division fact families

Lesson 6

Understanding Story Problems

Vocabulary Add, addition, plus, sum, subtract, subtraction, minus, difference, multiply, multiplication, times, product, divide, division, divided by, quotient, remainder, operations

Materials Counters (optional)

Math Background

- The four common operations in mathematics are addition, subtraction, multiplication, and division.

- The remainder in a division problem is the number left over when the two numbers cannot be divided evenly.

 Frontload the Lesson

What words do you need to understand when you solve story problems?

Essential Question

Talk About It

Build Background Have students rate the terms. Encourage them to tell what they know about the terms they rate with a 3.

Content and Language

You Will

Model Read the objectives aloud and explain them in your own words. Use diagrams and drawings to support your explanations.

Your Turn

Guide Discussion Ask students to read the objectives. Discuss what the objectives mean to them. Ask students to tell which ideas are most interesting to them.

Understanding Story Problems

Essential Question What words do you need to understand when you solve story problems?

You Will
- Read story problems and choose the right operation to solve them.
- Use all four operations to solve story problems.
- Use key vocabulary terms to discuss story problems and how to solve them.

Talk About It

Rate these mathematical terms according to the following scale.

1. I have never heard of this term before.
2. I have heard this term, but I do not know how to use it in math.
3. I understand this term and know how to use it in math.

_____ addition	_____ multiplication	_____ subtraction
_____ difference	_____ plus	_____ sum
_____ division	_____ product	_____ times
_____ divided by	_____ quotient	_____ operations
_____ minus	_____ remainder	

What do you know about each term? Explain, using the sentence starters for support.

I do not know what . . . means.
I think . . . means . . .
I know . . . means . . .

Your Turn
Look at the objectives listed under You Will at the top of the page. Working with a partner, predict what you will learn. Use the sentence starter below.

I am going to learn about . . .

Leveled Instruction

Early Beginner Partner early beginners with students at higher proficiency levels so they may provide added support. Expect single words, gestures, and simple responses as answers.

Beginner/Early Intermediate Expect phrases and simple sentences from these students when they are answering questions, especially when sentence starters are provided.

Intermediate Students should be able to complete activities with minimal assistance. Expect phrases and simple sentences in answering questions and joining discussions. Provide immediate feedback so students can self-correct.

Advanced/Transitioning Students should produce detailed answers with minimal assistance. They can offer students at lower proficiency levels support and assistance.

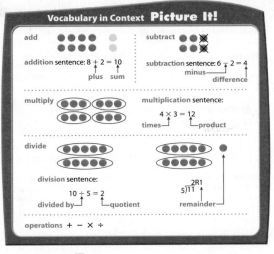

Vocabulary in Context Picture It!

add ●●●● ○   subtract ●● ✕
●●●● ○   ●● ✕

addition sentence: 8 + 2 = 10   subtraction sentence: 6 − 2 = 4
                    ↑plus ↑sum   ↑minus   ↑difference

multiply (●●●●)(●●●●)   multiplication sentence:
          (●●●●)(●●●●)   4 × 3 = 12
                                               times↗   ↖product

divide (●●●●●)(●●●●●)   (●●●●●)(●●●●●) ●
        (●●●●●)(●●●●●)   (●●●●●)(●●●●●)

division sentence: 2R1
         10 ÷ 5 = 2   5)11 ↑
   divided by↗ ↖quotient   remainder↗

operations + − × ÷

Talk About It

Talk with a partner. Complete the sentences. Look at the diagrams for help.

1. To put things together, use … **addition.**
2. To take away some things, use … **subtraction.**
3. If things are in equal groups, you can find the total number by using … **multiplication (or addition).**
4. To split things into equal groups, use … **division.**
5. The amount left over when you divide is called the … **remainder.**

Your Turn

Look at the operations and symbols above. How can you describe them? Use as many vocabulary terms as possible. Tell a partner.

22   Lesson 6

Academic Vocabulary

- Explain that operations in mathematics are processes used to solve problems. Other non-math uses of *operation* also refer to processes. For example, a medical operation is a process doctors use to repair a physical ailment.

Additional resources for building and reinforcing vocabulary are provided on pages T37–T41.

↻ Comprehensible Input
Guide students to understanding

Vocabulary in Context Picture It!

1. **Say the Term** Have students repeat, stressing each syllable. Then combine syllables and have students repeat.

2. **Introduce Meaning** Connect the term to the visual that illustrates it.

3. **Demonstrate** Use gestures and visuals to demonstrate. Use counters or other small objects to convey the meaning of *addition*. Show a group of 7 counters and a group of 5 counters. Push them together as you explain that addition means joining, or combining, two or more groups. Have the class help you write the number sentence for the situation, 7 + 5 = 12.

4. **Apply** Have students demonstrate understanding with Talk About It.

Repeat the routine for each vocabulary term.

Remind students that they can review vocabulary terms for the operations on pages 89–90 and record more terms as they learn them.

Talk About It

Guide Discussion Have students discuss the sentences with a partner. You might want to ask students to model each operation with counters. Provide this additional sentence completion if time permits:

Addition, subtraction, multiplication and division are all … **operations.**

Intervention

If students have difficulty with words ending with –*tion* and –*sion* …

Then review the –*tion* and –*sion* endings, pointing out that they are pronounced the same—*shun*. They also have the same meaning. Both suffixes point back to the base word and indicate something that is being done. Have students echo read the words after you several times.

Your Turn

Guide Discussion Have pairs of students keep track of the number of vocabulary terms they used during their discussion in Your Turn. Then have pairs share the results.

Understanding Story Problems

↻ Language Production

Comprehension Support Tell students that there are four story problems on the page. One of the operations will be used to solve each story problem.

Model Read the first problem aloud. *I can draw 12 blue counters for the 12 goats and 5 yellow counters for the cows. I will add 12 plus 5 to find the total number.* Write the number sentence on the board and state the answer: *Jenny feeds 17 animals.*

Have students complete the other problems. Allow them to use counters, if available, to plan their drawings.

Talk About It

Guide Discussion Provide time for students to plan their responses. Have partners discuss how they completed the sentences.

Your Turn

Guide Discussion As students write and solve their own word problem, you might want to have them provide a diagram or other artwork that illustrates the situation. Have them share their problem and describe it to a partner. Partners can record their work on copies of T44.

Read the problem. Draw a picture. The first picture is drawn for you. Then complete the number sentence to find the answer.

Addition
Jenny feeds 12 goats and 5 cows. How many animals does she feed?

●●●●●●●○○○
●●●●●●●○○○

__12__ + __5__ = __17__ animals

Subtraction
The chickens laid 22 eggs. The ducks laid 16 eggs. How many more eggs did the chickens lay?

Drawings will vary.

__22__ − __16__ = __6__ more eggs

Multiplication
Rico has 7 horses. Each horse has 4 horseshoes. How many horseshoes are there?

Drawings will vary.

__7__ × __4__ = __28__ horseshoes

Division
Ben has 30 pigs. He puts 6 pigs in each pen. How many pens will be filled with pigs?

Drawings will vary.

__30__ ÷ __6__ = __5__ pens

Talk About It 💬
Complete the sentences to tell about the problems.
1 In a number sentence, + stands for the word … plus.
2 The answer to a subtraction problem is called the … difference.
3 The product is the answer to a … problem. multiplication
4 If there had been any pigs left over in the division problem, the number of pigs left over would be called the … remainder.

Your Turn ✏️
Use one of the stories on this page as a model to write a story problem. Solve the problem. Tell your partner about the problem.

Understanding Story Problems   **23**

Leveled Language Proficiency

Students at each proficiency level should be able to perform the following tasks.

Listening/Speaking

Early Beginner Recognize a few vocabulary terms and follow very simple conversations with support. Make and respond to requests, using single words, gestures, or short phrases.

Beginner/Early Intermediate Follow simple directions; recognize some vocabulary terms. Say individual terms and simple phrases, and repeat longer phrases and short sentences.

Intermediate Show comprehension of vocabulary terms used during discussion. Participate in limited discussions using words and phrases.

Advanced/Transitioning Demonstrate understanding of discussions without requiring concrete references. Elaborate on discussion points using a variety of sentence types.

Your Turn

Write a number sentence to solve the problem. Then give the answer to the problem.

① Julia fills 10 bags with cherries. She puts 5 cherries in a bag. How many cherries does Julia have in all?

Number sentence: $10 \times 5 = 50$

Julia has __50__ cherries.

② There are 45 pumpkins in one patch and 38 pumpkins in another patch. How many pumpkins are there in all?

Number sentence: $45 + 38 = 83$

There are __83__ pumpkins in all.

③ Camilla grew 16 tomatoes. She gives them to 4 friends. Each friend gets the same number. How many tomatoes does she give to each friend?

Number sentence: $16 \div 4 = 4$

Each friend gets __4__ tomatoes.

Talk and Write About It 💬 ✏️

Complete the sentences about the story problems you solved.

Vocabulary			
addition	product	subtract	multiplication
remainder	sum	divide	operations

④ In Problem 1, I used __multiplication__ .

⑤ In Problem 2, I found the __sum__ .

⑥ In Problem 3, I needed to __divide__ .

Produce Language ✏️

Write about the steps you used to solve one of the problems. Use vocabulary terms in your sentences.

Leveled Language Proficiency

Students at each proficiency level should be able to perform the following tasks.

Reading/Writing

Early Beginner Read some vocabulary terms with support, along with a few common words. Write terms independently; copy terms and phrases.

Beginner Use visual and contextual support to determine meaning of terms, especially with the help of someone at a higher level of language proficiency. Use sentence starters and visual supports to write individual terms and phrases.

Early Intermediate Read most vocabulary terms in isolation or in context; read independently when text is made up of known words and simple sentences. Write simple sentences, with some errors.

Intermediate Read most vocabulary terms in context; read sentences made up of simple, phonetically regular words and sight words. Write in full sentences with some grammatical errors, using sentence starters as needed and including vocabulary terms as appropriate.

Advanced/Transitioning Read and write a variety of sentence types containing concrete and abstract ideas related to lesson content with minimal support.

↻ Assess Understanding

Your Turn

Model Read the introductions to the activity, and read the first problem. Discuss the operation and number sentence that are appropriate for the first problem. Read each problem aloud so that students can hear the words before working on their own. Then have students solve the problems.

Talk and Write About It

On Their Own Have students work independently or with a partner to complete the sentences.

Produce Language

On Their Own Have students use the terms they have learned in this lesson in their writing. Encourage them to tell what they learned about choosing the operation and writing the number sentence to solve a story problem.

Wrap Up

Table Talk Have students look back at the lesson's objectives. Allow time for them to reflect on what they have learned and then answer the essential question.

- ☑ **Learned** and applied language and operations related to solving story problems

- ☑ **Spoken** statements to describe the mathematical operations used to solve story problems

- ☑ **Written** statements about the process of solving story problems

Lesson 7

Estimation

Vocabulary Exactly, about, reasonable, unreasonable, round, nearest ten, estimate

Materials Index cards

 Math Background

- Estimating is a skill that often involves rounding strategies.

- To round a number to a certain place value, look at the digit to its right. If the digit is less than 5, round down. If the digit is 5 or more, round up. For example:

  52 rounds down to 50.
  57 rounds up to 60.

- The word *about* acts as a clue or a hint to provide an estimate rather than an exact answer.

Estimation

Essential Question What vocabulary do you need to know to understand and discuss estimation?

You Will
- Apply what you know about numbers and operations to estimate answers to math problems.
- Use rounding to help you make good estimates.
- Understand and use key terms related to estimation.

Talk About It

Make an index card for each vocabulary term below. Place each card in one of three piles.

Pile 1: I know what this term means.
Pile 2: I have heard of this term, but I am not sure how it is used in math.
Pile 3: I have not heard of this term.

exactly   round   estimate
reasonable   nearest ten   about
unreasonable

estimate

What do you know about each term? Explain, using the sentence starters for support.

I know ... means ...
I think ... means ...
I do not know what ... means.

Your Turn
Look at the objectives under You Will at the top of the page. Working with a partner, predict what you are going to learn. Use the sentence starter for support.

I am going to learn about ...

Estimation   **25**

Frontload the Lesson

 Essential Question

What vocabulary do you need to know to understand and discuss estimation?

Talk About It

Build Background Have students sort the terms. Encourage them to tell what they know about familiar terms.

Content and Language

You Will

Model Read the objectives aloud and explain them in your own words. Use examples in your explanations.

Your Turn

Guide Discussion Have students read the objectives. Have students discuss what the objectives mean to them.

Leveled Instruction

Early Beginner Partner students with those at higher language proficiency levels so that they might have assistance at hand. Expect single words and gestures as answers.

Beginner Students begin to respond with single English words or short phrases. At this level, students continue to benefit from partnerships with students at higher levels of language proficiency.

Early Intermediate Expect students to answer questions with phrases and simple sentences. Provide immediate feedback so students can self-correct.

Intermediate Students should be able to complete activities with minimal assistance. They should consistently answer questions and join in discussions using phrases and simple sentences.

Advanced/Transitioning Students at this level should be producing answers that include details and elaboration. Partner them with students at lower proficiency levels so they might offer assistance.

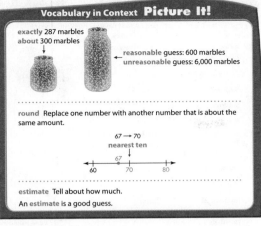

Vocabulary in Context **Picture It!**

exactly 287 marbles
about 300 marbles

reasonable guess: 600 marbles
unreasonable guess: 6,000 marbles

round Replace one number with another number that is about the same amount.

67 → 70
nearest ten

60   67   70   80

estimate Tell about how much.
An **estimate** is a good guess.

Talk About It
Talk with a partner. Complete the sentences.
1. A logical guess is an … **estimate.**
2. When you round 32 to 30, you round it to the … **nearest ten.**
3. There are … 24 hours in a day. **exactly**
4. An estimate of 100 days in a month is … **unreasonable.**

Your Turn
Choose three terms from the chart above. Use your own words to tell your partner what each term means.

26   Lesson 7

Academic Vocabulary

- Point out the connection between *round* numbers and physical roundness of the zero digit.

- Review the meaning of *about.* Students might read a story and tell what it is about. In math, *about* means "close to."

Additional resources for building and reinforcing vocabulary are provided on pages T37–T41.

 # Comprehensible Input

Guide students to understanding

Vocabulary in Context Picture It!

1. **Say the Term** Have students repeat, stressing each syllable. Then combine syllables and have students repeat.

2. **Introduce Meaning** Connect the term to the visual that illustrates it.

3. **Demonstrate** When teaching the term *nearest ten,* use a number line and explain several examples.

4. **Apply** Have students demonstrate understanding with Talk About It.

Repeat the routine for each vocabulary term.

Talk About It

Guide Discussion Have students discuss the sentences with a partner. Model the sentence starters. Then provide this additional sentence starter, if time permits:

A movie is … 2 hours long. **about**

Intervention

If students have difficulty discriminating between *estimate* as a noun and as a verb …

Then review the word in both its forms, focusing on the last syllable. Have students repeat, "I *estimate* ('mate') to find the *estimate* ('mit')."

Your Turn

Guide Discussion Encourage students to use examples to support their explanations.

Estimation   26

⟳ Language Production

Comprehension Support Tell students that they will use estimation to solve the three story problems on this page. Their first step is to round numbers to the nearest ten.

Model Read the first problem aloud. Be sure students do not confuse the meaning of *left* in *How many are left?* with the meaning of *left* as in *left hand.* Model rounding each number to the nearest ten. *The clown has 72 balloons. That's about 70. He gives away 48 balloons. That's about 50.* Use a number line to verify how you rounded the numbers. After rounding both numbers, use words and gestures to describe that the clown is giving balloons away. Subtract to find about how many he gives away. Emphasize that the answer is an estimate, and that's why we say *about* 20 balloons.

In Problem 3, discuss the phrase *in all*. Explain that this means the same as *total*. Also, explain that when a number is halfway between two tens, it is rounded up. So, when students round the numbers in the table, they should round 45 to 50.

Talk About It

Guide Discussion Have students work in pairs. Remind them to think about the story problem as they complete the sentences. Provide time for students to plan their responses.

Your Turn

Guide Discussion Have students write and solve their problems. Then have them work in pairs to talk about their estimates. Partners can record their work on copies of T44.

Do You Understand?

It's time for the Fourth of July parade! Read the story problems. Then fill in the missing numbers to find the estimates.

1. A clown has 72 balloons. He gives away 48. About how many balloons are left?

   Round 72 to the nearest ten: __70__

   Round 48 to the nearest ten: __50__

   Subtract: __70__ − __50__ = __20__

   Estimate: about __20__ balloons

2. Last year there were 11 floats in the parade. This year there will be 3 times as many. About how many floats will there be?

   Round 11 to the nearest ten: __10__

   Multiply: __10__ × __3__ = __30__

   Estimate: about __30__ floats

3. Use the table. About how many band members are there in all?

   Round 57 to the nearest ten: __60__

   Round 45 to the nearest ten: __50__

   Round 83 to the nearest ten: __80__

   Add: __60__ + __50__ + __80__ = __190__

   Estimate: about __190__ band members

Band	Marching Band Members
A	57
B	45
C	83

Talk About It 💬
Complete the sentences about these problems.

4. I rounded the numbers to the … nearest ten.
5. I computed with rounded numbers to find an … estimate.
6. My estimated answer tells … how many. about

Your Turn ✏️
Write a story problem and estimate the answer. Share your story problem with a partner. Tell how you estimated the answer.

Estimation **27**

Leveled Language Proficiency

Students at each proficiency level should be able to perform the following tasks.

Listening/Speaking

Early Beginner Recognize a few vocabulary terms and follow very simple conversations with support. Make and respond to requests, using single words, short phrases, or gestures.

Beginner/Early Intermediate Recognize some vocabulary terms, especially when visual support is provided. Say individual terms and respond to requests with phrases and simple sentences.

Intermediate Show comprehension of vocabulary terms used during discussion. Participate in limited discussions using words, phrases, and simple sentences.

Advanced/Transitioning Demonstrate understanding of discussions without requiring concrete references. Express oneself comfortably in oral contexts ranging from informal to formal interactions, using a variety of sentence structures.

Your Turn

Use rounding to find each estimate. Show your work.

① About how many beef tacos and chicken tacos are there in all?

Round 31 to 30.
Round 65 to 70.
30 + 70 = 100

About __100__ beef and chicken tacos

Paul's Taco Stand	
Taco	**Number**
Beef	31
Chicken	65
Fish	42
Bean	28
Cheese	17

② About how many more fish tacos are there than bean tacos?

Round 42 to 40.
Round 28 to 30.
40 − 30 = 10

About __10__ more fish tacos

③ Yesterday, there were 4 times as many cheese tacos. About how many cheese tacos were there yesterday?

Round 17 to 20.
4 × 20 = 80

About __80__ cheese tacos

Talk and Write About It

Complete the sentences.

Vocabulary

| about | round | exactly | unreasonable |
| estimate | nearest ten | reasonable | |

④ I estimated by rounding numbers to the __nearest ten__ .

⑤ When I round the numbers in a problem, the answer is an __estimate__ .

⑥ If my estimate is close to the exact amount, my estimate is __reasonable__ .

Produce Language ✎

Write about how rounding and estimating are related. Use an example. Use vocabulary terms in your sentences.

28   Lesson 7

Leveled Language Proficiency

Students at each proficiency level should be able to perform the following tasks.

Reading/Writing

Early Beginner Read common words, such as sight words, and some vocabulary terms, especially when supported by someone with a higher proficiency level. Write terms independently once learned; copy words and phrases from the board.

Beginner Use visual and contextual support to arrive at the meanings of terms. Use sentence starters and visual supports to write individual terms and phrases.

Early Intermediate Read most vocabulary terms in isolation and in context; read independently when text is made up of known words and simple sentences. Write phrases and simple sentences, with some errors.

Intermediate Read and follow directions; read and understand text that has some abstract ideas. Write complete sentences that include vocabulary terms, with some grammatical errors.

Advanced/Transitioning Carry out written instructions and independently read lessons with ease of comprehension. Write a variety of sentences, including details, with minimal support and errors.

⟳ Assess Understanding

Your Turn

Model Explain that students will use estimation to solve the problems on the page. Read the first problem and show them how to locate the numbers for each taco. Remind them of the steps they should follow to estimate. *I know that the first thing I should do is round the numbers to the nearest ten. I need to round 31 and 65 to the nearest ten, and then add them to estimate the answer.* Remind students that "halfway" numbers, such as 65, get rounded up to the next ten, 70.

Talk and Write About It

On Their Own Have students work with a partner to complete the sentences.

Produce Language

On Their Own Have students use the terms they have learned in this lesson in their writing. Encourage them to review the terms from Vocabulary in Context Picture It! on page 26 as needed.

Wrap Up

Table Talk Have students look back at the lesson's objectives. Allow time for them to reflect on what they have learned and then answer the essential question.

☑ **Learned** about rounding numbers and estimating answers

☑ **Spoken** statements to describe estimation and rounding numbers

☑ **Written** statements about estimation and rounding numbers

Fractions

Vocabulary Fraction, numerator, denominator, whole, equal parts, halves, half, thirds, third, fourths, fourth, fifths, fifth, sixths, sixth

Materials Green, red, and yellow crayons or markers

Math Background

- A fraction represents the division of a whole into equal parts. The whole may refer to a set, region, or segment. The top number, called the *numerator,* is the number of parts that the fraction represents. The bottom number, called the *denominator,* is the total number of parts in the whole.

Fractions

Essential Question What words do you need to understand when you discuss fractions?

You Will
- Identify and show fractions using figures, numbers, and terms.
- Understand and use key terms related to fractions.

Talk About It

Look at the list of terms below. In the first two columns of the chart, write terms you **know** or **want** to know more about.

equal parts	whole	fifth	fifths
fraction	half	halves	sixth
numerator	third	thirds	sixths
denominator	fourth	fourths	

Know	Want	Learned

What do you know about each term? Explain, using the sentence starters for support.

I know … means …
I want to know more about …

Your Turn

Look at the objectives under You Will at the top of the page. Working with a partner, predict what you are going to learn. Use the sentence starter for support.

I am going to learn about …

Fractions   29

Frontload the Lesson

Essential Question — What words do you need to understand when you discuss fractions?

Talk About It

Build Background Read the list of words aloud to the class. Model how to use the Know-Want-Learn chart. (See page T43 for additional copies of the chart.) Ask for volunteers to say what they might already know about terms they listed in the first two columns.

Content and Language

You Will

Model Read the objectives aloud and explain them in your own words. Use examples and figures to support your explanations.

Your Turn

Guide Discussion Have students read the objectives and discuss what the objectives mean to them.

Leveled Instruction

Early Beginner Provide single words and gestures as answers. Benefit from working with students at higher language proficiency to complete the activities.

Beginner Construct answers given sentence starters.

Early Intermediate Provide phrases and simple sentences as answers to the activities.

Intermediate Produce complete sentences and tackle the activities with little assistance.

Advanced/Transitioning Produce detailed answers with minimal assistance. These students can assist students at lower language proficiency levels.

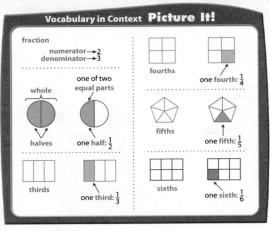

Talk About It 💬
Talk with a partner. Complete the sentences.
1. A fraction names a part of a ... whole.
2. One whole can be divided into ... equal parts (or halves, thirds, etc.).
3. The total number of equal parts is the ... of the fraction. denominator
4. A whole can be divided into three ... thirds.
5. In the fraction $\frac{4}{5}$, the 4 is the ... numerator.

Your Turn 💬
Describe one of the fractions in the box. Use as many vocabulary terms as you can. Tell a partner.

Academic Vocabulary

- Students might be familiar with other uses of *part*. Review additional common meanings of this word: a piece of a machine ("A car has many *parts*."); your share of work ("You should do your *part* to keep the room clean."); a role in a play or movie ("Who played the *part* of Harry Potter?").

- Point out the difference in both pronunciation and meaning between *have*, a verb and *half*, which refers to the fraction *one half*.

Additional resources for building and reinforcing vocabulary are provided on pages T37–T41.

↻ Comprehensible Input
Guide students to understanding

Vocabulary in Context Picture It!

1. **Say the Term** Have students repeat, stressing each syllable. Then combine syllables and have students repeat.

2. **Introduce Meaning** Connect the term to the visual that illustrates it.

3. **Demonstrate** Explain that a fraction describes something that is divided into equal parts. Demonstrate by dividing the class in half. (If you have an odd number of students, include yourself.) Explain: *There are X of you in the whole class. I have divided the class into two equal parts. There are Y of you in each part. So, the halves are equal.* Then do another demonstration using a piece of paper: *Now, I want to show fourths.* Fold the paper twice and open it so students can see the four equal parts.

4. **Apply** Have students demonstrate understanding with Talk About It.

Repeat the routine for each vocabulary term.

Talk About It

Guide Discussion Have students discuss the sentences with a partner. Model the sentence starters. Provide this additional sentence starter, if time permits:

If a whole is divided into six equal parts, each part is one ... sixth.

Intervention

If students have difficulty with the unvoiced /th/ sound at the end of the words ...

Then give them an articulation lesson on the sound: Model saying the term *third* and the initial sound /th/. Have students repeat until they are comfortable. Then have students blend the sound at the end of the term *fourth*. Model segmenting (*four–/th/*), then blending the sounds. Model the same way with the terms *fifth* and *sixth*.

Your Turn

Guide Discussion Have pairs of students compare the vocabulary terms they used during their discussion.

Fractions

↻ Language Production

Comprehension Support Tell students that this is the drawing of a garden. Talk about gardens. Then read the introductions aloud.

Model Describe the fraction of white flowers. *The garden is divided into five equal parts. One part has white flowers. So, the fraction that describes the white flowers is $\frac{1}{5}$. We say, "One fifth of the garden has white flowers."*

Talk About It

Guide Discussion Have students work in pairs. They should refer to the drawing and the fractions they wrote. Point out that the first sentence can be completed with either *equal parts* or *fifths*. Encourage them to say each fraction that is represented by numbers.

Your Turn

Guide Discussion Give students time to write their answers before joining a partner.

Look at the flower garden below. It is divided into 5 equal parts. Write the fraction of the garden that has blue flowers and the fraction that has pink flowers. Use the numbers for the part that has white flowers as a model.

There are 5 equal parts.

One part of the garden has white flowers.

$\frac{1}{5}$ of the garden has white flowers.

Blue flowers:
$\frac{1}{5}$ of the garden has blue flowers.

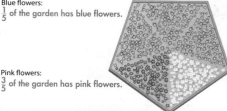

Pink flowers:
$\frac{3}{5}$ of the garden has pink flowers.

Talk About It 💬

How can you describe the garden? Complete the sentences.

① The garden is divided into five … equal parts (or fifths).

② Each part is one … of the garden. fifth

③ Each fraction of flowers in the garden has 5 in the … denominator.

Your Turn ✏️

Choose one of the ways shown below to divide a garden that is shaped like a rectangle. How would you describe it? Use the sentence starters for support. Share your ideas with a partner.

This garden is divided into …
The fraction … represents one part of this garden.

Leveled Language Proficiency

Students at each proficiency level should be able to perform the following tasks.

Listening/Speaking

Early Beginner Demonstrate comprehension of simple statements, including questions and commands. Make and respond to requests, asking for repetition when needed.

Beginner/Early Intermediate Demonstrate understanding of simple oral questions about academic content. Provide short answers, including vocabulary terms that have been learned.

Intermediate Demonstrate comprehension of oral input, including ordinary discourse and well-supported academic content. Explain how ideas or terms that are introduced are alike or different.

Advanced/Transitioning Demonstrate understanding of academic discussions without requiring concrete references. Support responses to oral questions or join discussions by providing additional details and explanations.

Your Turn

Draw a vegetable garden divided into 6 equal parts. Color 3 parts yellow for corn, color 2 parts red for tomatoes, and color 1 part green for peas. Write the fraction of the garden planted with each type of vegetable.

Students should divide this rectangle into 6 equal parts and then indicate that 3 parts are corn, 2 parts are tomatoes, and 1 part is peas.

The fraction of the garden that has corn is $\frac{3}{6}$.

The fraction of the garden that has tomatoes is $\frac{2}{6}$.

The fraction of the garden that has peas is $\frac{1}{6}$.

Talk and Write About It

Complete the sentences about the garden.

> **Vocabulary**
>
> | equal parts | sixth | thirds | fraction |
> | fourth | whole | half | numerator |

1. Peas are planted in one ___sixth___ of the garden.
2. All the parts for corn, tomatoes, and peas make up the ___whole___ garden.
3. Each type of vegetable is a different ___fraction___ of the garden.
4. Before I colored the garden, I divided it into six ___equal parts___.

Produce Language

Write the terms you learned about in this lesson in the third column of the chart on page 29. Write what you have learned about these terms. Use sentence starters from throughout the lesson for support.

Leveled Language Proficiency

Students at each proficiency level should be able to perform the following tasks.

Reading/Writing

Early Beginner Show willingness to read for meaning when visual support or the assistance of others is provided. Copy lists of words; write 1–2 vocabulary terms independently.

Beginner/Early Intermediate Read simple sentences with the help of a partner or an adult and visual support; read some vocabulary terms independently. Use sentence starters and other organizers to write individual words and phrases that use vocabulary terms.

Intermediate Show understanding of written material by the ability to follow directions or summarize text. Write full sentences and complex phrases about lesson concepts, using vocabulary terms; sentences may contain some grammatical and spelling errors.

Advanced/Transitioning Read and carry out simple and complex written instructions; read sentences about lesson ideas that use lesson vocabulary. Write complete sentences with very few errors.

↻ Assess Understanding

Your Turn

Model Explain that for this garden, students will divide it into equal parts themselves. Suggest that they sketch the divisions with a pencil so they can erase if their 6 parts do not look equal. Be sure they have yellow, red, and green crayons or markers and that they understand each vegetable is keyed to a color. *For corn, I will use yellow to color 3 of the 6 parts. Then I will write the fraction to describe it.*

Talk and Write About It

On Their Own Have students work alone for 10 minutes. They should refer to the plan, the fractions they wrote, and the colored garden to figure out how to complete the sentences. Once they have their answers, have students work in pairs.

Produce Language

On Their Own Have students complete the Know-Want-Learned chart from the beginning of the lesson. Have students write what they have learned about the terms they added to the third column and share their ideas with others. If some students have no new terms to add to column 3, ask them to write about any three or four terms in the lesson.

Wrap Up

Table Talk Have students look back at the lesson's objectives. Allow time for them to reflect on what they have learned and then answer the essential question.

☑ **Learned** and applied vocabulary related to fractions

☑ **Spoken** statements about fractions and what they describe

☑ **Written** statements about fractions and different ways of dividing a whole into equal parts

Fractions on a Number Line

Vocabulary Fraction, numerator, denominator, mixed number, whole number, number line, tick mark, equal parts, is less than, is greater than

Materials Index cards

Math Background

- A mixed number is made up of a whole number and a fraction. For example, $1\frac{1}{4}$.

- Number lines are useful to show how numbers compare. The number farther to the left is the lesser number.

Frontload the Lesson

Essential Question How do you use vocabulary terms to describe fractions on a number line?

Talk About It

Build Background Have students sort their word cards into three piles as you read each term aloud. Encourage students to tell what they know about the familiar terms.

Content and Language

You Will

Model Read the objectives aloud and explain them in your own words. Use diagrams and drawings to support your explanations.

Your Turn

Guide Discussion Have students read the objectives. Discuss what these objectives mean to them.

Fractions on a Number Line

Essential Question How do you use vocabulary terms to describe fractions on a number line?

You Will
- Identify fractions and mixed numbers.
- Use a number line to compare fractions and mixed numbers.
- Use math terms to discuss fractions, mixed numbers, and number lines.

Talk About It

Copy each term from Vocabulary in Context on a card. As your teacher reads each term, create three piles of cards.

1. Place terms that you know in **Pile 1.**
2. Place terms you have heard but are not sure what they mean in **Pile 2.**
3. Place terms you do not know in **Pile 3.**

denominator	is greater than	numerator
equal parts	is less than	number line
fraction	mixed number	tick mark

What do you know about each term? Explain, using the sentence starters for support.

I know … means …
I think … means …
I do not know what … means.

Your Turn
Look at the objectives under You Will at the top of the page. Working with a partner, predict what you are going to learn. Use the sentence starter for support.

I am going to learn about …

Leveled Instruction

Early Beginner Partner students with those at higher language proficiency levels so that they might have assistance at hand. Expect single words and gestures for responses.

Beginner/Early Intermediate Expect phrases and simple sentences. Encourage students to use sentence starters to help them construct their answers.

Intermediate Students should require minimal assistance when completing the activities. Expect phrases and simple sentences during discussions. Provide immediate feedback so students can self-correct.

Advanced/Transitioning Students should produce detailed answers with minimal assistance. Partner them with students at lower language proficiency levels so they might offer them assistance.

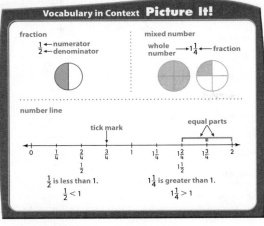

Talk About It 🗨
Talk with a partner. Complete the sentences.
① The top number in a fraction is the ... numerator.
② The bottom number in a fraction is the ... denominator.
③ Every mixed number ... 1. is greater than
④ By looking at a number line, I see that $\frac{1}{4}$ ... $\frac{1}{2}$. is less than
⑤ Tick marks show how a number line is divided into ... equal parts.

Your Turn ✏️
Write a mixed number. Describe it to a partner. Use the sentence starters if you need help.
The whole number in my mixed number is ...
The fraction in my mixed number is ...
The numerator is ...
The denominator is ...
It is greater than ...

Academic Vocabulary

- Students' knowledge of the verb *mix* might help them understand a *mixed number* as a whole number and a fraction. Review this definition of *mix*: "to combine different things." Discuss trail mix, or have students pantomime mixing different ingredients to make pancake batter.

Additional resources for building and reinforcing vocabulary are provided on pages T37–T41.

⟳ Comprehensible Input

Guide students to understanding

Vocabulary in Context Picture It!

1. **Say the Term** Have students repeat, stressing each syllable. Then combine syllables and have students repeat.

2. **Introduce Meaning** Connect the term to the visual that illustrates it.

3. **Demonstrate** Use a sheet of paper to model dividing the distance from 0 to 1 on a number line into equal parts. Use a ruler and draw a line across a sheet of paper. Label the left end of the line 0 and the right end 1. Then fold the paper in half, perpendicular to the line. Open it up and point to the fold. Say: *The fold is halfway between 0 and 1. It divides the line into two equal parts. We can write the fraction $\frac{1}{2}$ to show that $\frac{1}{2}$ is half of the whole number 1.* Write a tick mark and $\frac{1}{2}$ at the fold.

4. **Apply** Have students demonstrate understanding with Talk About It.

Repeat the routine for each vocabulary term.

Talk About It

Guide Discussion Model the sentence starters. Write the fraction $\frac{1}{4}$ on the board. Read the first sentence starter as you point to the numerator. Have students complete the sentence and correct as needed. Have pairs continue the routine with the other sentences. Provide this additional sentence starter, if time permits:

$1\frac{5}{6}$ is a ... mixed number.

Intervention

If students have difficulty with the pronunciation of *numerator* ...

Then write the word divided into syllables and say each syllable slowly as you point to it. nu•mer•a•tor. Have students echo it several times after you.

Your Turn

Guide Discussion Have pairs of students keep track of the number of vocabulary terms they used during their discussion. Then have pairs share their results.

Fractions on a Number Line

↻ Language Production

Comprehension Support Explain that students will use a number line to discuss how far some places are from Lola's house.

Model Read the directions aloud, and then discuss the number line. *The number line shows Lola's house at 0. The number 1 shows a distance of 1 mile from Lola's house. There are tick marks for each $\frac{1}{4}$ mile. Point to the $\frac{1}{4}$ mark. Point to other tick marks and have students give the distances from Lola's house.*

Talk About It

Guide Discussion Have students work in pairs and refer to the number line to complete the sentences. Provide time for them to plan their responses.

Your Turn

Guide Discussion Some students may wish to plan their oral responses by writing them down. Then have them work in pairs to discuss their sentences.

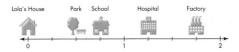
The number line shows how many miles it is from Lola's house to other places.

Write how far each place is from Lola's house.

Park: $\frac{1}{2}$ mile   Hospital: $1\frac{1}{4}$ miles

School: $\frac{3}{4}$ mile   Factory: $1\frac{3}{4}$ miles

Talk About It 💬
Complete the sentences about the distances on the number line.

1. Between 0 and 1, the number line is divided into four … equal parts.
2. The number I wrote for the distance to the factory is a … mixed number.
3. The fraction $\frac{1}{2}$ is … $\frac{3}{4}$. is less than
4. $1\frac{3}{4}$ … $1\frac{1}{4}$. is greater than

Your Turn 💬

Fill in the number line with fractions and mixed numbers. Use the sentence starters to tell a partner what you did.
The number line is divided into … thirds.
I wrote the fraction …
I wrote the mixed numbers …

Fractions on a Number Line   35

Leveled Language Proficiency

Students at each proficiency level should be able to perform the following tasks.

Listening/Speaking

Early Beginner Recognize a few vocabulary terms and follow very simple conversations with support. Make and respond to requests, using single words or short phrases.

Beginner/Early Intermediate Show basic understanding of key ideas, especially when visual support is provided. Speak in phrases and simple sentences, showing an increasing understanding of lesson vocabulary.

Intermediate Show comprehension of vocabulary terms and key ideas. Show an ability to express increasingly abstract ideas about vocabulary.

Advanced/Transitioning Understand complex sentence structures; follow abstract conversations involving lesson vocabulary. Speak on abstract topics, including those that involve lesson vocabulary, with few, if any, grammatical and syntactical errors.

Use the number lines to answer the questions.

1 Circle $\frac{1}{4}$ and $\frac{1}{3}$ on the number lines.

Is $\frac{1}{4}$ greater than $\frac{1}{3}$ or less than $\frac{1}{3}$?

$\underline{\quad\frac{1}{4} \text{ is less than } \frac{1}{3}.\quad}$

2 Circle $1\frac{1}{2}$ and $1\frac{3}{4}$ on the blue number line.

Is $1\frac{3}{4}$ greater than $1\frac{1}{2}$ or less than $1\frac{1}{2}$?

$\underline{\quad 1\frac{3}{4} \text{ is greater than } 1\frac{1}{2}.\quad}$

3 Circle $1\frac{1}{3}$ on the green number line.

What kind of number is $1\frac{1}{3}$?

$\underline{\quad 1\frac{1}{3} \text{ is a mixed number}.\quad}$

Talk and Write About It 🗩 ✏️

Complete the sentences.

Vocabulary			
denominator	fractions	numerator	is less than
is greater than	number line	equal parts	mixed numbers

4 The numbers shown on the number line between 0 and 1 are

$\underline{\quad\text{fractions}\quad}$.

5 The numbers shown on the number line between 1 and 2 are

$\underline{\quad\text{mixed numbers}\quad}$.

6 In the fraction $\frac{1}{3}$, the 3 is the $\underline{\quad\text{denominator}\quad}$.

Produce Language ✏️

Write how a number line can help you describe fractions and mixed numbers. Use examples and your vocabulary cards for support.

36 Lesson 9

Leveled Language Proficiency

Students at each proficiency level should be able to perform the following tasks.

Reading/Writing

Early Beginner Echo read and participate in some independent reading when strong visual support is provided. Copy vocabulary terms, and write one or two of them independently.

Beginner/Early Intermediate When given visual support, use vocabulary terms to complete sentence starters.

Intermediate Follow written directions. Write sentences, with some errors, that feature vocabulary terms.

Advanced/Transitioning Read instructions independently. Write a variety of sentences, including those which explain vocabulary terms with very few errors.

↻ Assess Understanding

Your Turn

Model Point to the number lines. *I see that the first number line is divided into thirds and the second one is divided into fourths.* Read aloud the problems so that students understand what they need to do. Remind them that when they compare two numbers on a number line, the smaller one is farther to the left. Since these two number lines are scaled the same way, numbers on the two number lines can be compared in the same way; the smaller number is on the left. Encourage students to use full sentences when they answer the questions.

Talk and Write About It

On Their Own Have students work independently to complete the sentences.

Produce Language

On Their Own Have students use the terms they have learned in this lesson in their writing. Encourage them to review the terms from Vocabulary in Context Picture It! on page 34 as needed.

Wrap Up

Table Talk Have students look back at the lesson's objectives. Allow time for them to reflect on what they have learned and then answer the essential question.

☑ **Learned** and applied vocabulary related to fractions, mixed numbers, and number lines

☑ **Spoken** statements to describe fractions and mixed numbers on a number line

☑ **Written** statements about fractions and mixed numbers on a number line

Number Sentences

Vocabulary Number sentences, addition sentence, subtraction sentence, multiplication sentence, division sentence, equation, missing number, value

Materials Sticky note (for teacher demonstration)

Math Background

- The term *number sentence* typically refers to a simple *equation* formed by numbers, an operation symbol ($+$, $-$, $\times$, $\div$), and the equal sign ($=$). Some number sentences are inequalities; they contain an *inequality* symbol ($>$, $<$, $\geq$, $\leq$).

- Missing numbers may be represented by a shape, blank, symbol, or, in later grades, by letter variables (such as x or y).

Frontload the Lesson

Essential Question What vocabulary do you need to discuss number sentences?

Talk About It

Build Background Have students rate the terms. Encourage them to tell what they know about the terms they rated with a 3.

Content and Language

You Will

Model Read the objectives aloud and explain them in your own words. Use symbols to support your explanations.

Your Turn

Guide Discussion Have students read the objectives and discuss what the objectives mean to them.

Number Sentences

Essential Question What vocabulary do you need to discuss number sentences?

You Will
- Identify four types of number sentences: addition, subtraction, multiplication, division.
- Find the value of a missing number in a number sentence.
- Understand and use key terms when discussing and solving number sentences.

Talk About It

Rate these mathematical terms according to the following scale.

① I have never heard of this term.

② I have heard this term, but I do not know how to use it in math.

③ I understand this term and know how to use it in math.

_____ addition sentence   _____ multiplication sentence
_____ division sentence   _____ number sentences
_____ equation   _____ subtraction sentence
_____ missing number   _____ value

What do you know about each term? Explain, using the sentence starters for support.

I do not know what … means.
I think … means …
I know … means …

Your Turn 💬
Look at the objectives under You Will at the top of the page. Working with a partner, predict what you are going to learn. Use the sentence starter for support.

I am going to learn about …

Leveled Instruction

Early Beginner Partner students with those at higher language proficiency levels so that they might have assistance at hand. Expect single words and gestures as answers.

Beginner Expect short and simple phrases and simple sentences as responses. Encourage students to use sentence starters to help them construct answers.

Early Intermediate Expect phrases and simple sentences from these students in answering questions and joining discussions.

Intermediate Students should produce complete sentences as answers. They should require minimal assistance in understanding information and questions.

Advanced/Transitioning Students should produce answers that include some details and elaboration. Partner them with students at lower language proficiency levels so they might offer them assistance.

Academic Vocabulary

- Help students see the connection between math *sentences* (numbers) and language arts *sentences* (words). Both types of sentences need certain elements in order to be complete. For example, students are asked to *fill in the blanks* for a word sentence. Students are also asked to *fill in the blank* or *find the value of a number* in a number sentence.

- Differentiate between the meaning of *value* in math as an assigned number or amount and *value* in culture as an important belief.

Additional resources for building and reinforcing vocabulary are provided on pages T37–T41.

↻ Comprehensible Input
Guide students to understanding

Vocabulary in Context Picture It!

1. **Say the Term** Have students repeat, stressing each syllable. Then combine syllables and have students repeat.

2. **Introduce Meaning** Connect the term to the visual that illustrates it.

3. **Demonstrate** Use a sticky note to model the term, *missing number*. Write $10 + 6 = 16$ on the board. Cover up the 10 with a sticky note. Say: *Some number plus 6 equals 16. I know that 10 plus 6 equals 16. So, the missing number is 10.* Then place the sticky note over the 6 and repeat the procedure.

4. **Apply** Have students demonstrate understanding with Talk About It.

Repeat the routine for each vocabulary term.

Remind students that they can review vocabulary terms for the four operations on pages 89–90 and record more terms as they learn them.

Talk About It

Guide Discussion Have students discuss the sentences with a partner. Model the sentence starters. Then provide this additional sentence starter, if time permits:

A number sentence that contains a plus sign is called an ... addition sentence.

Intervention

If students have difficulty with the initial /v/ sound, as in *value* ...

Then provide them with an articulation lesson on the /v/ sound: *Place your lower lip against your upper front teeth. Hold this position as you blow air out and make the sound in your throat.* Have students echo the sound (holding it several seconds) after you. Repeat several times. Then stretch the sound out at the beginning of *value* and have them echo you.

Your Turn

Guide Discussion Have pairs of students keep track of the number of vocabulary terms they used during their discussion. Then have pairs share their results.

⟳ Language Production

Comprehension Support Explain that you can write number sentences about real-world situations. If you have 2 apples and 6 oranges, you can write an addition sentence $2 + 6 = 8$ for how many pieces of fruit you have.

Model Read the problem aloud. Then call attention to the crates of oranges and the numbers below. *The number sentence says that 27 minus a missing number equals 6. I know that 27 minus 21 equals 6. So, 21 is the value of the square in this equation.* You might want to have students share ideas about how you determined that the value of the missing number is 21.

Talk About It

Guide Discussion Have students work in pairs to complete the number sentences.

Your Turn

Guide Discussion Have students begin by writing down one of the number sentences. Partners can record their number sentences on copies of T44. Ask each student to use vocabulary terms to describe the number sentence to a partner.

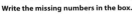

Do You Understand?

Ken sells fruit at his fruit stand. Write the missing numbers in the number sentences about Ken's fruit stand.

1 Ken starts with 27 oranges.
He sells most of them.
There are 6 left.
How many oranges did he sell?

$27 - \square = 6$

The missing number is ___21___ .

Ken sold ___21___ oranges.

2 Ken sells 4 bags of apples.
Each bag has the same number of apples.
He sells 40 apples in all.
How many apples are in each bag?

$4 \times \square = 40$

The value of $\square$ is ___10___ .

There are ___10___ apples in each bag.

Write the missing numbers in the box.

3 $12 \div \boxed{6} = 2$

4 $\boxed{8} + 24 = 32$

Talk About It 💬

What operations and symbols help you understand number sentences? Complete the sentences to explain.

5 The $\square$ in a number sentence stands for a ... missing number.

6 In Problem 1, I completed a ... subtraction sentence.

7 In Problem 2, I completed a ... multiplication sentence.

Your Turn ✏️

Choose one number sentence from above. Write a few sentences about it. Use the sentence starters for support. Share your sentences with a partner.

The number sentence I chose is ...

The value of ...

Leveled Language Proficiency

Students at each proficiency level should be able to perform the following tasks.

Listening/Speaking

Early Beginner Recognize a few vocabulary terms and follow very simple conversations with support. Make and respond to requests, using single words or short phrases.

Beginner/Early Intermediate Recognize some vocabulary terms, especially when visual support is provided. Say individual terms and respond to requests with phrases and simple sentences.

Intermediate Show comprehension of vocabulary terms used during discussion. Participate in limited discussions using words, phrases, and simple sentences.

Advanced/Transitioning Demonstrate understanding of discussions without requiring concrete references. Express oneself comfortably in oral contexts ranging from informal to formal interactions, using a variety of sentence structures.

Draw a line to match each problem to a number sentence on the right. Then find the missing number.

Number Sentences

1. There are 24 mangos.
   Jen divides them into groups.
   There are 8 mangos in each group.
   3

2. Enrique has some bananas.
   He buys 8 more.
   Now he has 24 bananas in all.
   16

3. Amy has some berries.
   She gives away 24 berries.
   There are 4 berries left.
   28

4. There are 4 buckets.
   Each bucket has the same number of apples in it.
   There are 24 apples in all.
   6

$\square - 24 = 4$

$4 \times \square = 24$

$24 \div \square = 8$

$\square + 8 = 24$

Talk and Write About It

Complete the sentences about the number sentences.

Vocabulary

addition sentence	division sentence
multiplication sentence	subtraction sentence
missing number	value
equation	number sentence

5. The first problem above matches a __division sentence__ .

6. To complete each number sentence, I found the __value__ of the square.

7. The + symbol is used in the __addition sentence__ .

8. A number sentence can also be called an __equation__ .

Produce Language

Write about finding the value of a missing number in a number sentence. Use an example. Use vocabulary terms in your sentences.

Leveled Language Proficiency

Students at each proficiency level should be able to perform the following tasks.

Reading/Writing

Early Beginner Echo read and participate in some independent reading when strong visual support is provided. Copy vocabulary terms, and write one or two of them independently.

Beginner/Early Intermediate Read simple sentences and vocabulary terms with the help of someone at a higher level of language proficiency. Use sentence starters to write individual words and phrases, including vocabulary terms.

Intermediate Follow written directions and independently retell what was read. Write simple sentences that use vocabulary terms properly, although with some grammatical errors.

Advanced/Transitioning Read and carry out written instructions and independently read lessons with ease of comprehension. Write a variety of sentences, including those which explain vocabulary terms, with few errors.

↻ Assess Understanding

Your Turn

Model Read aloud the instructions. Point out that each problem matches a number sentence. Then read the first problem. Help students match the first number sentence by pointing out the word *divide*. Then guide them to find the missing number. *Next, I need to find the missing number in the division sentence. 24 divided by some number equals 8. Which number works?*

Talk and Write About It

On Their Own Have students work independently or with a partner to complete the sentences.

Produce Language

On Their Own Have students use the terms they have learned in this lesson in their writing. Encourage them to review the terms from Vocabulary in Context Picture It! on page 38 as needed.

Wrap Up

Table Talk Have students look back at the lesson's objectives. Allow time for them to reflect on what they have learned and then answer the essential question.

☑ **Learned** and applied vocabulary related to number sentences

☑ **Spoken** statements to describe number sentences with missing numbers and also describe how to find their values

☑ **Written** statements about number sentences and missing numbers

Patterns

Vocabulary Patterns, repeating patterns, repeat, number patterns, rule, table

Math Background

- Some patterns are sequences of numbers. The numbers either repeat or change according to a rule. Applying the rule to one number in the sequence gives the next number in the sequence.

- Patterns can be found in tables when the two sets of data are related by a rule. Studying patterns in tables prepares students for functions in later grades.

Frontload the Lesson

What vocabulary will help you explain patterns?

Talk About It

Build Background Read the list of words aloud to the class. Model how to use the Know-Want-Learned chart. (See page T43 for additional copies of the chart.) Ask for volunteers to say what they might already know about various terms.

Content and Language

You Will

Model Read the objectives aloud and explain them in your own words. Use diagrams and drawings to support your explanations.

Your Turn

Guide Discussion Have students read the objectives. Discuss what these objectives mean to them.

Patterns

Essential Question What vocabulary will help you explain patterns?

You Will
- Identify and continue patterns.
- Find the rule for number patterns.
- Understand and use key terms related to patterns.

Talk About It

Look at the list of terms below. In the first two columns of the chart, write terms you **know** or **want** to know more about.

| pattern | number pattern | repeat |
| repeating pattern | rule | table |

Know	Want	Learned

What do you know about each term you wrote in the chart? Explain, using the sentence starters for support.

I know … means …
I want to know more about …

Your Turn 💬
Look at the objectives under You Will at the top of the page. Working with a partner, predict what you are going to learn. Use the sentence starter for support.

I am going to learn about …

Patterns   41

Leveled Instruction

Early Beginner Partner students with those at higher proficiency levels so that they might have assistance at hand. Expect gestures, pictures, single words, or simple phrases as responses.

Beginner Beginners can answer in short phrases, especially when sentence starters are provided.

Early Intermediate Expect phrases and simple sentences from these students in answering questions and joining discussions. Provide immediate feedback so students can self-correct.

Intermediate Students should produce complete sentences that show their comprehension of activity information and questions.

Advanced/Transitioning Students should produce a variety of sentence types when answering questions or making comments. They can offer students at lower proficiency levels support and assistance.

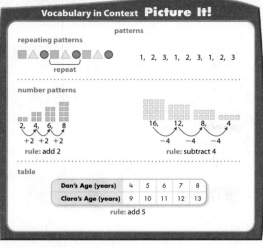

Vocabulary in Context **Picture It!**

patterns

repeating patterns

■ ▲ ● ■ ▲ ● ■ ▲ ●   1, 2, 3, 1, 2, 3, 1, 2, 3

repeat

number patterns

2, 4, 6, 8
+2 +2 +2
rule: add 2

16, 12, 8, 4
−4 −4 −4
rule: subtract 4

table

| Dan's Age (years) | 4 | 5 | 6 | 7 | 8 |
| Clara's Age (years) | 9 | 10 | 11 | 12 | 13 |

rule: add 5

Talk About It
Talk with a partner. Complete the sentences.
1. 1, 3, 5, 7 is an example of a … **number pattern**
2. In the pattern A B A B A B A B, the letters A and B … **repeat.**
3. In the pattern 3, 5, 7, 9, "add 2" is the … **rule.**
4. Dan's and Clara's ages are shown in a … **table**

Your Turn
Look at the pattern below. Use vocabulary terms to describe it to a partner.

Academic Vocabulary

- Explain that *patterns* are common in daily life, such as rhythmic sounds in music, or a repeated design on wrapping paper or fabric.

- Clarify that in this context, a *rule* describes how to find numbers in a pattern. It explains how the pattern works, as soccer rules explain and govern that game.

- Distinguish the math meaning of *table* from the piece of furniture.

Additional resources for building and reinforcing vocabulary are provided on pages T37–T41.

Cultural Connection

Visual patterns are familiar elements in the art and design of many cultures. African and Asian fabric designs and Arabic mosaic tiles are some common examples.

↻ Comprehensible Input

Guide students to understanding

Vocabulary in Context Picture It!

1. **Say the Term** Have students repeat, stressing each syllable. Then combine syllables and have students repeat.

2. **Introduce Meaning** Connect the term to the visual that illustrates it.

3. **Demonstrate** Draw arrays of small circles on the board to show the pattern, 2, 4, 6, 8. Draw a row of 2 circles. To the right, draw 4 circles (2 rows of 2). Then draw 6 circles (3 rows of 2) and 8 circles (4 rows of 2). Point out that there are 2 circles added to each array in the pattern to find the next number of circles, so the rule is to add 2.

4. **Apply** Have students demonstrate understanding with Talk About It.

Repeat the routine for each vocabulary term.

Remind students that they can review vocabulary terms for the four operations on pages 89 and 90 and record more terms as they learn them.

Talk About It

Guide Discussion Have students discuss the sentences with a partner. Model the sentence starters. Provide time for students to plan their answers. Then provide this additional sentence completion, if time permits:

The number pattern 8, 1, 1, 8, 1, 1, 8, 1, 1, can also be called a … **repeating pattern.**

Intervention

If students have difficulty with the initial /p/ sound, as in *pattern* …

Then provide them with an articulation lesson on the /p/ sound: *Close and press your lips together. Then quickly open your lips to give off a puff of breath.* Have students echo the sound after you. Repeat several times. Then stretch the sound out at the beginning of *pattern* and have them echo you.

Your Turn

Guide Discussion Have pairs of students keep track of the vocabulary terms they used during their discussion. Then have pairs share their results.

Language Production

Comprehension Support Explain that the sections of the trains can be called cars. Read the table and show students that the price of the train depends upon the number of train cars. Review the dollar sign and how to read money amounts.

Model Show students how to find a rule in the table. Explain to students that the rule should relate the number of train cars to the price. Give students a few minutes to look for a pattern in the numbers in the table. Then discuss the fact that the prices are all multiples of 5. Go through the first 4 columns of the table to show students they can multiply the number of train cars by 5 to get the price. *So, the rule is to multiply by 5.* Help students complete the table by multiplying by 5.

Guide students through the remaining patterns by finding the change from one number to the next.

Talk About It

Guide Discussion Have students work in pairs to complete the sentences. Provide time for them to plan their responses.

Your Turn

Guide Discussion Have students plan their oral responses by writing their pattern and its description. Then have them work in pairs to discuss the patterns. Partners can record their work on copies of T44.

Do You Understand?

① Anya is buying a toy train. The price depends on the number of train cars.

	Train Prices					
Number of Train Cars	1	2	3	4	5	6
Price	$5	$10	$15	$20	$25	$30

Write a rule for the table. Then complete the table.

Rule: __Multiply the number of train cars by 5__

Look at the number patterns. Write the rule. Then write the next number.

②

③

The rule is __subtract 2__ .   The rule is __add 4__ .

The next number is __1__ .   The next number is __20__ .

Talk About It 💬
Complete the sentences about the patterns.

④ The information about the train prices is given in a … table.
⑤ To find a rule for the table, I looked for a … pattern.
⑥ To find the next number in Problem 2, first I needed to find the … rule.
⑦ The pattern in Problem 3 is **not** a … repeating pattern

Your Turn ✏️
Write a number pattern that follows a rule. Describe it to a partner. Use the sentence starters for support.
The pattern is …
The rule is …

Leveled Language Proficiency

Students at each proficiency level should be able to perform the following tasks.

Listening/Speaking

Early Beginner Recognize a few vocabulary terms and follow very simple conversations with support. Make and respond to requests, using single words, short phrases, or gestures.

Beginner Recognize some vocabulary terms, especially when visual support is provided. Say individual terms and respond to requests with simple phrases.

Early Intermediate Show understanding of oral questions that use key terms. Reply to questions with short answers and requests for clarification.

Intermediate Show comprehension of vocabulary terms used during discussions. Participate in limited discussions using words and phrases.

Advanced/Transitioning Demonstrate understanding of discussions that use a variety of sentence structures. Use key terms and other grade-level vocabulary during discussions.

Your Turn

Write the rule for each table. Complete each table.

①

Number of Markers	Number of Boxes
4	1
12	3
20	5
28	7
36	9

②

Price of Cheese Pizza	Price with 2 Toppings
$7	$10
$8	$11
$10	$13
$12	$15
$13	$16

Rule: __divide by 4__ .

Rule: __add 3__ .

③ Choose a rule from the box. Write a number pattern using the rule.

add 5	subtract 5
add 10	subtract 10

Pattern: _____
Patterns will vary.

Talk and Write About It 💬 ✏️
Complete the sentences about patterns.

Vocabulary

pattern	repeat	rule
repeating pattern	table	number pattern

④ To find the rule in each table, I looked for a __pattern__ .

⑤ To make my pattern in Problem 3, I followed a __rule__ .

⑥ In the pattern 5, 1, 8, 5, 1, 8, 5, 1, 8, the __repeat__ is 5, 1, 8.

Produce Language ✏️
Write the terms you learned about in this lesson in the third column of the chart on page 41. Write what you have learned about these terms. Use sentence starters from throughout the lesson for support.

Leveled Language Proficiency

Students at each proficiency level should be able to perform the following tasks.

Reading/Writing

Early Beginner Read independently when strong visual support is provided, after being walked through a reading at least once. Write individual vocabulary terms once the meanings are understood.

Beginner/Early Intermediate Read simple sentences with the help of someone at a higher level of language proficiency. Complete sentence starters with individual words and phrases, including vocabulary terms.

Intermediate Follow written directions and demonstrate comprehension of reading done independently. Write simple sentences that use vocabulary terms properly, though with some grammatical errors.

Advanced/Transitioning Carry out written instructions and independently read lessons with ease of comprehension. Write a variety of sentences, and use correct mechanics when editing them.

⟳ Assess Understanding

Your Turn

Model Explain to students that for each table, they should find a rule to relate the number in the left column to the number in the right column. Students may need extra assistance with the second table, because the intervals between prices vary.

Then model making a pattern using the rule "add 20." *First I choose a number to start with. Then I follow the rule by adding 20 to get the next number. Let's say I start with 10. For the next number in the pattern, I add 10 plus 20, which is 30. For the next number after that, I add 30 plus 20, and I get 50.* Write the pattern on the board as you provide the explanation.

Talk and Write About It

On Their Own Have students work in pairs to complete the sentences.

Produce Language

On Their Own Have students complete the Know-Want-Learn chart from the beginning of the lesson. Have students write what they have learned about these terms and share their ideas with others. If some students have no new terms to add to column 3, ask them to write about any three or four terms in the lesson.

Wrap Up

Table Talk Have students look back at the lesson's objectives. Allow time for them to reflect on what they have learned and then answer the essential question.

☑ **Learned** and applied vocabulary related to patterns

☑ **Spoken** statements about patterns

☑ **Written** statements about patterns

Lines

Vocabulary Line, line segment, horizontal line, vertical line, intersecting lines, parallel lines, perpendicular lines

Math Background

- A line extends infinitely in both directions. A line segment is part of a line that stops on each end.

- Parallel lines have no point in common. Intersecting lines have one point in common.

- Perpendicular lines form four right angles.

Frontload the Lesson

What terms do you need to know to understand and discuss lines?

Talk About It

Build Background Read each term above the chart. Explain the meaning of the chart columns and model how to place terms in the first two columns. (See page T43 for additional copies of the chart.) Ask for volunteers to say what they might already know about various terms.

Content and Language

You Will

Model Read the objectives aloud and model restating them in your own words. Draw examples of lines and line segments to support your explanations.

Your Turn

Guide Discussion Have students read the objectives. Discuss what these objectives mean to them. Invite students to work with a partner to practice speaking.

Lines

Essential Question What terms do you need to know to understand and discuss lines?

You Will
- Recognize the properties of lines and line segments.
- Understand the relationship between pairs of lines.
- Use math vocabulary to describe lines.

Talk About It

Look at the list of terms below. In the first two columns of the chart, write terms you **know** or **want** to know more about.

line	intersecting lines
line segment	perpendicular lines
horizontal line	parallel lines
vertical line	

Know	Want	Learned

Explain what you know about the terms you wrote in the chart. Use the sentence starters for help.

I know … means … in math.
I think … means …

Your Turn
Look at the objectives listed under You Will at the top of the page. Working with a partner, predict what you will learn. Use the sentence starter below.

I am going to learn about …

Lines **45**

Leveled Instruction

Early Beginner Early beginners may not use many English words in their responses. Encourage them to use gestures and pictures to communicate responses.

Beginner Have students partner with students of higher language proficiency to complete activities. Expect short and simple sentences as responses.

Early Intermediate Students may rely on sentence starters to express their ideas. Model using these sentence starters if necessary.

Intermediate Encourage students to try to express their ideas without sentence starters. They should use complete sentences, though they will probably make some grammatical errors.

Advanced/Transitioning You can expect these students to form sentences of increasing complexity. Have students use a more varied vocabulary, and encourage them to try new sentence structures.

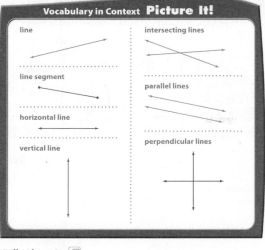

Talk About It

Talk with a partner to complete the sentences.

1. Part of a line that stops at each end is a ... line segment.
2. A line that goes across is a ... horizontal line.
3. A line that goes up and down is a ... vertical line.
4. Lines that never cross are ... parallel lines.

Your Turn

Choose a term on this page. Draw three different examples of it. Show your drawings to a partner. Ask your partner to describe them.

Academic Vocabulary

- Point out that in a drawing of a *line,* there are arrowheads at each end as a reminder that the line continues in both directions. Points are drawn at the ends of a *line segment* to indicate that the line segment stops at each end.

- Relate *intersecting lines* to street *intersections.* You can illustrate this concept by having students refer to the map shown on page 47.

- *Perpendicular lines* are often described as lines that form right angles. Students will study angles in the next lesson and learn about *right angles.* In this lesson, merely point out the square-shaped corners formed by perpendicular lines.

- The following words are cognates with Spanish, and should be easy for some students to understand: *horizontal, vertical, parallel, perpendicular.*

Additional resources for building and reinforcing vocabulary are provided on pages T37–T41.

Cultural Consideration

If available, students might enjoy sharing street maps of the town where they were born or the capital city of the country where they were born.

⟳ Comprehensible Input

Guide students to understanding

Vocabulary in Context Picture It!

1. **Say the Term** Have students repeat, stressing each syllable. Then combine syllables and have students repeat.

2. **Introduce Meaning** Connect the term to the visual that illustrates it.

3. **Demonstrate** Use gestures and visuals to demonstrate. As *horizontal lines* and *vertical lines* are discussed, sweep your hand across or up and down to designate the appropriate direction.

4. **Apply** Have students demonstrate understanding with Talk About It.

Repeat the routine for each vocabulary term.

Talk About It

Guide Discussion Have students discuss the sentences with a partner. If time permits, have students look for examples of lines in the classroom. Have them describe an example by completing a sentence such as the following:

The window sill looks like a ... horizontal line.

Intervention

If students confuse intersecting and perpendicular lines ...

Then explain that perpendicular lines are special intersecting lines that form square corners where they meet.

Your Turn

Guide Discussion Have pairs of students share their drawings and their discussions.

↻ Language Production

Comprehension Support Direct students' attention to the map. Read the names of the streets and talk about some of the buildings pictured.

Model Help students locate Cedar Street and Rose Street. *On the map, Cedar Street and Rose Street look like lines. They cross and form square corners. So, Cedar Street and Rose Street look like perpendicular lines.* Have students complete the descriptions of other streets on the map.

Talk About It

Guide Discussion Have students complete the Talk About It sentences on their own or with a partner. Remind students that if they need help with the terms, they can check their descriptions of the streets or Vocabulary in Context Picture It!

Your Turn

Guide Discussion Partners can record their drawings on copies of page T44. Have pairs of students join together to make groups of four. Have students share their drawings and describe them to other members of the group.

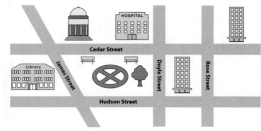

Do You Understand?

On this map, Cedar Street and Rose Street look like perpendicular lines.

Map of Downtown

Use vocabulary terms to describe other streets on this map.

James Street and Cedar Street

Sample answer: intersecting lines

Doyle Street and Hudson Street

Sample answer: perpendicular lines

Doyle Street and Rose Street

Sample answer: parallel lines

Talk About It 🗨
Complete the sentences to help describe lines.

① Lines that go across are … horizontal lines.

② Lines that never cross each other are … parallel lines.

③ Lines that cross each other are … intersecting lines.

④ Lines that cross each other and form square corners are … perpendicular lines.

Your Turn ✎
Draw two lines. Describe these lines to a partner using vocabulary terms.

Lines 47

Leveled Language Proficiency

Students at each proficiency level should be able to perform the following tasks.

Listening/Speaking

Early Beginner Recognize a few vocabulary terms and follow very simple conversations with support. Repeat simple phrases, and use vocabulary terms to answer questions.

Beginner Follow simple directions; recognize some vocabulary terms. Say individual terms and simple phrases, and repeat longer phrases and short sentences.

Early Intermediate Begin to follow more abstract discussion about vocabulary terms. Speak in phrases and simple sentences, showing an increasing understanding of lesson vocabulary.

Intermediate Understand abstract ideas; recognize vocabulary as individual terms and in the context of spoken sentences. Show an ability to express abstract ideas about vocabulary.

Advanced/Transitioning Understand complex sentence structures; follow abstract conversations involving lesson vocabulary. Speak on abstract topics, including those that involve lesson vocabulary, with few, if any, grammatical and syntactical errors.

Your Turn

Draw a street map. Write a name on each street. Show streets that look like:

- intersecting lines
- perpendicular lines
- parallel lines

Check students' drawings.

Write the names of a pair of streets that can be described by each term.

1. Intersecting lines: _____ and _____ . Check students' answers.
2. Perpendicular lines: _____ and _____ . Check students' answers.
3. Parallel lines: _____ and _____ . Check students' answers.

Talk and Write About It 🗨️ ✏️

Complete the sentences about lines.

Vocabulary		
lines	horizontal lines	parallel lines
line segment	vertical lines	perpendicular lines
intersecting lines		

4. Lines that go up and down are _vertical lines_ .
5. Part of a line that stops at each end is a _line segment_ .
6. Lines that never intersect are _parallel lines_ .

Produce Language ✏️

Write the terms you learned about in this lesson in the third column of the chart on page 45. Write about these terms. Use sentence starters from throughout the lesson for support.

↻ Assess Understanding

Your Turn

Model Draw a simple map on the board with straight streets. Write a name on each street. Have students decide if any pair of streets looks like intersecting lines, perpendicular lines, or parallel lines. Have students draw their own maps independently. Tell students to include at least five streets on the map. Be sure that they understand that the map should show the three types of pairs of lines.

Talk and Write About It

On Their Own Have students work independently to complete the sentences.

Produce Language

On Their Own Have students write the terms they have learned in this lesson in the chart on page 45. Have students write what they have learned about these terms and share their ideas with others. If some students did not need to add any terms to the third column, have them write about any three or four vocabulary terms.

Wrap Up

Table Talk Have students look back at the lesson's objectives. Allow time for them to reflect on what they have learned and then answer the essential question.

☑ **Learned** and applied vocabulary related to lines

☑ **Spoken** statements about lines

☑ **Written** statements about lines

Leveled Language Proficiency

Students at each proficiency level should be able to perform the following tasks.

Reading/Writing

Early Beginner Read a few short, common words and some vocabulary terms, if given visual support or help from a partner or adult. Copy words and phrases from the board; write 1–2 vocabulary terms independently.

Beginner/Early Intermediate Read simple sentences with the help of a partner or an adult and visual support; read some vocabulary terms independently. Use sentence starters and other organizers to write individual words and phrases that use vocabulary terms.

Intermediate Read and understand lesson vocabulary both in and out of context, and read simple directions independently. Write full sentences and complex phrases about lesson concepts, using vocabulary terms; sentences may contain some grammatical and spelling errors.

Advanced/Transitioning Read and carry out simple and complex written instructions; read sentences about lesson ideas that use lesson vocabulary. Write complete sentences with very few errors, using sentence starters only as necessary and including abstract ideas in writing.

Lesson 13

Angles

Vocabulary Angle, rays, vertex (vertices), right angle, acute angle, obtuse angle, perpendicular lines

Materials Index cards, pencils, markers or crayons (red, blue, and green), two rulers (for teacher demonstration)

Math Background

- Two *rays* with the same endpoint form an *angle*. The endpoint is called the *vertex*.

- *Right angles* measure 90 degrees. They are the corners of a square. *Acute angles* measure less than 90 degrees, and *obtuse angles* measure between 90 degrees and 180 degrees.

- *Perpendicular lines* intersect to form 4 right angles.

↻ Frontload the Lesson

Essential Question
What vocabulary terms should you use to identify and describe angles?

Talk About It

Build Background Read the terms aloud as students place the cards into piles. Once they have finished, encourage them to share the meanings of the terms they placed in Pile 1.

↻ Content and Language

You Will

Model Read the objectives aloud and explain them in your own words. Use diagrams and gestures to support your explanations.

Your Turn

Guide Discussion Have students read the objectives. Invite them to use their own words to describe what the objectives mean to them.

Angles

Essential Question What vocabulary terms should you use to identify and describe angles?

You Will
- Identify and describe different types of angles.
- Recognize right angles, acute angles, and obtuse angles.
- Understand and use key terms related to angles.

Talk About It

Copy each term from Vocabulary in Context on a card. As your teacher reads each term, create three piles of cards.

1. Place terms that you know in **Pile 1**.
2. Place terms you have heard but are not sure what they mean in **Pile 2**.
3. Place terms you do not know in **Pile 3**.

What do you know about each term? Explain, using the sentence starters for support.

I know … means …
I think … means …
I do not know what … means.

Your Turn 💬
Look at the objectives under You Will at the top of the page. Working with a partner, predict what you are going to learn. Use the sentence starter for support.

I am going to learn …

Leveled Instruction

Early Beginner Partnering early beginners with students at higher proficiency levels will provide them added support. Single words, gestures, and pictures are the types of answers early beginners will give.

Beginner/Early Intermediate Expect phrases and simple sentences from these students when they are answering questions. Encourage students to use sentence starters to help them construct their answers.

Intermediate Intermediate students should be able to complete activities with minimal assistance. Expect them to answer questions using full sentences with some details.

Advanced/Transitioning Students should be able to produce detailed answers with minimal assistance. They can offer students at lower proficiency levels support and assistance.

angle

rays

vertex
(plural: vertices)

right angle

acute angle

obtuse angle

perpendicular lines

Talk About It

Talk with a partner. Complete the sentences.

1. The point where the rays of an angle meet is the … **vertex.**
2. An angle that opens less than a right angle is an … **acute angle.**
3. An angle that opens more than a right angle is an … **obtuse angle.**
4. Two lines that cross each other and form right angles are … **perpendicular lines.**

Your Turn

Draw a right angle, an acute angle, and an obtuse angle. Under each angle, write the term that tells what kind of angle you drew. Write a sentence to describe each angle. Use the sentence starters for help.

This is a right angle because …

This is an acute angle because …

This is an obtuse angle because …

50 Lesson 13

Academic Vocabulary

- The following words are cognates with Spanish and should be easy for some students to understand: *angle, rays, acute angle, obtuse angle, perpendicular.*

- A *ray* is part of a line that continues in one direction only. Compare this to a ray of light from a flashlight or the sun. The ray of light continues in only one direction, away from the light source.

- Be sure that students understand that *right* in *right angle* does not refer to the direction (right vs. left) or correctness (right vs. wrong).

- Discuss *vertices,* the plural form of *vertex.* Stress the correct pronunciation of the word.

Additional resources for building and reinforcing vocabulary are provided on pages T37–T41.

Cultural Consideration

Avoid the tendency to teach acute angles by references such as this: "An acute angle is a cute, small angle." Not all cultures view smallness as "cute."

↻ Comprehensible Input

Guide students to understanding

Vocabulary in Context Picture It!

1. **Say the Term** Have students repeat, stressing each syllable. Then combine syllables and have students repeat.

2. **Introduce Meaning** Connect the term to the visual that illustrates it.

3. **Demonstrate** Use two rulers to model angles. For example, hold the two rulers so that they form a *right angle.* Close the angle a little to illustrate an *acute angle.* Begin, again, with a right angle. Then open it a little to illustrate an *obtuse angle.* Be sure students understand *more* and *less.* Clarify, using gestures, as needed, so students understand that an acute angle is open *less* than a right angle, and an obtuse angle is open *more* than a right angle.

4. **Apply** Have students demonstrate understanding with Talk About It.

Repeat the routine for each vocabulary term.

Talk About It

Guide Discussion Have students discuss the sentences with a partner. Provide the following additional sentence starter, if time permits:

The corner of a book looks like a … **right angle.**

Intervention

If students have difficulty identifying the different types of angles …

Then have them use two pencils to make each type of angle as you demonstrated earlier with rulers. They should begin with a right angle. Then they should close it a bit to make an acute angle. Begin with a right angle, again, and open it to show an obtuse angle. Call out each type of angle and have students make the angle with their pencils.

Your Turn

Guide Discussion Have students form pairs to share their angles and sentences.

Language Production

Comprehension Support Explain that students will look for right angles, acute angles, and obtuse angles formed by the lines in the drawing of the castle. Distribute an index card to each student. Be sure students have red, blue, and green markers or crayons.

Model Show students how to fit the corner of the index card into some of the angles in the drawing. *The corner of the card fits into the corner of a window. It's a right angle, so I will circle its vertex in red.* Compare other angles to a corner of the card to identify acute angles and obtuse angles.

As an alternate approach, for each student draw a right angle on a sheet of tracing paper or wax paper. (Use a permanent marker to draw on wax paper.) Have the student slide the paper over the picture of the castle to hunt for right angles, acute angles, and obtuse angles.

Talk About It

Guide Discussion Have students work in pairs. They should refer to the directions for the activity, their colored circles, and Vocabulary in Context Picture It! as needed to complete the sentences.

Your Turn

Guide Discussion As students plan their drawing and their explanation, remind students to think about which type of angles are formed by perpendicular lines.

Each corner of an index card is a right angle. You can use the card to go on an angle hunt. Move a corner of the card around the drawing of the castle to check for right angles. When you find a right angle, circle the vertex in red. Then look for acute and obtuse angles. Circle the vertices of acute angles in blue. Circle the vertices of obtuse angles in green.

Check students' work.

Talk About It
What angles did you find? Complete the sentences to explain.
1. The angles that look like square corners are … right angles.
2. The angles that open less than a right angle are … acute angles.
3. The angles that open more than a right angle are … obtuse angles.

Your Turn
Use your index card to draw a pair of perpendicular lines. Use vocabulary terms to explain to a partner why the lines are perpendicular.

Leveled Language Proficiency

Students at each proficiency level should be able to perform the following tasks.

Listening/Speaking

Early Beginner Demonstrate understanding of one-step oral directions. Make and respond to requests, using single words, gestures, or short phrases.

Beginner Demonstrate comprehension of some vocabulary terms, especially when visual support is provided. Say individual terms and respond to requests with simple phrases.

Early Intermediate Demonstrate comprehension of multiple-step oral directions. Participate in discussions when clarification is readily available.

Intermediate Demonstrate comprehension of the main points of a discussion. Explain thinking processes used to arrive at answers.

Advanced/Transitioning Demonstrate understanding of academic discussions without requiring concrete references. Elaborate on discussion points using a variety of sentence types.

Your Turn

Draw a picture in the space below. Include all three types of angles. Use red for the rays of a right angle. Use blue for the rays of an acute angle. Use green for the rays of an obtuse angle.

Check students' work.

Talk and Write About It 💬 ✏️

Complete the sentences about angles.

Vocabulary		
acute angle	obtuse angle	right angle
rays	vertex	perpendicular lines

1. Every angle is made up of two _____rays_____ .

2. Every angle has one _____vertex_____ .

3. An angle that makes a square corner is a _____right angle_____ .

4. Right angles can be formed by ___perpendicular lines___ .

Produce Language ✏️

Write about how the three types of angles are alike. Then write about how they are different. Use the sentence starters for help.

The angles are all formed by …

Right angles are different from acute angles because …

52   Lesson 13

Leveled Language Proficiency

Students at each proficiency level should be able to perform the following tasks.

Reading/Writing

Early Beginner Read some vocabulary terms with support, along with a few common words. Write terms and copy phrases with support.

Beginner Use visual and contextual support to determine meaning of terms, especially with the help of someone at a higher level of language proficiency. Use sentence starters and visual supports to write individual terms and phrases.

Early Intermediate Read most vocabulary terms in context; read independently when text is made up of known words and simple sentences. Write simple sentences, with some errors.

Intermediate Apply reading strategies, including identifying the main idea and details, to aid independent reading. Write complete sentences that include vocabulary terms.

Advanced/Transitioning Read and write a variety of sentence types containing concrete and abstract ideas related to lesson content with minimal support.

↻ Assess Understanding

Your Turn

Model Be sure each student has an index card and red, blue, and green markers or crayons. Draw a simple sketch on the board of a house without its roof. *Now, I'm going to draw an obtuse angle to make a roof. So, I will use a green marker to draw it. I will use the index card to check to be sure this angle is more open than a right angle.* Encourage students to draw at least two of each type of angle.

Talk and Write About It

On Their Own Have students work alone for 10 minutes. Once they have chosen the term for each sentence, have students share their work in pairs.

Produce Language

On Their Own Have students work independently to write their comparisons. Remind them to refer to Vocabulary in Context Picture It! if they need help.

Wrap Up

Table Talk Have students look back at the lesson's objectives. Allow time for them to reflect on what they have learned and then answer the essential question.

☑ **Learned** and applied vocabulary related to different types of angles

☑ **Spoken** statements to identify acute, obtuse, and right angles and how they are formed

☑ **Written** statements to describe the different types of angles

Lesson 14

Shapes

Vocabulary Polygon, angle, side, vertex (vertices), circle, triangle, quadrilateral, pentagon, hexagon, octagon, square, rectangle, right angle

Materials Index cards

 Math Background

- Polygons are flat, closed shapes with at least three straight sides. Circles are not polygons, since they have no straight sides.

- Each polygon has the same number of angles as it has sides.

↻ Frontload the Lesson

 What words do you use when you discuss shapes?

Talk About It

Build Background Once students have finished making and sorting the cards, encourage them to share the meanings of the terms they placed in pile 1.

↻ Content and Language

You Will

Model Read the objectives aloud and explain them in your own words. Be sure to clarify *compare, contrast,* and *key terms.* Ask for volunteers to draw some shapes on the board and tell what they know about them.

Your Turn

Guide Discussion Have students read the objectives. Invite them to restate the objectives in their own words.

Shapes

Essential Question What words do you use when you discuss shapes?

You Will
- Identify and describe different types of shapes.
- Compare and contrast different types of shapes.
- Understand and use key terms that you need to give details about shapes.

Talk About It

Make an index card for each vocabulary term below. Place each card in one of three piles.

Pile 1: I know what this term means.
Pile 2: I have heard this term, but I am not sure how it is used in math.
Pile 3: I have not heard of this term.

Polygon

right angle	pentagon	square
circle	angle	triangle
quadrilateral	rectangle	vertex
hexagon	octagon	side
polygon		

What do you know about each term? Explain, using the sentence starters for support.

I know … means …
I think … means …
I do not know what … means.

Your Turn 💬
Look at the objectives under You Will at the top of the page. Working with a partner, predict what you are going to learn. Use the sentence starter for support.

I am going to learn about …

Leveled Instruction

Early Beginner Be sure students know that gesturing and answering with single words or short phrases are fine ways for them to respond.

Beginner Students should respond with single words or short phrases. Students continue to benefit from partnerships with students at higher levels of language proficiency.

Early Intermediate Expect students to answer questions with phrases and simple sentences. Encourage students to use sentence starters to help them construct their answers.

Intermediate Anticipate that students can complete the activities with minimal assistance. They should consistently answer questions using full sentences.

Advanced/Transitioning Students should be producing answers that include details and elaboration. Rather than needing assistance, they should be able to provide it to students at lower proficiency levels.

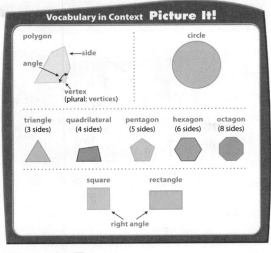

polygon

side

angle

vertex
(plural: vertices)

circle

triangle
(3 sides)

quadrilateral
(4 sides)

pentagon
(5 sides)

hexagon
(6 sides)

octagon
(8 sides)

square

rectangle

right angle

Talk About It

Talk with a partner. Complete the sentences.

1. Two sides of a polygon that meet form an … angle.
2. A square has 4 … angles. right
3. A triangle has 3 angles and 3 … sides.
4. A … is not a polygon. circle
5. Since squares and rectangles have 4 sides, each one can also be called a … quadrilateral.

Your Turn

Choose a shape to draw and describe. Use vocabulary terms in your description. Use them to label your drawing, too.

54 Lesson 14

Academic Vocabulary

- The following words are cognates with Spanish, and should be easy for some students to understand: *triangle, pentagon, hexagon, rectangle, octagon, circle.*

- Discuss words with related prefixes, such as *triangle* and *tricycle, quadrilateral* and *quadruplets,* and *octagon* and *octopus.*

- Review other common meanings for *side.* Indicate the *side* of your body. Talk about the *sides,* or opposing teams, in sports events: *In a soccer game, two teams play each other. Both sides try to score goals.*

- Point out that the sides of a room meet at a *corner* of the room. The sides of a polygon meet at a *vertex.* Discuss and carefully pronounce the singular form and the plural form, *vertices.*

Additional resources for building and reinforcing vocabulary are provided on pages T37–T41.

↻ Comprehensible Input

Guide students to understanding

Vocabulary in Context Picture It!

1. **Say the Term** Have students repeat, stressing each syllable. Then combine syllables and have students repeat.

2. **Introduce Meaning** Connect the term to the visual that illustrates it.

3. **Demonstrate** As you introduce each polygon, have students help you count the number of sides, vertices, and angles.

4. **Apply** Have students demonstrate understanding with Talk About It.

Repeat the routine for each vocabulary term.

Talk About It

Guide Discussion Have students discuss the sentences with a partner. Model the sentence starters. If time permits, provide another sentence starter:

A hexagon has one more side than a … pentagon.

Intervention

If students have trouble with the pronunciation of *pentagon, hexagon,* and *octagon* …

Then point out that the *a* in each word makes the schwa ("uh") sound. Stretch out the pronunciation of each word and have students echo you. Then say the three words quickly in a row and have students echo you. Note that the stress is on the first syllable in each word. These three words are cognates in Spanish, but the stress is on the second syllable in that language.

Your Turn

Guide Discussion Have pairs share their labeled shapes and sentences. If both students in a pair chose the same shape, have them compare their answers.

Language Production

Comprehension Support Discuss the road signs and their meanings. Explain that each sign has a shape. Students should draw a line from each sign to the label on the left that names it. There is no sign that is a hexagon. If any of your students are from Malaysia, they might have seen this shape used to identify the highways.

Model Model thinking about the attributes of the shapes in order to make the matches. *I see that the yield sign has 3 sides and 3 angles. That means it is a triangle. I will draw a line from the word* triangle.

Talk About It

Guide Discussion Have students work in pairs. Encourage them to refer to the representations of the different polygons in Vocabulary in Context Picture It! as needed to recall details about each shape.

Your Turn

Guide Discussion Give students time to write their answers before forming pairs to orally share their ideas. Some students may need to be reminded that a circle is not a polygon.

Do You Understand?

Draw a line from the name of each shape to the sign with that shape. You might not find every shape.

octagon
circle
hexagon
pentagon
rectangle
square
triangle

Rectangle could also be matched to the square sign.

Which shape did you **not** find? ___hexagon___

Talk About It
How can you describe shapes? Complete the sentences to explain.
1. One shape that is not a polygon is a . . . circle.
2. All 4 sides of a . . . are the same length. square
3. The polygon with 3 sides is a . . . triangle.
4. Both a square and a . . . have 4 right angles. rectangle
5. An octagon has two more sides than a . . . hexagon.

Your Turn
Write a few sentences to describe polygons. Give some examples. Use the sentence starters for support. Share your ideas with a partner.
A polygon is . . .
One example of a polygon is . . .
It has . . . and . . .

Shapes **55**

Leveled Language Proficiency

Students at each proficiency level should be able to perform the following tasks.

Listening/Speaking

Early Beginner Demonstrate understanding of oral directions that are well-supported with visual cues. Respond to requests, expressing confusion at times.

Beginner/Early Intermediate Connect new information received orally to previous knowledge. Ask and respond to questions to clarify commands or information.

Intermediate Demonstrate comprehension of more complex instructions and information, including those utilizing common words with multiple meanings. Express how two things within an academic context are alike or different.

Advanced/Transitioning Demonstrate comprehension of all types of classroom discussions, whether basic or more complex sentence structures are employed. Elaborate on discussion points, extending ideas through different modes of discourse.

Your Turn

These kites are all polygons. Fill in the chart to describe them.

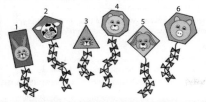

Kite	Type of Polygon	Number of Sides	Number of Angles
①	rectangle	4	4
②	pentagon	5	5
③	triangle	3	3
④	octagon	8	8
⑤	square	4	4
⑥	hexagon	6	6

Talk and Write About It

Complete the sentences about shapes.

Vocabulary			
right angle	triangle	square	hexagon
pentagon	rectangle	circle	angle

⑦ A hexagon has twice as many sides as a ___triangle___ .

⑧ Each corner of a square is the vertex of a ___right angle___ .

⑨ A ___pentagon___ has 5 sides .

Produce Language

Draw two polygons. Write sentences to describe each one.

Leveled Language Proficiency

Students at each proficiency level should be able to perform the following tasks.

Reading/Writing

Early Beginner Read some vocabulary terms with support, along with a few common words. Write terms and copy phrases with support.

Beginner Read and comprehend previously learned vocabulary terms. Write lists of words and phrases in response to writing tasks.

Early Intermediate/Intermediate Read independently when text is made up of known words and simple sentences. Write complete sentences, ranging from very simple to those that include some details.

Advanced/Transitioning Independently read grade-level text. Write a variety of sentence types, including details, with minimal support and errors.

⟳ Assess Understanding

Your Turn

Model Show how the kite numbers relate to the numbers in the chart. *I see that kite number 1 has 4 sides and 4 angles. I will write that in the top row of the chart. This kite has 4 right angles, so I know it is either a square or a rectangle. Which shape is it? Yes, I will write* rectangle. Have students complete the chart.

Talk and Write About It

On Their Own Have students work alone for 10 minutes. Once they have chosen the term for each sentence, have students share their work in pairs. Be sure that students understand the meaning of *twice* in Problem 7. Clarify as needed.

Produce Language

On Their Own Model constructing sentences to show how two polygons compare. Write these sentences on the board so that the two sentences about an octagon are side by side with the two sentences about a pentagon: *An octagon has _____ sides. A pentagon has _____ sides. An octagon has _____ angles. A pentagon has _____ angles.*

Wrap Up

Table Talk Have students look back at the lesson's objectives. Allow time for them to reflect on what they have learned and then answer the essential question.

☑ **Learned** and applied vocabulary used to name and describe different types of shapes

☑ **Spoken** statements to name, describe, and compare shapes

☑ **Written** statements to describe and compare shapes

Lesson 15

Triangles and Quadrilaterals

Vocabulary Polygon, opposite sides, parallel lines, triangle, equilateral triangle, isosceles triangle, scalene triangle, right triangle, acute triangle, obtuse triangle, quadrilateral, square, rectangle, rhombus, parallelogram, trapezoid

Math Background

- Triangles are polygons with 3 sides and 3 angles. Quadrilaterals are polygons with 4 sides and 4 angles.

- Triangles can be classified by their sides (*equilateral, isosceles, scalene*) or by their angles (*right, obtuse, acute*).

↻ Frontload the Lesson

Essential Question What vocabulary terms should you use to identify and describe triangles and quadrilaterals?

Talk About It

Build Background Once students have finished the first two columns of the chart, encourage them to share the meanings of the terms they wrote in those columns. (See page T43 for additional copies of the chart.)

↻ Content and Language

You Will

Model Read the objectives aloud and explain them in your own words. Use figures drawn on the board to support your explanations.

Your Turn

Guide Discussion Have students read the objectives. Ask students to explain what the objectives mean to them.

Triangles and Quadrilaterals

Essential Question What vocabulary terms should you use to identify and describe triangles and quadrilaterals?

You Will
- Identify different types of triangles and quadrilaterals.
- Use key terms to describe triangles and quadrilaterals.

Talk About It

Look at the list of terms below. In the first two columns of the chart, write terms you **know** or **want** to know more about.

polygon	quadrilateral	trapezoid
acute triangle	rectangle	triangle
obtuse triangle	rhombus	scalene triangle
opposite sides	right triangle	isosceles triangle
parallel lines	square	equilateral triangle
parallelogram		

Know	Want	Learned

What do you know about each term? Explain, using the sentence starters for support.

I know ... means ...
I want to know more about ...

Your Turn
Look at the objectives under You Will at the top of the page. Working with a partner, predict what you are going to learn. Use the sentence starter for support.

I am going to learn about ...

Leveled Instruction

Early Beginner Students should partner with students at higher language proficiency to complete the activities. Single words and gestures should be expected as answers.

Beginner Encourage students to use sentence starters to help them construct answers.

Early Intermediate Expect phrases and simple sentences from these students as answers to the activities.

Intermediate Students should produce complete sentences and tackle the activities with little assistance.

Advanced/Transitioning Students should produce detailed answers with minimal assistance and partner with students at lower language proficiency levels to offer them assistance.

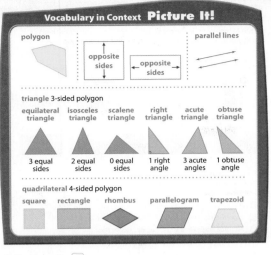

Vocabulary in Context Picture It!

polygon
opposite sides
opposite sides
parallel lines

triangle 3-sided polygon

equilateral triangle	isosceles triangle	scalene triangle	right triangle	acute triangle	obtuse triangle
3 equal sides	2 equal sides	0 equal sides	1 right angle	3 acute angles	1 obtuse angle

quadrilateral 4-sided polygon

square   rectangle   rhombus   parallelogram   trapezoid

Talk About It

Talk with a partner. Complete the sentences.

1. A polygon with 3 sides is a … triangle.
2. A polygon with 4 sides is a … quadrilateral.
3. Lines that never cross are … parallel lines.
4. Sides that are across from each other are … opposite sides.

Your Turn

Choose one quadrilateral and one triangle to draw and describe. Use vocabulary terms in your descriptions. Use them to label your drawings, too.

Academic Vocabulary

- Point out and teach the prefixes *tri-* (meaning "three") and *quadr-* (meaning "four") in *triangle* and *quadrilateral*. Explain that *triangle* means "three angles" and *quadrilateral* means "four-sided."

- Show students that *parallelogram* contains the word *parallel*. Explain that a parallelogram has two pairs of parallel sides.

- Explain that the word *right* in a right triangle's name does not mean "correct." It refers to the right angle.

Additional resources for building and reinforcing vocabulary are provided on pages T37–T42.

Cultural Consideration

Be aware that there are various definitions of *trapezoid*. Students schooled outside of the United States might have learned some properties of the trapezoid that are different from what they are learning in their math class here.

⟳ Comprehensible Input

Guide students to understanding

Vocabulary in Context Picture It!

1. **Say the Term** Have students repeat, stressing each syllable. Then combine syllables and have students repeat.

2. **Introduce Meaning** Connect the term to the visual that illustrates it.

3. **Demonstrate** Use visuals, gestures, and classroom objects to demonstrate. For example, when teaching *opposite sides,* point to opposite sides of the classroom.

4. **Apply** Have students demonstrate understanding with Talk About It.

Repeat the routine for each vocabulary term.

Talk About It

Guide Discussion Have students discuss the sentences with a partner. Model the sentence starters. Then provide this additional sentence completion, if time permits:

A triangle with an obtuse angle is called an … obtuse triangle.

Intervention

If students have trouble with *equal* as used here to describe sides …

Then explain that the term refers to having the same length, not to the mathematical process of reaching a total. Model using a ruler to measure the opposite sides of a parallelogram and show that the lengths are the same, or *equal.*

Your Turn

Guide Discussion Have pairs share their quadrilaterals and triangles. If both students in a pair chose the same quadrilateral or triangle, have them compare their answers.

↻ Language Production

Comprehension Support Explain that each piece of paper doll clothing is shaped like a quadrilateral or triangle, or it has one of these shapes somewhere on it.

Model *I see that part of the first blouse is shaped like a square. So, a line is drawn to the term square. Now you have to match the other polygons with the correct terms.*

Talk About It

Guide Discussion Have students work in pairs. Encourage them to refer to the representations of the different quadrilaterals and triangles in Vocabulary in Context Picture It! as needed to recall details about each shape.

Your Turn

Guide Discussion Give students time to complete their drawings and descriptions before forming pairs to orally share their ideas. Partners can record their work on copies of T44.

Do You Understand?

Look for polygons on the paper doll clothes. Draw a line from the polygon to the name of the polygon. The first one is done for you.

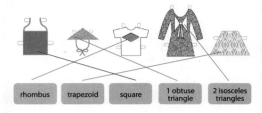

| rhombus | trapezoid | square | 1 obtuse triangle | 2 isosceles triangles |

Talk About It 🗨
How can you describe quadrilaterals and triangles? Complete the sentences to explain.

1. A polygon with 3 sides and 1 right angle is a … right triangle.
2. A parallelogram is a kind of … quadrilateral (or polygon).
3. All three angles in an … are acute. acute triangle
4. Both a square and a … have 4 equal sides. rhombus

Your Turn ✏
Draw your own shirt for a paper doll. Use a quadrilateral or a triangle in your drawing. Write a few sentences to describe it. Use the sentence starters for support. Share your ideas with a partner.

Look for the … on this shirt.
This shape has … sides.
One of the angles is …

Leveled Language Proficiency

Students at each proficiency level should be able to perform the following tasks.

Listening/Speaking

Early Beginner Demonstrate comprehension of simple statements, including questions and commands. Make and respond to requests, asking for repetition when needed.

Beginner Demonstrate comprehension of oral directions that include visual support. Give one-step directions.

Early Intermediate Demonstrate comprehension of oral questions about academic content. Respond to questions with short answers.

Intermediate Demonstrate comprehension of more complex instructions and information, including those requiring categorization. Explain how academic ideas fit into concept-based categories.

Advanced/Transitioning Demonstrate understanding of academic discussions without requiring concrete references. Support conclusions by stating facts or explaining reasoning.

Your Turn

You can see triangles and quadrilaterals all around you. Fill in the Polygon names chart to describe the ones that are pictured. may vary. Check students' answers.

Name	trapezoid	isosceles triangle	rectangle	right triangle
Sides	4	3	4	3
Angles	4	3	4	3
Parallel Sides	1 pair	0	2 pairs	0

Draw an example of each polygon.

① obtuse triangle   ② rhombus   ③ parallelogram

Check students' work.

Talk and Write About It 💬 ✏️

Complete the sentences about triangles and quadrilaterals.

Vocabulary
obtuse triangle rectangle   right triangle   rhombus
parallelogram   quadrilateral isosceles triangle trapezoid
acute triangle   parallel lines scalene triangle   square

④ A _right triangle_ has one right angle.

⑤ A trapezoid is a kind of _quadrilateral_ .

⑥ All angles are right angles in a square and in a _rectangle_ .

Produce Language ✏️

Write the terms you learned about in this lesson in the third column of the chart on page 57. Write what you have learned about these terms.

Leveled Language Proficiency

Students at each proficiency level should be able to perform the following tasks.

Reading/Writing

Early Beginner Show willingness to read for meaning when support is provided. Copy lists of words; write 1–2 vocabulary terms independently.

Beginner/Early Intermediate Read simple sentences with help and visual support; read some vocabulary terms independently. Use sentence starters and other organizers to write individual words and phrases that use vocabulary terms.

Intermediate Show understanding of written material by following directions or summarizing text. Write full sentences and complex phrases about lesson concepts, using vocabulary terms; sentences may contain some errors.

Advanced/Transitioning Read and carry out simple and complex written instructions; read sentences about lesson ideas that use lesson vocabulary. Write complete sentences with very few errors.

↻ Assess Understanding

Your Turn

Model Review how the information for the trapezoid has been filled in as an example. *The front of the flower pot is a trapezoid. It has 4 sides and 4 angles. Only 2 sides, or 1 pair of sides, are parallel.* Have students complete the chart and then draw the polygons described in Problems 1–3.

Talk and Write About It

On Their Own Have students work alone to choose the term for each sentence. Then have students share their work in pairs.

Produce Language

On Their Own Have students complete the Know-Want-Learned chart from the beginning of the lesson. Have students write what they have learned about these terms and share their ideas with others. If students have no new terms to add to column 3, ask them to write about three or four of the terms in the lesson.

Wrap Up

Table Talk Have students look back at the lesson's objectives. Allow time for them to reflect on what they have learned and then answer the essential question.

☑ **Learned** and applied vocabulary used to name and describe different types of triangles and quadrilaterals

☑ **Spoken** statements to name, describe, and compare triangles and quadrilaterals

☑ **Written** statements to describe and compare triangles and quadrilaterals

Figures in Our World

Vocabulary Shapes, circle, triangle, square, rectangle, symmetric figure, line of symmetry, solid figures, rectangular prism, edge, vertex, face, cube, pyramid, cylinder, cone, sphere, figures

Materials 2- and 3-dimensional grocery store items and containers, or other everyday objects that represent the figures in this lesson; red, blue, green, and black pencils or crayons

Math Background

- Two-dimensional flat figures are often called, simply, *shapes*. Three-dimensional figures are also called *solid figures*.

Frontload the Lesson

Essential Question

How can you describe figures in the world around you?

Talk About It

Build Background Encourage students to share their own definitions of the terms they rated 3.

Content and Language

You Will

Model Read the objectives aloud and explain them in your own words. Use objects in the classroom and grocery store items and containers to support your explanations.

Your Turn

Guide Discussion Have students read the objectives. Ask students to explain what the objectives mean to them.

Essential Question How can you describe figures in the world around you?

You Will
- Identify shapes and solid figures.
- Understand and use key terms to describe and compare shapes and solid figures.

Talk About It

Rate these mathematical terms according to the following scale:

1 I do not know this term.
2 I have heard this term, but I do not know how to use it in math.
3 I understand this term and know how to use it in math.

____ shape	____ rectangle	____ cube
____ solid figure	____ rectangular prism	____ sphere
____ cone	____ pyramid	____ circle
____ vertex	____ figures	____ square
____ line of symmetry	____ edge	____ triangle
____ face	____ cylinder	____ symmetric figure

What do you know about each term? Explain, using the sentence starters for support.

I do not know what … means.
I think … means …
I know that … means …

Your Turn
Look at the objectives under You Will at the top of the page. Working with a partner, predict what you are going to learn. Use the sentence starter for support.

I am going to learn about …

Leveled Instruction

Early Beginner Students should partner with those at higher language proficiency to complete the activities. They might answer with single words or construct responses in their native language.

Beginner/Early Intermediate Encourage students to use sentence starters when answering. Expect them to use complete simple sentences.

Intermediate Students should require minimal assistance when completing the activities. Their answers should be given as complete sentences with some detail.

Advanced/Transitioning Students should produce detailed answers with minimal assistance and partner with students at lower language proficiency levels to offer them assistance.

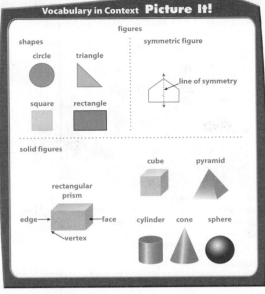

Vocabulary in Context **Picture It!**

figures

shapes

circle   triangle

square   rectangle

symmetric figure

line of symmetry

solid figures

cube   pyramid

rectangular prism

edge   face

vertex

cylinder   cone   sphere

Talk About It

Talk with a partner. Complete the sentences.

1. Triangles and circles are … **shapes.**
2. A shape that can be folded into two matching halves has a … **line of symmetry.**
3. Cubes and pyramids are … **solid figures.**
4. A solid figure shaped like a ball is a … **sphere.**

Your Turn

Choose a solid figure to describe. Use vocabulary terms.

62   Lesson 16

Academic Vocabulary

- Review common meanings of *edge*. An edge is a boundary line, as in the *edge* of the school's property. An edge is also the sharp side of a tool used for cutting, as in the *edge* of a knife. Then use a geometric model or a box to illustrate the mathematical meaning of *edge*.

- Have students indicate their own *faces*. Then introduce *face* used as a verb. Have students stand up. Say, "*Face* the front of the room." Turn your own body to face the front. Next say, "Now *face* the back of the room." Then use a geometric model or a box to illustrate the mathematical meaning of *face*.

- Discuss the two meanings of *circle* used in this lesson. A *circle* is a round shape (noun). Also, *circle* means to draw a round shape (verb). This second meaning of the word is used in the activity on page 63.

Additional resources for building and reinforcing vocabulary are provided on pages T37–T42.

↻ Comprehensible Input
Guide students to understanding

Vocabulary in Context Picture It!

1. **Say the Term** Have students repeat, stressing each syllable. Then combine syllables and have students repeat.

2. **Introduce Meaning** Connect the term to the visual that illustrates it.

3. **Demonstrate** Use visuals to demonstrate. Display typical grocery store or everyday items representing both shapes and solid figures. (Examples include square napkins, circular paper plates, cylindrical oatmeal containers or cans, cubic tea boxes, ice cream cones, and so on.)

4. **Apply** Have students demonstrate understanding with Talk About It.

Repeat the routine for each vocabulary term.

Talk About It

Guide Discussion Have students discuss the sentences with a partner. Model the sentence starters. Then provide this additional sentence completion, if time permits:

A rectangular prism has faces that are shaped like … **rectangles.**

Intervention

If students have trouble with the consonant blends in *prism* and *sphere* …

Then practice blending /pr/, /sm/, and /sf/.

Your Turn

Guide Discussion Have students form pairs to share their descriptions for Your Turn. If both students in a pair chose the same figure to describe, have them compare their answers and then select a second figure to describe together.

↻ Language Production

Comprehension Support Explain that students will follow the directions to circle figures they see in the picture. Be sure they have red, blue, green, and black pencils or crayons.

Model *The instructions for Problem 1 say to find a sphere and a triangle and to circle them in red. A sphere is a solid figure that looks like a ball, so I will look for that. A triangle is a shape with three sides, so I will look for that.* Read Problems 2–4 and have students complete them.

Talk About It

Guide Discussion Have students work in pairs. Encourage them to refer to the representations of the different figures in Vocabulary in Context as needed to recall details about each one. Allow sufficient time for them to plan their responses.

Your Turn

Guide Discussion Explain that the first sentence should end with either *shape* or *solid figure*. Give students time to complete their descriptions. Then have partners present their descriptions to each other as clues in a "Which object in the picture is it?" game.

Do You Understand?

You can see figures all around you. Look at the picture. Follow the directions to identify the figures. Check students' work.

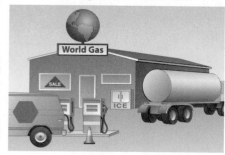

1. Use red to circle these figures: sphere, triangle.
2. Use blue to circle these figures: rectangle, rectangular prism.
3. Use green to circle these figures: cylinder, cone.
4. Find a type of polygon that you have not circled. Use black to draw a line of symmetry on it.

Talk About It
How can you describe figures? Complete the sentences to explain.

5. A corner in a solid figure is called a ... vertex.
6. The flat surface of a rectangular prism, cube, or pyramid is called a ... face.
7. A figure shaped like a soup can is a ... cylinder.

Your Turn
Choose one figure from the picture and write a description. Use the sentence starters for support. Share with a partner. See if your partner can point to the right figure in the picture.

This figure is a ...
It has ...
It is called a ...

Figures in Our World **63**

Leveled Language Proficiency

Students at each proficiency level should be able to perform the following tasks.

Listening/Speaking

Early Beginner Demonstrate comprehension of oral directions, especially those supported with visual cues. Make and respond to simple requests.

Beginner/Early Intermediate Demonstrate comprehension of information received orally as it connects to prior knowledge. Participate in classroom activities by using words and phrases supported by appropriate gestures and expressions.

Intermediate Demonstrate comprehension of key terms and phrases presented orally by sorting them into categories. Compare and contrast information orally.

Advanced/Transitioning Demonstrate understanding of questions based on academic content, including those using key terms in various contexts. Participate in discussions and other academic interactions, including those based on abstract topics, using a variety of sentences.

Your Turn
Draw a line from each picture to the type of figure it is.

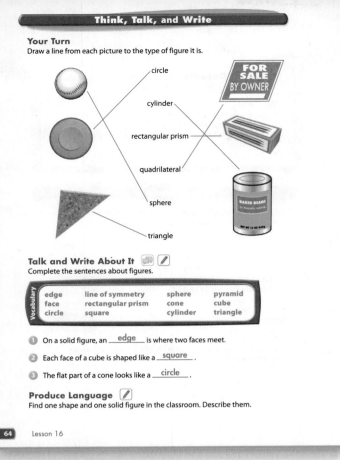

circle

cylinder

rectangular prism

quadrilateral

sphere

triangle

Talk and Write About It
Complete the sentences about figures.

Vocabulary			
edge	line of symmetry	sphere	pyramid
face	rectangular prism	cone	cube
circle	square	cylinder	triangle

1. On a solid figure, an ___edge___ is where two faces meet.
2. Each face of a cube is shaped like a ___square___ .
3. The flat part of a cone looks like a ___circle___ .

Produce Language
Find one shape and one solid figure in the classroom. Describe them.

64   Lesson 16

Leveled Language Proficiency

Students at each proficiency level should be able to perform the following tasks.

Reading/Writing

Early Beginner Use visual support and the assistance of others when reading. Copy lists of words; write 1–2 vocabulary terms independently.

Beginner Read and understand previously learned key terms. Write lists of words and phrases in response to an assigned writing task.

Early Intermediate/Intermediate Independently figure out words in context using vocabulary strategies. Write directions, instructions, and explanations in simple sentences that are arranged in logical order.

Advanced/Transitioning Independently read instructions and academic text. Write complete sentences with very few errors.

↻ Assess Understanding

Your Turn

Model Explain that students will match the objects to the words. Then they will draw a line connecting them.

Talk and Write About It

On Their Own Have students work alone at first. Once they have chosen the word for each sentence, have students share their work in pairs.

Produce Language

On Their Own Encourage students to use labeled drawings of the real-world objects to support their definitions.

Wrap Up

Table Talk Have students look back at the lesson's objectives. Allow time for them to reflect on what they have learned and then answer the essential question.

- ☑ **Learned** and applied vocabulary used to name and describe figures
- ☑ **Spoken** statements to name, describe, and compare figures
- ☑ **Written** statements to describe specific examples of figures

Units of Measure

Vocabulary Length, customary units, inch, foot, yard, mile, metric units, millimeter, centimeter, meter, kilometer, weight, ounce, pound, ton, mass, gram, kilogram, capacity, cup, quart, gallon, milliliter, liter

Materials Index cards, ruler, yardstick, meterstick, 1-inch paperclip, transparent measuring cup that measures liquid capacity in customary and/or metric units, Measurement Match activity (page 95)

Math Background

- Mass, the amount of matter that an object contains, is measured in metric units (grams). Weight, the pull of gravity on an object, is measured in customary units.

♻ Frontload the Lesson

Essential Question

What do you need to know about the names of different units of measure?

Talk About It

Build Background Read the terms aloud as students sort them into piles. Encourage them to share their own definitions of the terms they place in Pile 1.

♻ Content and Language

You Will

Model Read the objectives aloud and explain them in your own words. Use gestures and objects to support your explanations.

Your Turn

Guide Discussion Have students read the objectives. Ask volunteers to explain what the objectives mean to them.

Essential Question What do you need to know about the names of different units of measure?

You Will
- Identify customary and metric units of measure for length, weight or mass, and capacity.
- Determine the best units to use when measuring length, weight or mass, and capacity.
- Use the correct terms when discussing units of measure.

Talk About It

Copy each term from Vocabulary in Context on a card. As your teacher reads each term, create three piles of cards.

1. Place terms that you know in **Pile 1.**
2. Place terms you have heard but are not sure what they mean in **Pile 2.**
3. Place terms you do not know in **Pile 3.**

What do you know about each term? Explain, using the sentence starters for support.

I know … means …
I think … means …
I do not know what … means.

capacity

length

weight

Your Turn
Look at the objectives listed under You Will at the top of the page. Predict what you are going to learn. Use the sentence starter for support.

I am going to learn about …

Leveled Instruction

Early Beginner Partner early beginners with students at higher proficiency levels so they may provide added support. Expect single words, gestures, and simple responses as answers.

Beginner/Early Intermediate Expect phrases and simple sentences from these students when they are answering questions, especially when sentence starters are provided.

Intermediate Students should be able to complete activities with minimal assistance. Expect phrases and simple sentences in answering questions and joining discussions. Provide immediate feedback so students can self-correct.

Advanced/Transitioning Students should produce detailed answers with minimal assistance. They can offer students at lower proficiency levels support and assistance.

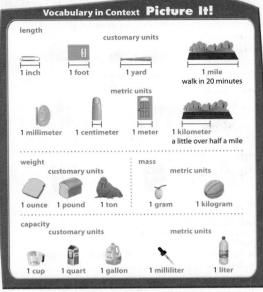

length
customary units
1 inch 1 foot 1 yard 1 mile
walk in 20 minutes

metric units
1 millimeter 1 centimeter 1 meter 1 kilometer
a little over half a mile

weight
customary units
1 ounce 1 pound 1 ton

mass
metric units
1 gram 1 kilogram

capacity
customary units
1 cup 1 quart 1 gallon

metric units
1 milliliter 1 liter

Talk About It

Talk with a partner. Complete the sentences.

① Yards and inches are customary units of ... length.

② Liters and milliliters are ... units of capacity. metric

Your Turn

Choose a unit of measure. Tell a partner what you could measure using that unit.

Academic Vocabulary

- Be sure students understand that units of *length* are used to tell how *long* (or *tall, wide, thick*) an object is, units of *weight* are used to tell how *heavy* an object is, units of *mass* are used to tell how much *matter* is in an object, and units of *capacity* are used to tell how much (usually liquid) an object can *hold*.

- Help students distinguish the customary unit of measure *foot/feet* from the anatomical terms. Also, help students understand the difference between the customary unit of measure *yard* and the term describing an area of ground.

- Students may call all types and sizes of drinking vessels *cups*. Confirm that this is a proper use of the word, but that the unit of measure *cup* refers to a specific amount.

Additional resources for building and reinforcing vocabulary are provided on pages T37–T41.

Cultural Consideration

Students from cultures using the metric system might be confused by customary measures. Consider providing additional equivalency information.

↻ Comprehensible Input

Guide students to understanding

Vocabulary in Context Picture It!

1. **Say the Term** Have students repeat, stressing each syllable. Then combine syllables and have students repeat.

2. **Introduce Meaning** Connect the term to the visual that illustrates it.

3. **Demonstrate** Use gestures and objects to demonstrate. For example, when discussing *inch*, hold up a paperclip and point out its length.

4. **Apply** Have students demonstrate understanding with Talk About It.

Repeat the routine for each vocabulary term.

Talk About It

Guide Discussion Have students discuss the sentences with a partner. Model the sentence starters. Then provide this additional sentence completion, if time permits:

Two customary units of weight are pounds and ... ounces (or tons).

Intervention

If students have trouble with the concept of capacity ...

Then show students a transparent measuring cup and the marks showing the different units of measure. If possible, have volunteers fill the cup with water to different levels that you specify.

Your Turn

Guide Discussion Have students share their ideas with a partner. You might want to suggest that they look for examples in the classroom.

Language Production

Comprehension Support Explain that students will circle the word below each picture that names the better unit of measure.

Model *If I measure the length of this shoe, would I use inches or yards?* Use a yardstick to point out the size of one inch and one yard. *An inch is about the length of a paperclip. A shoe would be many inches long. A yard is about the width of a door.* (Sweep your hand across the width of a door.) *So, a yard is much longer than this shoe! So, I would circle* inch. Be sure students notice the categories on the page: length, weight or mass, and capacity. Encourage them to refer to the examples of objects provided in Vocabulary in Context as needed.

Talk About It

Guide Discussion Have students work in pairs. Encourage them to refer back to Vocabulary in Context as needed. Allow sufficient time for them to plan their responses.

Your Turn

Guide Discussion Give students time to identify an object and select a unit of length and a unit of weight. Then have them form pairs, point out to each other the objects they chose, and share their ideas about measuring those objects.

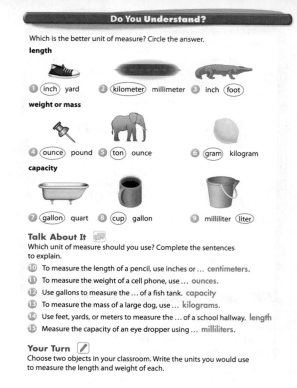

Do You Understand?

Which is the better unit of measure? Circle the answer.

length

1 (inch) yard   2 (kilometer) millimeter   3 inch (foot)

weight or mass

4 (ounce) pound   5 (ton) ounce   6 (gram) kilogram

capacity

7 (gallon) quart   8 (cup) gallon   9 milliliter (liter)

Talk About It
Which unit of measure should you use? Complete the sentences to explain.

10 To measure the length of a pencil, use inches or… centimeters.
11 To measure the weight of a cell phone, use … ounces.
12 Use gallons to measure the … of a fish tank. capacity
13 To measure the mass of a large dog, use … kilograms.
14 Use feet, yards, or meters to measure the … of a school hallway. length
15 Measure the capacity of an eye dropper using … milliliters.

Your Turn ✎
Choose two objects in your classroom. Write the units you would use to measure the length and weight of each.

Leveled Language Proficiency

Students at each proficiency level should be able to perform the following tasks.

Listening/Speaking

Early Beginner Demonstrate comprehension of simple statements supported by gestures. Respond to requests, admitting to confusion whenever it is experienced.

Beginner/Early Intermediate Demonstrate understanding of terms, especially when supported with visuals, actions, or realia. Use terms and grade-level vocabulary when speaking.

Intermediate Demonstrate comprehension of terms used during discussion, using resources to clarify meanings as needed. Respond accurately to questions about academic content and to requests.

Advanced/Transitioning Demonstrate understanding of questions based on academic content, including those requiring inference. State facts or other reasons that support conclusions.

Your Turn

Tear out the Measurement Match activity on page 95.

Write the letter for the picture that could match the measures below.

weight		
B	C	A
4 ounces	9 pounds	50 pounds

length		
E	F	D
10 centimeters	20 yards	1 meter

capacity		
H	I	G
3 cups	5 milliliters	10 gallons

Talk and Write About It 💬 ✏️

Complete the sentences about units of measure.

Vocabulary			
centimeters	yards	grams	capacity
kilograms	pounds	inches	weight
metric units	mass	measure	length

1. To measure the length of a pen, use <u>inches (or centimeters)</u>.
2. A pound is a unit of <u>weight</u>.
3. Centimeters and meters are <u>metric units</u> of length.
4. To measure mass, use <u>grams or kilograms</u>.
5. A liter is a metric unit of <u>capacity</u>.
6. A yard is a customary unit of <u>length</u>.

Produce Language ✏️

You want to know how tall you are. What is the best unit of measure to use? Explain why.

68   Lesson 17

Leveled Language Proficiency

Students at each proficiency level should be able to perform the following tasks.

Reading/Writing

Early Beginner Echo read and participate in some independent reading when strong visual support is provided. Copy vocabulary terms, and write one or two of them independently.

Beginner/Early Intermediate Read simple sentences and vocabulary terms with the help of someone at a higher level of language proficiency. Use sentence starters to write individual words and phrases, including vocabulary terms.

Intermediate Follow written directions and retell what was read independently. Write simple sentences that use vocabulary terms properly, although with some grammatical errors.

Advanced/Transitioning Read and carry out written instructions and independently read lessons with ease of comprehension. Write a variety of sentences, including those that explain vocabulary terms, with few errors.

Assess Understanding

Your Turn

Model Explain that each category (weight, length, capacity) begins with a list of three different measurements. Students will decide which picture matches each measure and write the letter for it in the blank below the measure. Determining weight may be difficult for students, so have them use the process of elimination. *For weight, the three measurements are 4 ounces, 9 pounds, and 50 pounds. The dog has the greatest weight. The greatest weight is 50 pounds. Match the dog with the weight 50 pounds. The banana has the least weight. The least weight is 4 ounces. Match the banana with 4 ounces.*

Talk and Write About It

On Their Own Have students work alone for 5 minutes to match the measurements. Then have partners compare their matches and complete the sentences.

Produce Language

On Their Own Have students write about what they have learned about units of length.

Wrap Up

Table Talk Have students look back at the lesson's objectives. Allow time for them to reflect on what they have learned and then answer the essential question.

☑ **Learned** and applied vocabulary related to units of measure for length, weight or mass, and capacity

☑ **Spoken** statements to describe the different units of measure and when they should be used

☑ **Written** statements to describe the length, weight or mass, and capacity of different objects

Lesson 18

Measurement Tools

Vocabulary Length, ruler, inch, foot, yardstick, yard, meterstick, centimeter, meter, capacity, measuring cup, cup, pint, quart, milliliter, liter, weight, mass, pan balance, ounce, gram, pound, kilogram

Materials Index cards, ruler, yardstick, meterstick, transparent measuring cup that measures liquid capacity in customary and metric units, pan balance

Math Background

- Rulers, yardsticks, and metersticks are tools used to measure length. Measuring cups can be used to measure capacity. Weight or mass are measured using pan balances, sometimes called *balance scales*.

Measurement Tools

Essential Question How can you discuss measurement tools and what they measure?

You Will
- Identify measurement tools.
- Determine which tool to use to measure the length, the weight or mass, or the capacity of an object.
- Use key terms for units of measure and measurement tools.

Talk About It

Copy each term from Vocabulary in Context onto an index card. Place each card in one of three piles.

Pile 1: I know what this term means.
Pile 2: I have heard of this term, but I am not sure how it is used in math.
Pile 3: I have not heard of this term.

What do you know about each term?
Explain, using the sentence starters for support.

I know ... means ...
I have heard of ..., but I don't know how to use it in mathematics.
I have not heard of ...

yardstick

Your Turn

Look at the objectives under You Will at the top of the page. Working with a partner, predict what you are going to learn. Use the sentence starter for support.

I am going to learn about ...

Frontload the Lesson

How can you discuss measurement tools and what they measure?

Talk About It

Build Background Once students have made the cards and placed them into piles, encourage them to share the definitions of any terms they placed in Pile 1.

Content and Language

You Will

Model Read the objectives aloud and explain them in your own words. Use measuring tools to support your explanations.

Your Turn

Guide Discussion Have students read the objectives. Ask volunteers to explain what the objectives mean to them.

Leveled Instruction

Early Beginner Provide answers in the form of single words, gestures, and pictures. May benefit from partnering with students at higher proficiency levels who can provide assistance.

Beginner Answer in short phrases, especially when sentence starters are provided.

Early Intermediate Provide phrases and simple sentences in answering questions and joining discussions.

Intermediate Produce complete sentences that show their comprehension of activity information and questions.

Advanced/Transitioning Produce a variety of sentence types when answering questions or making comments. Can offer students at lower proficiency levels support and assistance.

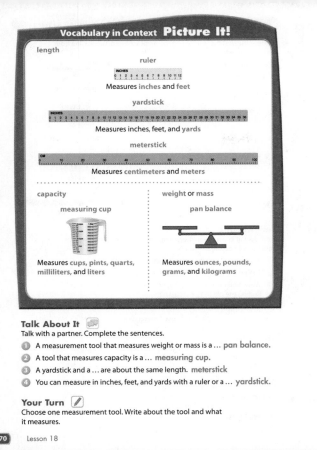

Vocabulary in Context Picture It!

length
ruler
Measures **inches** and **feet**

yardstick
Measures inches, feet, and **yards**

meterstick
Measures **centimeters** and **meters**

capacity
measuring cup
Measures **cups, pints, quarts, milliliters,** and **liters**

weight or mass
pan balance
Measures **ounces, pounds, grams,** and **kilograms**

Talk About It
Talk with a partner. Complete the sentences.
1. A measurement tool that measures weight or mass is a ... pan balance.
2. A tool that measures capacity is a ... measuring cup.
3. A yardstick and a ... are about the same length. meterstick
4. You can measure in inches, feet, and yards with a ruler or a ... yardstick.

Your Turn
Choose one measurement tool. Write about the tool and what it measures.

Academic Vocabulary

- Students are probably familiar with *tools* used to make or repair things. Ask them to name some of these tools (hammer, screwdriver, scissors, jack, etc.) Explain that, like these tools, measurement tools are used to perform certain tasks.

- Point out that, during physical education, students might be asked to *balance* on a structure.

- *Ruler* names a measurement tool for length, but it also names the leader of a country. Explain that a person who is a *ruler* rules, or leads the government of a country.

- If you use a measuring cup that has ounces marked, point out that this unit is called a *fluid ounce*, not to be confused with the *ounce*, a unit of weight. Fluid ounces are a unit of capacity, like cups, pints, and quarts, which students will learn more about in a later grade.

Additional resources for building and reinforcing vocabulary are provided on pages T37–T41.

Cultural Consideration

Invite volunteers familiar with the metric system to "teach" other students what they know.

↻ Comprehensible Input
Guide students to understanding

Vocabulary in Context Picture It!

1. **Say the Term** Have students repeat, stressing each syllable. Then combine syllables and have students repeat.

2. **Introduce Meaning** Connect the term to the visual that illustrates it.

3. **Demonstrate** Invite students to measure with each type of measurement tool in your classroom. Point out the different units of measure on each tool. Since some measurement tools include both customary and metric units, be sure students see and understand how the two types of units can be shown on a single tool.

4. **Apply** Have students demonstrate understanding with Talk About It.

Repeat the routine for each vocabulary term.

Talk About It

Guide Discussion Have students discuss the sentences with a partner. Model the sentence starters. Then provide this additional sentence completion, if time permits:

You can find the mass of an object using a ... pan balance.

Intervention

If students have trouble remembering the units measured by each tool ...

Then set up three measurement centers in your classroom: length, capacity, and weight or mass. Place the correct tools in each center. Make index cards, writing one unit of measure on each card. Have students match the cards to the tools.

Your Turn

Guide Discussion Have students form pairs to share their descriptions for Your Turn. If both members of a pair chose the same tool to describe, have them compare descriptions and then choose a different tool to describe together.

↻ Language Production

Comprehension Support Explain that students will match the terms listed on the left with the measurement tools pictured on the right.

Model *For Problem 1, I need to find a tool that will help me measure the length of a sheet of paper. I can use a ruler for that. I will draw a line to that tool.* Read each measure aloud for students.

Talk About It

Guide Discussion Have students work in pairs. Encourage them to refer to pictured tools or actual measurement tools in your classroom, as needed. Allow sufficient time for students to plan their responses.

Your Turn

Guide Discussion Have students estimate the length and weight or mass of their favorite pet or animal. Then have students form pairs to share the tools they would use to measure its length and weight or mass.

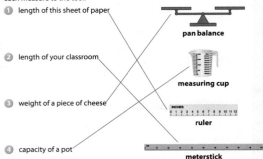

Do You Understand?

Choose the best tool for finding the measure listed. Draw a line from each measure to the tool.

1 length of this sheet of paper

2 length of your classroom

3 weight of a piece of cheese

4 capacity of a pot

pan balance

measuring cup

ruler

meterstick

Talk About It 💬
How do you know which measurement tool to use? Complete the sentences to explain.

5 You can measure length in inches with a yardstick or a … ruler.
6 To find the weight of this book, use a … pan balance.
7 When you measure the amount of liquid in a pitcher, you are finding the pitcher's … capacity.
8 You can measure a pencil's mass with a … pan balance.
9 To measure a rug's length, use a meterstick or a … ruler (or yardstick).

Your Turn ✏️
Choose a favorite pet or animal. Write the measurement tools you would use to measure its length and weight. Use the sentence starters for support.

My favorite animal is …
I need to see how many … long it is.
So, I would use a … to measure its length.
I need to see how many … it weighs.
So, I would use a … to measure its weight.

Measurement Tools 71

Leveled Language Proficiency

Students at each proficiency level should be able to perform the following tasks.

Listening/Speaking

Early Beginner Demonstrate comprehension of words, phrases, and simple sentences supported by gestures and visuals. Make and respond to requests, using single words or short phrases.

Beginner Demonstrate comprehension of some vocabulary terms, especially when visual support is provided. Say individual terms and respond to requests with simple phrases.

Early Intermediate Demonstrate understanding of questions based on academic content. Speak in phrases and simple sentences, showing an increasing understanding of lesson vocabulary.

Intermediate Demonstrate comprehension of multiple-step directions. Participate in classroom discussions, asking for clarification as needed.

Advanced/Transitioning Connect ideas during academic discussions. Elaborate on ideas during contributions to discussions.

Your Turn

Name the best tool and unit of measure for each object.

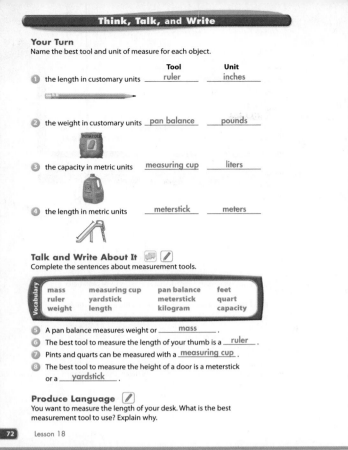

	Tool	Unit
1 the length in customary units	ruler	inches
2 the weight in customary units	pan balance	pounds
3 the capacity in metric units	measuring cup	liters
4 the length in metric units	meterstick	meters

Talk and Write About It

Complete the sentences about measurement tools.

Vocabulary			
mass	measuring cup	pan balance	feet
ruler	yardstick	meterstick	quart
weight	length	kilogram	capacity

5 A pan balance measures weight or ___mass___ .

6 The best tool to measure the length of your thumb is a ___ruler___ .

7 Pints and quarts can be measured with a ___measuring cup___ .

8 The best tool to measure the height of a door is a meterstick or a ___yardstick___ .

Produce Language

You want to measure the length of your desk. What is the best measurement tool to use? Explain why.

Leveled Language Proficiency

Students at each proficiency level should be able to perform the following tasks.

Reading/Writing

Early Beginner Read independently when strong visual support is provided, after being walked through a reading at least once. Write individual vocabulary terms after the meanings are understood.

Beginner/Early Intermediate Read simple sentences with the help of someone at a higher level of language proficiency. Complete sentence starters with individual words and phrases, including vocabulary terms.

Intermediate Follow written directions and demonstrate comprehension of reading done independently. Write simple sentences.

Advanced/Transitioning Carry out written instructions and independently read lessons with ease of comprehension. Write a variety of sentences, and use correct mechanics when editing them.

↻ Assess Understanding

Your Turn

Model Explain that students will decide what tool and units of measure they would use to measure the pictured object. *For Problem 1, I need to figure out how to measure the length of the pencil in customary units. If I need help remembering the name of a tool or unit of measure, I will look back at Vocabulary in Context for help.*

Talk and Write About It

On Their Own Have students work alone for 10 minutes. Once they have chosen the word for each sentence, have students share their work in pairs.

Produce Language

On Their Own Have students write about what they have learned about using measurement tools for length.

Wrap Up

Table Talk Have students look back at the lesson's objectives. Allow time for them to reflect on what they have learned and then answer the essential question.

- ☑ **Learned** and applied vocabulary related to measurement tools and the units they measure

- ☑ **Spoken** statements to describe measurement tools and when they should be used

- ☑ **Written** statements to describe the use of measurement tools to measure the length, weight or mass, and capacity

Lesson 19

Perimeter and Area

Vocabulary Perimeter, distance, dimensions, width, length, area, unit, square unit, square centimeter, square inch

Materials Yardstick or measuring tape, square sticky notes, Inch Tiles (page 97), scissors

Math Background

- The perimeter of a figure is the distance around it. For polygons, add the lengths of the sides to find the perimeter.

- The area of a figure is the number of square units that fit inside it. For rectangles, multiply length by width to find the area.

↻ Frontload the Lesson

What words should you use to talk about perimeter and area?

Talk About It

Build Background Once students have rated the terms, ask volunteers to share the definitions of any terms they rated 3.

↻ Content and Language

You Will

Model Read the objectives aloud and explain them in your own words. Use a yardstick or measuring tape to show how to find the perimeter and area of your desktop to support your explanations.

Your Turn

Guide Discussion Have students read the objectives and explain what the objectives mean to them.

Essential Question What words should you use to talk about perimeter and area?

You Will
- Understand what perimeter and area measure.
- Find the perimeter and area of rectangles.
- Understand and use key terms related to perimeter and area.

Talk About It

Rate these mathematical terms according to the following scale.

1. I do not know this term.
2. I have heard this term, but I do not know how to use it in math.
3. I understand this term and I know how to use it in math.

_____ area	_____ square unit
_____ distance	_____ width
_____ length	_____ unit
_____ dimensions	_____ square inch
_____ perimeter	_____ square centimeter

Explain what you know about each term, using the sentence starters.

I do not know what … means.
I think … means …
I know … means … in math.

Your Turn
Look at the objectives under You Will at the top of the page. Working with a partner, predict what you are going to learn. Use the sentence starter for support.

I am going to learn about …

Leveled Instruction

Early Beginner Partnering early beginners with students at higher proficiency levels will provide them added support. Expect students to give answers consisting of single words, gestures, and pictures.

Beginner/Early Intermediate Expect phrases and simple sentences from these students when they are answering questions. Encourage the use of sentence starters to help students construct their answers.

Intermediate Expect students to be able to complete activities with minimal assistance. Encourage them to answer using full sentences with some details.

Advanced/Transitioning Expect students to produce detailed answers with minimal assistance. They can offer students at lower proficiency levels support and assistance.

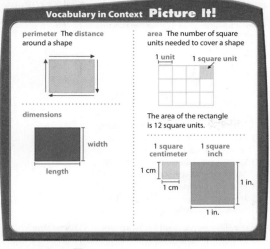

Vocabulary in Context Picture It!

perimeter The distance around a shape

dimensions

width

length

area The number of square units needed to cover a shape

1 unit   1 square unit

The area of the rectangle is 12 square units.

1 square centimeter   1 square inch

1 cm

1 cm

1 in.

1 in.

Talk About It
Talk with a partner. Complete the sentences.
1. The distance around a shape is its … **perimeter.**
2. The number of square units that fit inside a shape is its … **area.**
3. When I find how far it is from my desk to the door, I am finding the … **distance.**
4. Length and width are … **dimensions.**

Your Turn
Describe *perimeter* and *area*. Use your own words and/or drawings. Share your description with a partner.

Academic Vocabulary

- Students have probably heard *area* used to refer to a particular place. Your classroom might have a reading *area,* or your city or town might have a historical *area.* Be sure students know the difference between this use of the word and the term *area* that refers to a measurement.

- The following words are cognates with Spanish, and should be easy for some students to understand: *distance, perimeter,* and *dimensions.*

- Explain that *length* and *width* can refer to either set of sides of a rectangle. Introduce students to other uses of *length.* The word is used to describe distance, as in the *length* of a trip or race. It is also used to describe a piece of something, as in a *length* of ribbon or rope.

- Relate the words *length/long* and *width/wide* and point out how the spelling changes in examples, such as "How *long* is the rectangle?" and "What is the rectangle's *length*?"

Additional resources for building and reinforcing vocabulary are provided on pages T37–T41.

⟳ Comprehensible Input
Guide students to understanding

Vocabulary in Context Picture It!

1. **Say the Term** Have students repeat, stressing each syllable. Then combine syllables and have students repeat.

2. **Introduce Meaning** Connect the term to the visual that illustrates it.

3. **Demonstrate** Make an array of 3 rows of 4 sticky notes each on the board. Identify the perimeter and the area.

4. **Apply** Have students demonstrate understanding with Talk About It.

Repeat the routine for each vocabulary term.

Talk About It

Guide Discussion Have students discuss the sentences with a partner. Model the sentence starters. Then provide this additional sentence completion, if time permits:

A square unit that is smaller than a square inch is a … **square centimeter.**

Intervention

If students have trouble understanding how to count units of measure to find perimeter …

Then use tape to outline a 6 × 8 rectangle on a tiled floor, or create the rectangle using 48 eight-inch square pieces of construction paper. Have students start at one corner and walk around the shape, stepping along the edge of each piece of paper and counting their steps to find the total (28).

Your Turn

Guide Discussion Have students form pairs to share their descriptions for Your Turn.

↻ Language Production

Comprehension Support Have students cut out the one-inch tiles from page 97 to find the perimeter and area of the business card. If available, show students a business card and discuss how business cards are used.

Model *I can cover the bottom of the card with 3 tiles. The length of the card is 3 inches. I can cover the whole card with 2 rows of 3 tiles. The width of the card is 2 inches. The perimeter is the distance around the card. So the perimeter is 3 + 2 + 3 + 2 which equals 10 inches.* Monitor students as they find the area of the card.

Talk About It

Guide Discussion Have students work in pairs. Encourage them to talk about how they found the perimeter and area of the card. Ask volunteers to talk about the area and perimeter of the rectangles they made from tiles. Allow sufficient time for them to plan their responses.

Your Turn

Guide Discussion Give students time to complete their writing. Then have students form pairs to share their ideas.

Do You Understand?

Cover this business card with 1-inch tiles from page 97. Find the perimeter and area.

Moons Bank

Steve Riley
Manager
32 Parkland Dr.
Boston, Ma 02154
617-555-5555

1. How many tiles long is the card? __3__ tiles
   What is the length of the card? __3__ inches
2. How many tiles wide is the card? __2__ tiles
   What is the width of the card? __2__ inches
3. What is the perimeter of the card? __10__ inches
4. How many tiles cover the card? __6__ tiles
   What is the area of the card? __6__ square inches

With the tiles, make a rectangle that has a perimeter of 12 inches. What is the area of this rectangle? __Check students' answers.__

With the tiles, make a rectangle that has an area of 12 square inches. What is the perimeter of this rectangle? __Check students' answers.__

Talk About It 💬
Complete the sentences.

5. The distance around the card is its ... perimeter.
6. The number of inch tiles that cover the card is its ... area.
7. To find the area of the card, count the tiles or multiply the ... by the width. length

Your Turn ✏️
Write how to find the perimeter and area of a square. Use the sentence starters for help. Share your ideas with a partner.

To find the perimeter of a square, you ...
To find the area of a square, you ...

Leveled Language Proficiency

Students at each proficiency level should be able to perform the following tasks.

Listening/Speaking

Early Beginner Demonstrate understanding of one-step oral directions. Make and respond to requests, expressing confusion at times.

Beginner Demonstrate comprehension of some vocabulary terms, especially when visual support is provided. Say individual terms and respond to requests with simple phrases.

Early Intermediate Use both verbal and nonverbal cues to comprehend oral directions. Participate in small group activities when the role is clearly defined and understood.

Intermediate Demonstrate comprehension of the main points of a discussion. Explain thinking processes used to arrive at answers.

Advanced/Transitioning Connect ideas during academic discussions. Elaborate on discussion points using a variety of sentence types.

Your Turn

Draw the shapes described.

① Draw a square with a perimeter of 16 units.

② Draw a rectangle with an area of 20 square units.

Students should draw the shapes specified, using the grids. Check that the perimeter or area match the specifications.

③ Draw a square with a perimeter of 24 units.

④ Draw a rectangle with an area of 18 square units.

Talk and Write About It ✏️

Complete the sentences about perimeter and area.

Vocabulary

width	square units	area	length
perimeter	distance	dimensions	unit

⑤ The length and width of a figure are its __dimensions__.

⑥ The distance around a figure is the __perimeter__.

⑦ The area of a figure is given in __square units__.

Produce Language ✏️

What is the difference between area and perimeter? Write about how they are different. You can include drawings as examples.

Leveled Language Proficiency

Students at each proficiency level should be able to perform the following tasks.

Reading/Writing

Early Beginner Read some vocabulary terms with support, along with a few common words. Write terms independently; copy phrases.

Beginner Use visual and contextual support to determine meaning of terms, especially with the help of someone at a higher level of language proficiency. Use sentence starters and visual supports to write individual terms and phrases.

Early Intermediate Read most vocabulary terms in context; read independently when text is made up of known words and simple sentences. Write simple sentences, with some errors.

Intermediate Apply reading strategies, including identifying main idea and details, to aid independent reading. Write complete sentences that include vocabulary terms.

Advanced/Transitioning Read and write a variety of sentence types containing concrete and abstract ideas related to lesson content with minimal support.

↻ Assess Understanding

Your Turn

Model Explain that students will decide how to draw rectangles on the grids so that the shapes have the correct perimeter or area. *It's important that I think about the shape I am supposed to draw. For Problem 1, I am supposed to draw a square. I need to remember that a square has 4 sides that are all the same length.* Encourage students to work in pencil so that they can erase, if necessary.

Talk and Write About It

On Their Own Have students work alone for 10 minutes. Once they have chosen the word for each sentence, have students share their work in pairs.

Produce Language

On Their Own You might provide students with words that signal contrast/differences such as *but, however, while.* Encourage them to use the vocabulary terms in their sentences.

Wrap Up

Table Talk Have students look back at the lesson's objectives. Allow time for them to reflect on what they have learned and then answer the essential question.

☑ **Learned** and applied vocabulary related to perimeter and area

☑ **Spoken** statements to describe perimeter and area

☑ **Written** statements telling how to find the perimeter and area of shapes

Lesson 20

Time

Vocabulary Time, clocks, quarter, hour hand, minute hand, minutes, hour, day, calendar, month, date, weeks, year, Sunday, Monday, Tuesday, Wednesday, Thursday, Friday, Saturday, January, February, March, April, May, June, July, August, September, October, November, December

Materials Index cards, clock, calendar for the current year

Math Background

- Units of time measured by clocks are seconds, minutes, and hours. Units measured by calendars are days, weeks, months, and years.

⟳ Frontload the Lesson

Essential Question

How do you use vocabulary terms to talk about telling time and the calendar?

Talk About It

Build Background Once students have made and sorted their terms cards, encourage them to share the definitions of any terms they placed in Pile 1.

⟳ Content and Language

You Will

Model Read the objectives aloud and explain them in your own words. Use clocks or calendars in your classroom to support your explanations.

Your Turn

Guide Discussion Have students read the objectives. Ask students to explain what the objectives mean to them.

Time

Essential Question How do you use vocabulary terms to talk about telling time and the calendar?

You Will
- Tell time and talk about time using clocks.
- Use a calendar.
- Understand and use key terms related to time.

Talk About It

Work with a partner. Make an index card for each vocabulary term below. Place each card in one of three piles.

Pile 1: I know what this term means.
Pile 2: I have heard this term, but I am not sure how it is used in math.
Pile 3: I have not heard of this term.

hour hand	date	month
day	quarter	minute hand
calendar	hour	week
clocks	minutes	year
time		

What do you know about each term? Explain, using the sentence starters for support.

I know that … means …
I think … means …
I do not know what … means.

Your Turn
Look at the objectives under You Will at the top of the page. Working with a partner, predict what you are going to learn. Use the sentence starter for support.

I am going to learn about …

Time 77

Leveled Instruction

Early Beginner Gesturing and answering with single words, short phrases, and pictures are fine ways for students to respond.

Beginner Students should respond with single English words or short phrases. Students continue to benefit from partnerships with students at higher levels of language proficiency.

Early Intermediate Expect students to answer questions with phrases and simple sentences. Encourage the use of sentence starters to help them construct their answers.

Intermediate Anticipate that students can complete the activities with minimal assistance. They should consistently answer questions using full sentences.

Advanced/Transitioning Students should produce answers that include details and elaboration. Rather than needing assistance, they should be able to provide it to students at lower proficiency levels.

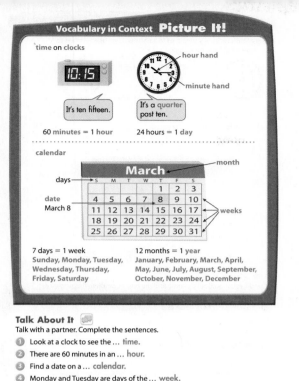

Vocabulary in Context Picture It!

time on clocks

10:15 hour hand

minute hand

It's ten fifteen.

It's a quarter past ten.

60 minutes = 1 hour   24 hours = 1 day

calendar

month

March

days

S	M	T	W	T	F	S
					1	2	3

date
March 8

4	5	6	7	8	9	10
11	12	13	14	15	16	17
18	19	20	21	22	23	24
25	26	27	28	29	30	31

weeks

7 days = 1 week
Sunday, Monday, Tuesday,
Wednesday, Thursday,
Friday, Saturday

12 months = 1 year
January, February, March, April,
May, June, July, August, September,
October, November, December

Talk About It
Talk with a partner. Complete the sentences.
1. Look at a clock to see the … time.
2. There are 60 minutes in an … hour.
3. Find a date on a … calendar.
4. Monday and Tuesday are days of the … week.

Your Turn
Tell what time it is now. Describe the time in two different ways.

78   Lesson 20

Academic Vocabulary

- The following words are cognates with Spanish, and should be easy for some students to understand: *quarter, minute, hour, day, calendar.*

- Students have probably heard *time* used in a variety of ways: Summer is the best *time* of the year. Keep *time* by clapping your hands. I will *time* you when you run the race.

- *Week* may be confused with *weak.* Point to a *week* on the calendar. Then explain that *weak* means "not strong."

- The term *date* can refer to an appointment you have to meet someone. For example: We have a *date* for lunch. A *date* is also a type of fruit.

- Point out the difference between *hour* and *our.*

Additional resources for building and reinforcing vocabulary are provided on pages T37–T41.

Cultural Consideration

Calendars from other cultures may not begin on Sunday. Many European, Latin American, and Chinese calendars begin on Monday. Also, students may be used to writing the date of the month with the number for the day first and the month second.

↻ Comprehensible Input
Guide students to understanding

Vocabulary in Context Picture It!

1. **Say the Term** Have students repeat, stressing each syllable. Then combine syllables and have students repeat.

2. **Introduce Meaning** Connect the term to the visual that illustrates it.

3. **Demonstrate** Use a clock as you discuss terms related to telling time. Explain that for the first half of an hour, we sometimes use the term *past,* but for the second half, we often use the term *to.* Give examples, such as *three forty* and *twenty to four;* and *two thirty* and *half past two.*

4. **Apply** Have students demonstrate understanding with Talk About It.

Repeat the routine for each vocabulary term.

Talk About It

Guide Discussion Have students discuss the sentences with a partner. Model the sentence starters. Then provide this additional sentence completion, if time permits:

The first month of the year is … **January.**

Intervention

If students have trouble differentiating between *day* and *date* …

Then point out that the name of each day ends with *day,* and that *date* (a longer word than *day*) includes more information: the number for the day, the month, and sometimes the year.

Your Turn

Guide Discussion Have students form pairs to share their descriptions for Your Turn.

↻ Language Production

Comprehension Support Discuss the vocabulary terms using a real clock and a real calendar. Have students practice saying the names for the days of the week and the months of the year. Guide students through the times displayed on the clocks at the top of the page. Then guide them in labeling the calendar.

Model *The first clock says four o'clock. Let's write that time. Now say the time with me.* Monitor students as they work. Then model labeling the calendar. *The word at the top of the calendar is June. June is a month. Let's write* month *on the blank.*

Talk About It

Guide Discussion Have students work in pairs. Encourage them to look at the classroom clock and calendar or the representations from Vocabulary in Context Picture It! as references. Allow sufficient time for them to plan their responses.

As you discuss time on a clock, you might want mention A.M. and P.M. Explain that A.M. is used for times between 12:00 at night (*midnight*) and 12:00 during the day (*noon*). P.M. is used for times between noon and midnight. Discuss examples such 9:10 A.M. and 3:30 P.M.

Your Turn

Guide Discussion Give students time to complete their sentences. Then have students form pairs to share their answers.

Do You Understand?

Look at the clocks. Say the times to a partner. Then use numbers to write the times under the clocks.

4:00   6:30   8:15

Look at the calendar. Label the parts.

month

June

day →	S	M	T	W	T	F	S
		1	2	3	4	5	6
date →	7	8	9	10	11	12	13	← week
	14	15	16	17	18	19	20
	21	22	23	24	25	26	27
	28	29	30				

Talk About It 💬
How do you talk about the time and the date? Complete the sentences to explain.
1 You tell the time in hours and … minutes.
2 June has 30 … days.
3 There are 7 days in 1 … week.
4 The day before Tuesday is … Monday.

Your Turn ✏️
What is today's date? Write sentences about today. Use the sentence starters for support. Share your ideas with a partner.
Today is …
There are … days in this month.

Time **79**

Leveled Language Proficiency

Students at each proficiency level should be able to perform the following tasks.

Listening/Speaking

Early Beginner Demonstrate understanding of oral directions that are well-supported with visual cues. Respond to requests, expressing confusion at times.

Beginner/Early Intermediate Demonstrate comprehension of oral questions about content that has been learned. Respond to requests and contribute to discussions using a range of formats from phrases to simple sentences.

Intermediate Demonstrate comprehension of more complex instructions and information, using resources to help clarify the meanings of words. Participate in classroom discussions and activities, asking for more clarification as needed.

Advanced/Transitioning Use context to identify the meanings of words during discussions and activities. Participate fully in classroom discussions, supporting conclusions by stating logical reasons.

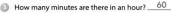

Think, Talk, and Write

Your Turn
Look at the clock. Answer the questions.

1. What is the time in numbers? _7:45_
2. What is the time in words? _seven forty-five_
   (or a quarter to eight)
3. How many minutes are there in an hour? _60_

Look at the calendar. Answer the questions.

May						
S	M	T	W	T	F	S
			1	2	3	4
5	6	7	8	9	10	11
12	13	14	15	16	17	18
19	20	21	22	23	24	25
26	27	28	29	30	31	

4. What is the name of this month? _May_
5. How many days are in this month? _31_
6. What is the shaded date? _May 9_

Talk and Write About It 💬 ✏️
Complete the sentences about clocks and calendars.

Vocabulary			
quarter	day	weeks	calendar
date	hours	year	clocks

7. A clock shows _hours_ and minutes.
8. A calendar shows 12 months of a _year_ .
9. May 17 is a _date_ .

Produce Language ✏️
Write about the day and the date of your birthday this year.

80 · Lesson 20

Leveled Language Proficiency

Students at each proficiency level should be able to perform the following tasks.

Reading/Writing

Early Beginner Read some vocabulary terms with support, along with a few common words. Write terms independently; copy phrases.

Beginner Read and comprehend previously learned vocabulary terms. Write lists of words and phrases in response to writing tasks.

Early Intermediate/Intermediate Read independently when text is made up of known words and simple sentences. Write complete sentences, ranging from very simple to those that include some details.

Advanced/Transitioning Independently read grade-level text. Write a variety of sentence types, including details, with minimal support and errors.

↻ Assess Understanding

Your Turn

Model Read Problem 1 to students and help them write the time with numbers. *You can say this as either* seven forty-five *or* a quarter to eight. You might want to draw a clock face and divide it into fourths. Then explain that *quarter* means *fourth. A quarter of an hour is 15 minutes.*

Talk and Write About It

On Their Own Have students work independently to choose the word for each sentence. Then have students share their work in pairs.

Produce Language

On Their Own Be sure students have access to this year's calendar.

Wrap Up

Table Talk Have students look back at the lesson's objectives. Allow time for them to reflect on what they have learned and then answer the essential question.

☑ **Learned** and applied vocabulary for discussing times and dates

☑ **Spoken** statements to describe times and dates

☑ **Written** statements to describe times and dates

Collecting and Organizing Data

Vocabulary Survey, record, data, data set, organize, tally chart, tally mark

Materials Index cards

Math Background

- One quick way to count and sort data is by making a *tally chart*.

- *Tally marks* are shown in groups of five, with the fifth mark drawn across the previous four. Tally marks can be counted and represented as numbers.

$$||||\ = 4 \qquad \cancel{||||}\ ||\ = 7$$

↻ Frontload the Lesson

Essential Question What words should you use to help you discuss ways to collect and organize data?

Talk About It

Build Background After students have made their vocabulary cards, read each term as they sort the cards. Encourage students to share the meanings of terms they placed in Pile 1.

↻ Content and Language

You Will

Model Read the objectives aloud and explain them in your own words. Use charts or graphs around the classroom to support your explanations. Share a sample survey question: Are you right-handed or left-handed?

Your Turn

Guide Discussion Have students read the objectives. Ask students to explain what the objectives mean to them.

Collecting and Organizing Data

Essential Question What words should you use to discuss ways to collect and organize data?

You Will
- Identify some ways you can collect and organize data.
- Explain what a set of data shown in a chart means.
- Understand and use key terms related to collecting and organizing data.

Talk About It

Copy each term from Vocabulary in Context on a card. As your teacher reads each term, create three piles of cards.

1. Place terms that you know in **Pile 1.**
2. Place terms you have heard but are not sure what they mean in **Pile 2.**
3. Place terms you do not know in **Pile 3.**

What do you know about each term? Explain, using the sentence starters for support.

I know … means …
I think … means …
I do not know what … means.

Your Turn
Look at the objectives under You Will at the top of the page. Working with a partner, predict what you are going to learn. Use the sentence starter for support.

I am going to learn about …

Leveled Instruction

Early Beginner Partnering early beginners with students at higher proficiency levels will provide them added support. Single words, gestures, and pictures are the types of answers to expect from early beginners.

Beginner/Early Intermediate Expect phrases and simple sentences from these students when they are answering questions. Encourage students to use sentence starters to help them construct their answers.

Intermediate Intermediate students should be able to complete activities with minimal assistance. Expect them to answer questions using full sentences with some details.

Advanced/Transitioning Students should be able to produce detailed answers with minimal assistance. They can offer students at lower proficiency levels support and assistance.

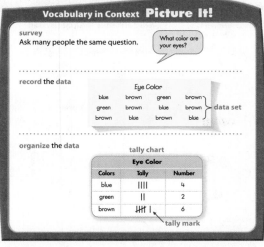

Academic Vocabulary

- Help students learn the two different pronunciations of *record*. When used as a verb, the stress is on the second syllable (ri KORD). As a noun, the term is pronounced REK urd. Students may be familiar with sports records. They might think of recording in the context of music or video. Explain that you can also record by writing.

- The following words are cognates with Spanish, and should be easy for some students to understand: *data, organize.*

- Clarify that *data* can be pronounced dā′ tə or dat′ ə. Note that *data* is plural, so one says the *data are,* not *the data is.* However, it is not necessary to emphasize the point at this time.

Additional resources for building and reinforcing vocabulary are provided on pages T37–T41.

↻ Comprehensible Input
Guide students to understanding

Vocabulary in Context Picture It!

1. **Say the Term** Have students repeat, stressing each syllable. Then combine syllables and have students repeat.

2. **Introduce Meaning** Connect the term to the visual that illustrates it.

3. **Demonstrate** Ask students to stand up if they are wearing red. Have a volunteer slowly count the number of people who are standing as you demonstrate how to write tally marks to record the count. Be sure students see that the fifth mark is slanted.

4. **Apply** Have students demonstrate understanding with Talk About It.

Repeat the routine for each vocabulary term.

Talk About It

Guide Discussion Have students discuss the sentences with a partner. Model the sentence starters. Then provide this additional sentence completion, if time permits:

When I take a survey, I ask questions and … the answers. **record**

Intervention

If students express confusion about how to use the term *survey* …

Then help them become comfortable using the term as a noun as well as a verb. Provide examples, such as "I will survey my class to learn their favorite colors." "I took a survey of my class this morning."

Your Turn

Guide Discussion Have students form pairs to share their explanations for Your Turn.

↻ Language Production

Comprehension Support Read the introduction aloud and guide students to see that 12 responses have been recorded to the question. Make sure students understand the context of traveling to school. Refer to the pictures in the tally chart. Explain that if students live very close to the school, they might walk instead of riding.

Model Point out that the data set has already been recorded. *Now I will organize the data into the tally chart.* Model making tally marks for each occurrence of "car" in the data set. Then fill in the number column for "car." *I write the number of tally marks in the number column. I made two tally marks for car, so I will write "2."*

Talk About It

Guide Discussion Have students work in pairs to complete the questions and the sentences.

Your Turn

Guide Discussion Give students time to write their sentences. Then have students share with a partner.

Do You Understand?

Renda surveyed 12 people. She recorded the data. Finish the tally chart to organize Renda's data.

How Did You Get to School Today?

Bus	Bus	Walk	Bus
Car	Bus	Car	Walk
Walk	Bus	Bus	Bus

Travel	Tally	Number
(car)	II	2
(bus)	ⷌ II	7
(shoe)	III	3

Answer the questions.

1. How many people get to school in a car? __2 people__
2. How many people walk to school? __3 people__
3. How do **most** people in the survey get to school? __bus__

Talk About It 💬
How do you collect and organize data? Complete the sentences to explain.

4. Asking 12 people how they get to school is a … survey.
5. The answers Renda recorded are the … data set (or data).
6. The tally chart has twelve … tally marks.

Your Turn ✏️
What information would you like to find out? Write how you would collect and organize the data. Use the sentence starters for help. Share your ideas with a partner.

First I would …
To record the data, I would …
Then I would …

Collecting and Organizing Data **83**

Leveled Language Proficiency

Students at each proficiency level should be able to perform the following tasks.

Listening/Speaking

Early Beginner Demonstrate understanding of one-step oral directions. Make and respond to requests, using single words, gestures, or short phrases.

Beginner Demonstrate comprehension of some vocabulary terms, especially when visual support is provided. Say individual terms and respond to requests with simple phrases.

Early Intermediate Demonstrate comprehension of academic questions by responding with short answers. Participate in discussions, using appropriate words and phrases.

Intermediate Demonstrate comprehension of the main points of a discussion. Explain how ideas compare and contrast.

Advanced/Transitioning Demonstrate understanding of a wide range of academic discussions and discourse. Rephrase ideas, accurately expressing meaning.

Your Turn

Survey 8 people. Ask: What is your favorite color?
Record the data. Then organize the data in the tally chart.

Favorite Color		

Students write the color name given by each person they surveyed.

Favorite Color		
Color	Tally Marks	Number

Students list the color names and indicate the number of responses using tally marks and then numbers.

Talk and Write About It

Complete the sentences about collecting and organizing data.

Vocabulary			
survey	record	tally marks	organize
tally chart	data	data set	tally mark

1 I ask 8 people the same question to take a _____survey_____ .

2 The answers to the survey are called _data (or data set)_ .

3 You can organize the data in a _tally chart_ using tally marks.

Produce Language

Write the steps you followed to collect and organize the data about favorite colors.

Leveled Language Proficiency

Students at each proficiency level should be able to perform the following tasks.

Reading/Writing

Early Beginner Read some vocabulary terms with support, along with a few common words. Write terms independently; copy phrases.

Beginner Use visual and contextual support to determine meaning of terms, especially with the help of someone at a higher level of language proficiency. Use sentence starters and visual supports to write individual terms and phrases.

Early Intermediate Read most vocabulary terms in context; read independently when text is made up of known words and simple sentences. Write simple sentences, with some errors.

Intermediate Apply reading strategies, including identifying main idea and details, to aid independent reading. Write complete sentences that include vocabulary terms.

Advanced/Transitioning Read and write a variety of sentence types containing concrete and abstract ideas related to lesson content with minimal support.

⟳ Assess Understanding

Your Turn

Model Write a box on the board with the label "Favorite Color." Model recording data by asking a volunteer for his or her favorite color. *I will record that your favorite color is … Now ask 7 other people.*

Talk and Write About It

On Their Own Once students have collected their data set, have them work alone for 10 minutes on their tally charts and sentence completions. Then have them share their sentences with a partner.

Produce Language

On Their Own Have students share their survey results and written steps with a partner. Encourage them to compare and contrast the results.

Wrap Up

Table Talk Have students look back at the lesson's objectives. Allow time for them to reflect on what they have learned and then answer the essential question.

☑ **Learned** and applied vocabulary related to collecting and organizing data

☑ **Spoken** statements to describe how to collect and organize data

☑ **Written** statements telling about the steps you follow to collect and organize data

Lesson 22

Representing Data

Vocabulary Graphs, pictograph, key, symbol, bar graph, title, scale, line plot, line graph

Materials Newspaper clippings or printouts of graphs

Math Background

- *Pictographs* use pictures or *symbols* to represent data.

- *Line graphs* display changes in data over time.

- *Line plots* display numerical data which are represented by Xs stacked in columns over a number line.

Frontload the Lesson

How can you talk about different types of graphs?

Talk About It

Build Background Encourage students to share the meanings of terms they placed in the first two columns of the chart. (See page T43 for additional copies.)

Content and Language

You Will

Model Read the objectives aloud and explain them in your own words. Use graphs from printed media to support your explanations.

Your Turn

Guide Discussion Have students read the objectives. Ask students to explain what the objectives mean to them.

Essential Question How can you talk about different types of graphs?

You Will
- Identify different types of graphs.
- Read graphs.
- Understand and use key terms related to graphs.

Talk About It

Look at the list of terms below. In the first two columns of the chart, write terms you **know** or **want** to know more about.

graph	symbol	scale
pictograph	bar graph	line graph
key	title	line plot

Know	Want	Learned

What do you know about each term? Explain, using the sentence starters for support.

I know … means …
I want to know more about …

Your Turn
Look at the objectives under You Will at the top of the page. Working with a partner, predict what you are going to learn. Use the sentence starter for support.

I am going to learn about …

Representing Data 85

Leveled Instruction

Early Beginner Beginners should partner with students at higher language proficiency to complete the activities. Single words and gestures, as well as pictures, should be expected as answers.

Beginner Encourage students to use sentence starters to help them construct answers.

Early Intermediate Expect phrases and simple sentences from these students as answers to questions.

Intermediate Students should produce complete sentences and tackle the activities with little assistance.

Advanced/Transitioning Students should produce detailed answers with minimal assistance and partner with students at lower language proficiency levels to offer them assistance.

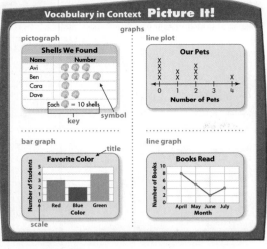

Vocabulary in Context **Picture It!**

graphs

pictograph

Shells We Found

Name	Number
Avi	
Ben	
Cara	
Dave	

Each 🐚 = 10 shells

key — symbol

line plot

Our Pets

```
X
X       X
X   X   X
X   X   X           X
+---+---+---+---+---+
0   1   2   3   4
```

Number of Pets

bar graph — title

Favorite Color

Number of Students
5 4 3 2 1 0
Red Blue Green
Color

scale

line graph

Books Read

Number of Books
10 8 6 4 2 0
April May June July
Month

Talk About It 🗨
Talk with a partner. Complete the sentences.

1. A key tells how to read the symbols in a … *pictograph.*
2. In the line graph, the numbers 0, 2, 4, 6, 8, and 10 are the … *scale.*
3. "Our Pets" is the title of the … *line plot.*
4. A graph that connects points with line segments is a … *line graph.*

Your Turn 🗨
Describe one of the graphs above to a partner. Use the sentence starters for help.
The type of graph is …
The title is …

86   Lesson 22

Academic Vocabulary

- The term *key* has several other common meanings that you should review with students. A *key* opens a lock. A *key* is a button on a computer keyboard, a small island, or part of a piano. The adjective *key* describes something very important: We have a *key* decision to make.

- Students have probably learned the term *scale* in reference to weights and measurement or in music. Help them to understand that the *scale* on a bar or line graph shows the units of a graph.

Additional resources for building and reinforcing vocabulary are provided on pages T37–T41.

↻ Comprehensible Input
Guide students to understanding

Vocabulary in Context Picture It!

1. **Say the Term** Have students repeat, stressing each syllable. Then combine syllables and have students repeat.

2. **Introduce Meaning** Connect the term to the visual that illustrates it.

3. **Demonstrate** Help students to see how the name of each graph describes it. For example, when you discuss pictographs, point out that *picto-* is related to *picture.* The symbols are pictures related to the data being represented (for example, soccer balls when talking about soccer games).

4. **Apply** Have students demonstrate understanding with Talk About It.

Repeat the routine for each vocabulary term.

Talk About It

Guide Discussion Have students discuss the sentences with a partner. Model the sentence starters. Then provide this additional sentence completion, if time permits:

The seashells in the pictograph are … **symbols.**

Intervention

If students confuse line graph and line plot …

Then point out that a line graph is often drawn on what is commonly known as *graph* paper. If you have samples of line graphs and line plots, take turns holding them up, and have students repeat *graph* and *plot.*

Your Turn

Guide Discussion Have students form pairs to share their descriptions. If both partners chose the same graph to describe, have them compare their ideas and then choose a second graph to describe together.

⟳ Language Production

Comprehension Support Read the introduction aloud and point out the four graphs and the questions that go with each one. Help students understand the context of the graphs. Explain that a hike (noun) is a long walk. When you hike (verb) outdoors, you usually walk along a trail. Support your explanation with pictures from a magazine, if available.

Model Examine and identify the graphs with students. *The first graph has the title, "Sara's Hikes." I see a scale along the side of the graph from 0 to 4. I see line segments connected to points. This looks like a line graph.* After identifying all four graphs, guide students through the questions. Read the first question aloud. *For this question I look at the line plot. The Xs in the line plot represent trails. The numbers on the number line tell how many miles for each trail. I want to know how many trails are two miles, so I count the Xs above the 2.*

Talk About It

Guide Discussion Have students work in pairs to complete the sentences.

Your Turn

Guide Discussion Students are to compare and contrast graphs in general. Students who have difficulty with this task may compare the specific graphs shown on this page. Give students time to complete their sentences. Then have students form pairs to share their ideas. If partners compared the same two types of graphs, encourage them to work together to make comparisons with a third type of graph.

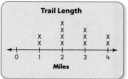

Do You Understand?

Write the name for each type of graph. Then answer the questions.

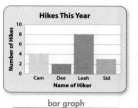

① Look at the line plot. How many trails are 2 miles? 4
② Look at the bar graph. Who hiked the most? Leah
③ Look at the pictograph. Who hiked 2 miles? Gary

Talk About It 💬
Complete the sentences about the graphs.
④ The numbers from 0 to 4 in the line graph are the … scale.
⑤ Only the pictograph has a … key.
⑥ "Hikes This Year" is the … of the bar graph. title

Your Turn ✐
Choose two types of graphs to compare. Use the sentence starters for help. Share your ideas with a partner.
A … graph shows …
A … graph is different because …

Leveled Language Proficiency

Students at each proficiency level should be able to perform the following tasks.

Listening/Speaking

Early Beginner Demonstrate comprehension of simple statements, including questions and commands. Make and respond to requests, asking for repetition when needed.

Beginner Demonstrate comprehension of oral directions that include visual support. Give one-step directions.

Early Intermediate Demonstrate comprehension of oral questions about academic content. Respond to questions with short answers.

Intermediate Demonstrate comprehension of more complex instructions and information, including those requiring the categorization of terms. Explain how academic ideas fit into concept-based categories.

Advanced/Transitioning Demonstrate understanding of academic discussions without requiring concrete references. Support conclusions by stating facts or explaining reasoning.

Your Turn

The graphs show data about some soccer matches. Write the name for each type of graph. Tell a partner a fact about each graph.

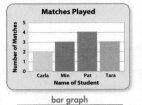

Matches Played

bar graph

Practice Time

line graph

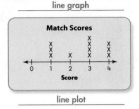

Goals This Year

pictograph

Match Scores

line plot

Talk and Write About It 💬 ✏️

Complete the sentences about graphs.

Vocabulary			
bar graph	symbols	line graph	key
pictograph	title	line plot	scale

1. All of the graphs above have a __title__ .
2. A graph that uses pictures or symbols is a __pictograph__ .
3. A graph that uses bars is called a __bar graph__ .

Produce Language ✏️

Write the terms you learned about in this lesson in the third column of the chart on page 85. Then write what you have learned about different kinds of graphs.

88 Lesson 22

Leveled Language Proficiency

Students at each proficiency level should be able to perform the following tasks.

Reading/Writing

Early Beginner Show willingness to read for meaning when visual support or the assistance of others is provided. Copy lists of words; write 1–2 vocabulary terms independently.

Beginner/Early Intermediate Read simple sentences with visual support and the help of a partner or an adult; read some vocabulary terms independently. Use sentence starters and other organizers to write individual words and phrases that use vocabulary terms.

Intermediate Show understanding of written material by the ability to follow directions or summarize text. Write full sentences and complex phrases about lesson concepts, using vocabulary terms; sentences may contain some grammatical and spelling errors.

Advanced/Transitioning Read and carry out simple and complex written instructions; read sentences about lesson ideas that use lesson vocabulary. Write complete sentences with very few errors.

↻ Assess Understanding

Your Turn

Model Before you talk about the graphs, discuss soccer matches with students. Some may play on a soccer team. Then provide an example of a fact about the bar graph. Show students that the bar for Tara goes to 3, and then say: *Tara played in 3 matches.* Ask students to find a different fact about the graph.

Talk and Write About It

On Their Own Have pairs of students share their work from Your Turn. Then have them complete the sentences together.

Produce Language

On Their Own Have students complete the Know-Want-Learned chart from the beginning of the lesson. Then have them write about what they have learned about different kinds of graphs.

Wrap Up

Table Talk Have students look back at the lesson's objectives. Allow time for them to reflect on what they have learned and then answer the essential question.

☑ **Learned** and applied vocabulary related to identifying and reading graphs

☑ **Spoken** statements about types of graphs and graph components

☑ **Written** statements about identifying and reading graphs

STUDENT BOOK RESOURCES

My Addition & Subtraction Words

Addition	Subtraction
add	subtract
plus (+)	minus (−)
sum	difference
total	fewer than
addend	left

page 89

My Multiplication & Division Words

Multiplication	Division
multiply	divide
times (×)	divided by (÷)
product	quotient
factors	divisor
array	dividend

page 90

Comparing Schools Four Corners Activity

Corner 1

Name of school _____
Number of students _____
Find a school on page 93 where the number of students is **less than** the number of students shown in this corner. Cut and paste that school here:

Corner 2

Name of school _____
Number of students _____
Find a school on page 93 where the number of students is **greater than** the number of students shown in this corner. Cut and paste that school here:

Use with Lesson 2. 91

page 91

Comparing Schools Four Corners Activity

Corner 3

Name of school _____
Number of students _____
Find a school on page 93 where the number of students is **equal to** the number of students shown in this corner. Cut and paste that school here:

Corner 4

Name of school _____
Number of students _____
Draw a small picture of **your** school here:

Ask your teacher how many students attend your school.
Write that number here: _____
Is that number less than, greater than, or equal to the number of students shown in this corner? _____

92 Use with Lesson 2.

page 92

pages 93–94

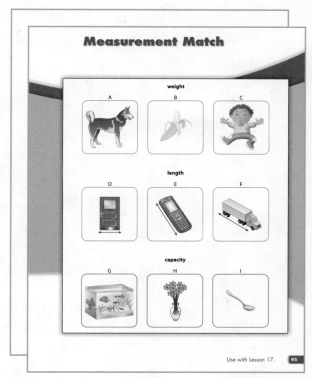

pages 95–96

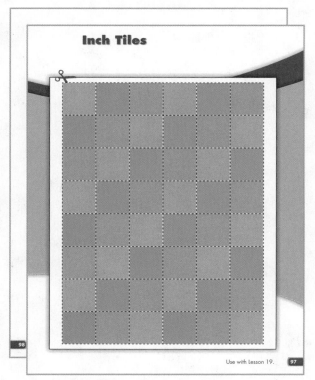

pages 97–98

CONTENTS
Grade 4

Place Value

Vocabulary Digits, place value, hundred thousands, ten thousands, thousands, hundreds, tens, ones, value, standard form, expanded form, word form

Math Background

- A number can be expressed in standard form, expanded form, and word form.
  standard form: 582
  expanded form: 500 + 80 + 2
  word form: five hundred eighty-two

- The value of any digit depends on its place-value position. In the number 2,536, the *place value* of the 5 is hundreds; the *value* of the 5 is 500.

- The expanded form is the sum of the values of each digit.

Place Value

Essential Question What vocabulary terms should you know and use when you discuss place value?

You Will
- Represent numbers through 999,999.
- Use standard form, word form, and expanded form to write numbers.
- Use math vocabulary to express place-value ideas.

Talk About It

Rate these mathematical terms according to the following scale.

1. I do not know this term.
2. I have heard this term, but I do not know how to use it in math.
3. I understand this term and I know how to use it in math.

_____ place value	_____ digit
_____ ones	_____ tens
_____ hundreds	_____ thousands
_____ ten thousands	_____ hundred thousands
_____ expanded form	_____ standard form
_____ value	_____ word form

Explain what you know about each term, using the sentence starters.

I do not know what … means.
I think … means …
I know … means … in math.

Your Turn
Look at the objectives under You Will at the top of the page. Working with a partner, predict what you are going to learn. Use the sentence starter for support.

I am going to learn about …

Place Value   **1**

Frontload the Lesson

Essential Question

What vocabulary terms should you know and use when you discuss place value?

Talk About It

Build Background Have students tell what they already know about these terms related to place value.

Content and Language

You Will

Model Read the objectives aloud and explain them in your own words. Use visual examples to support your explanations.

Your Turn

Guide Discussion Have students read the objectives. Have them discuss what the objectives mean to them.

Leveled Instruction

Early Beginner Early beginners may not use many English words in their responses. Encourage them to use gestures to communicate. Allow students to respond in their native languages.

Beginner Have students partner with students of higher English language proficiency to complete activities. Expect short and simple sentences as responses.

Early Intermediate Encourage students to use sentence starters for support. Model using these sentence starters if necessary.

Intermediate Encourage students to express their ideas without sentence starters if possible. They should use complete sentences. Anticipate some grammatical errors.

Advanced/Transitioning Expect students to form sentences of increasing complexity. Have them use more advanced terms, and encourage them to try new sentence structures.

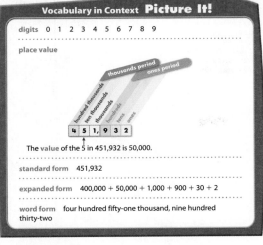

Vocabulary in Context Picture It!

digits 0 1 2 3 4 5 6 7 8 9

place value

thousands period
ones period

hundred thousands
ten thousands
thousands
hundreds
tens
ones

4 5 1, 9 3 2

The value of the 5 in 451,932 is 50,000.

standard form   451,932

expanded form   400,000 + 50,000 + 1,000 + 900 + 30 + 2

word form   four hundred fifty-one thousand, nine hundred thirty-two

Talk About It

Talk with a partner to complete the sentences.

1. In the number 451,932, the 3 is in the ... place. tens
2. The value of the 7 in 701,254 is ... 700,000.
3. 6,000 + 300 + 40 + 5 is written in ... expanded form.
4. The expanded form of a number shows each digit's ... value.

Your Turn

Write a 5-digit number. Use all different digits. Write the place value of each digit. Tell your number to a partner. Tell the value of each digit.

2   Lesson 1

Academic Vocabulary

- Use the familiar context of *place* (where something is; a location) to help students understand that the location of a digit in a number means the same thing as place. Point to your desk and say, *This is my place.* Point to a digit in a number and say, *This is the (tens) place.*

- Model the correct pronunciation of the soft *g* in *digit.* Explain that in English, when a *g* is followed by *e* or *i*, it usually has a /j/ sound.

- Differentiate between *values* in math (worth) and *values* in culture (important beliefs).

Additional resources for building and reinforcing vocabulary are provided on pages T37–T41.

Cultural Consideration

In some countries, decimal points are used the way we use commas in the United States. One hundred thousand would be written 100.000 rather than 100,000. Clarify this for students as needed.

↻ Comprehensible Input

Guide students to understanding

Vocabulary in Context Picture It!

1. **Say the Term** Have students repeat, stressing each syllable. Then combine syllables and have students repeat.

2. **Introduce Meaning** Connect the term to the visual that illustrates it.

3. **Demonstrate** Use gestures and visuals to demonstrate. For example, when teaching the term *digit,* write a 3-digit number and point to each digit, one at a time. Show how to write other numbers using the same 3 digits.

4. **Apply** Have students demonstrate understanding with Talk About It.

Repeat the routine for each vocabulary term.

Talk About It

Guide Discussion Have students discuss their responses with a partner. Then ask students to state the word form of each of the numbers in the sentence starters. Provide this additional sentence completion if time permits:

7,000 + 600 + 40 + 9 is the ... for the number 7,649. **expanded form**

Intervention

If students have difficulty writing word names for numbers in standard notation ...

Then generate a list, with student help, of the correct spellings of the numbers 1–19, the decade terms, *hundred,* and *thousand.*

Your Turn

Guide Discussion Have pairs of students share and discuss the numbers they wrote in Your Turn.

Place Value   **2**

↻ Language Production

Comprehension Support Tell students that a population tells how many people are in a certain place. Give as an example the population of the classroom. Explain that the map shows 4 cities and their populations. Read the name of each city aloud. Students will write the populations in the table below.

Model Guide the students to write the population of Seattle, Washington, in the place-value chart. *This is the population of Seattle, Washington: six hundred seventeen thousand, three hundred thirty-four. This number has 6 digits. I'll write the ones digit first.* Model writing the digits from right to left, stating the place value for each digit. Guide students to complete the rest of the chart.

Talk About It

Guide Discussion Have students complete the Talk About It sentences with a partner. Encourage them to discuss how the place-value chart supports their answers.

Your Turn

Guide Discussion Have students work in groups of three or four to share their numbers.

The numbers in the map are the populations of some cities in the United States. Write each population in the place-value chart.

Seattle 617,334
Rhinelander 7,649
Naples 21,653
Arlington 332,969

Talk About It
How can you describe these numbers? Complete the sentences.
1. The number 7,649 has four … **digits**.
2. The number 21,653 has a 1 in the … place. **thousands**
3. In the number 617,334, the … of the 7 is 7,000. **value**
4. "Three hundred thirty-two thousand, nine hundred sixty-nine" is the … for the number 332,969. **word form**

Your Turn ✏
Write a 6-digit number in the place-value chart above. Say the word form of your number to your group. Then tell the value of each digit.

Place Value   **3**

Leveled Language Proficiency

Students at each proficiency level should be able to perform the following tasks.

Listening/Speaking

Early Beginner Recognize a few vocabulary terms and follow very simple conversations with support. Repeat simple phrases, and use vocabulary terms to answer questions.

Beginner Follow simple directions. Recognize and use some vocabulary terms. Say individual terms and simple phrases, and repeat longer phrases and short sentences.

Early Intermediate Begin to follow more abstract discussion about vocabulary terms and math ideas. Speak in phrases and simple sentences, showing an increasing understanding of lesson vocabulary.

Intermediate Understand abstract ideas; recognize vocabulary as individual terms and in the context of spoken sentences. Show an ability to express abstract ideas about vocabulary.

Advanced/Transitioning Understand complex sentence structures; follow abstract conversation involving lesson vocabulary. Speak on abstract topics, including those that involve lesson vocabulary, with few if any grammatical and syntactical errors.

Your Turn

The population of Fresno, California, is 479,921. Write the population in the place-value chart. Then write the population in standard form, word form, and expanded form.

hundred thousands	ten thousands	thousands	hundreds	tens	ones
4	7	9	9	2	1

Standard form: 479,921

Word Form: four hundred seventy-nine thousand, nine hundred twenty-one

Expanded Form: 400,000 + 70,000 + 9,000 + 900 + 20 + 1

Talk and Write About It 💬 ✏️

Complete the sentences about the number 479,921.

Vocabulary				
ones	digits	tens	ten thousands	
value	hundreds	thousands	hundred thousands	

① The 7 is in the ___ten thousands___ place.

② 400,000 is the ___value___ of the 4.

③ The number has six ___digits___ .

Produce Language ✏️

Explain how knowing about place value helps you to read and write numbers. Use as many vocabulary terms as you can.

4 Lesson 1

↻ Assess Understanding

Your Turn

Model Write a 6-digit number on the board and say the number aloud. Identify and label the number as standard form. Beneath, write the number in word form and expanded form. Label those forms. Read the Your Turn instructions with students and have them do the activity.

Talk and Write About It

On Their Own Have students work alone for ten minutes. Then have them share their completed sentences with a partner.

Produce Language

On Their Own Have students review how they rated the vocabulary terms on page 1. Have students use the terms in their writing. Remind them that they may use examples to support their explanations.

Wrap Up

Table Talk Have students look back at the lesson's objectives. Allow time for them to reflect on what they have learned and then answer the essential question.

☑ **Learned** and applied vocabulary related to place value of numbers through 999,999

☑ **Spoken** statements about place value

☑ **Written** statements about place value

Leveled Language Proficiency

Students at each proficiency level should be able to perform the following tasks.

Reading/Writing

Early Beginner Read some short, common words and easier vocabulary terms, if given visual support or help from a partner or adult. Copy terms and phrases from the board; write 1–2 vocabulary terms independently.

Beginner Read a growing number of everyday words and some lesson vocabulary terms. Use sentence starters and visual supports to write individual terms and phrases.

Early Intermediate Read most vocabulary terms in isolation or in context; read sentences made up of simple phonetically regular words and sight words. Write simple sentences with support to describe ideas and explain knowledge of vocabulary with some errors.

Intermediate Read lesson vocabulary both in and out of context, and read and follow simple directions. Read and understand some abstract ideas. Write in full sentences with some spelling and grammatical errors, using sentence starters as needed and including vocabulary as appropriate.

Advanced/Transitioning Read and write complete sentences, with very few errors and with minimal support, that contain concrete and abstract ideas related to lesson vocabulary. Use sentence starters only as necessary.

Comparing and Ordering Numbers

Vocabulary Compare, equals, is equal to (=), greater, is greater than (>), less, is less than (<), symbols, order, least, greatest

Materials: Index cards

 Math Background

- Any two numbers can be compared using the terms (and symbols) *is equal to* (=), *is greater than* (>), or *is less than* (<).

- If the *order* of the numbers in an inequality is reversed, the symbol is also reversed. For example, when comparing 9 and 7, both 9 > 7 and 7 < 9 are correct.

 # Frontload the Lesson

Essential Question **How do you use words and symbols (<, >, =) to compare and order numbers?**

Talk About It

Build Background Have students tell what they already know about these terms related to comparing and ordering numbers.

Content and Language

You Will

Model Read the objectives aloud and explain them in your own words. Use visual examples, gestures, and symbols to support your explanations.

Your Turn

Guide Discussion Have students read the objectives and explain what the objectives mean to them.

Comparing and Ordering Numbers

Essential Question How do you use words and symbols (<, >, =) to compare and order numbers?

You will
- Use the symbols <, >, and = to compare and order numbers.
- Use math vocabulary to compare and order numbers.

Talk About It

Rate these mathematical terms according to the following scale.

1. I do not know this term.
2. I have heard this term, but I do not know how to use it in math.
3. I understand this term and know how to use it in math.

_____ compare
_____ equals (is equal to)
_____ least
_____ symbols

_____ is greater than
_____ is less than
_____ order
_____ greatest

Explain what you know about these terms, using the sentence starters.

I know … means … in math.
I think … means …
I do not know what … means.

Your Turn
Look at the objectives listed under You Will at the top of the page. Working with a partner, predict what you are going to learn. Use the sentence starter for support.

I am going to learn about …

Leveled Instruction

Early Beginner Early beginners may use few English words in their responses. Encourage them to use gestures and pictures to communicate.

Beginner Have students partner with students of higher English language proficiency to complete activities. Expect short and simple sentences as responses.

Early Intermediate Encourage students to use sentence starters for support. Model using these sentence starters as needed.

Intermediate Encourage students to come up with their own complete sentences, if possible. Expect some grammatical mistakes.

Advanced/Transitioning Students should form sentences of increasing complexity. Have them use more advanced terms and try different sentence structures.

compare Tell how things are the same or different.

equals The same amount as

● ● ● ● ● ● ● ●   ● ● ● ● ● ● ● ●
● ● ● ● ● ● ● ●   ● ● ● ● ● ● ● ●

$$12 + 4 \quad \text{equals} \quad 16.$$
$$12 + 4 \quad \text{is equal to} \quad 16.$$
$$12 + 4 \quad = \quad 16$$

greater Bigger

● ● ● ● ●   ● ● ● ● ●
● ● ● ● ●   ● ● ●

15 is greater than 13.
$$15 \quad > \quad 13$$

less Smaller

● ● ● ● ● ● ● ●   ● ● ● ● ● ● ●
● ● ● ● ● ● ● ●   ● ● ● ● ● ● ●
● ● ● ● ● ● ● ●   ● ● ● ● ● ● ●

24 is less than 31.
$$24 \quad < \quad 31$$

symbols $= \quad > \quad <$ numbers in order
4, 11, 16, 22, 50
↑   ↑
least   greatest

Talk About It
Talk with a partner to complete the sentences.

1. 134 … 88. is greater than
2. 50 + 50 … 100. is equal to (or equals)
3. 100 < 213 means one hundred … two hundred thirteen. is less than
4. The numbers 6, 11, 18, 37 are written in order from least to … greatest.

Your Turn
Think about the new vocabulary terms and symbols. Write a number sentence for each of the symbols $=$, $<$, and $>$.

6   Lesson 2

Academic Vocabulary

- *Than* may be confused with *then*. Pronounce each word carefully and have students repeat. Explain that *than* is used to compare and *then* is a time word. Give example sentences.

- Discuss words similar in meaning to *greater than* (larger, bigger, more, higher) and *less than* (fewer, littler, smaller, lower). Be sure students understand that *greatest* means the biggest one of all, and *least* means the smallest one of all.

- Compare some of the everyday meanings of the verb *order*, as in to order a pizza, or to command someone. Then discuss its mathematical meaning—to arrange numbers from least to greatest or greatest to least.

Additional resources for building and reinforcing vocabulary are provided on pages T37–T41.

↻ Comprehensible Input
Guide students to understanding

Vocabulary in Context Picture It!

1. **Say the Term** Have students repeat, stressing each syllable. Then combine syllables and have students repeat.

2. **Introduce Meaning** Connect the term to the visual that illustrates it.

3. **Demonstrate** Use gestures, and visuals or manipulatives, to demonstrate *greater than* and *less than*. For example, you can verify how two numbers compare in size by showing them on a number line, balance scale, or by using counters or place-value blocks that represent the numbers.

4. **Apply** Have students demonstrate understanding with Talk About It.

Repeat the routine for each vocabulary term.

Talk About It

Guide Discussion Have students discuss their responses with a partner. Then provide this additional sentence completion if time permits:

The numbers 24, 20, 17, 8 are written in order from greatest to … **least.**

Intervention

If students have difficulty remembering the meaning of the inequality symbols $<$ and $>$ …

Then show students that the symbol always opens to the greater number and points to the lesser one.

Your Turn

Guide Discussion Some students might think that a number sentence must contain an equal sign. Point out that some number sentences contain the $>$ symbol or the $<$ symbol. Discuss the examples in Vocabulary in Context Picture It! Then have students write their own. Ask students to share their number sentences with a partner.

↻ Language Production

Comprehension Support Talk about the table with students. Read aloud the headings for each column and the days of the week. Ask questions to check understanding, such as *How many DVDs were rented on Friday?* 3,302 and *On which day were 2,382 DVDs rented?* Saturday

Model Work through the comparison explained at the top of the page. *I find* Sunday *in the table and read across that row to see that 1,968 DVDs were rented. Then I find* Saturday *in the table. I read across its row to see that 2,382 DVDs were rented. I compare the two numbers. I know that 1,968 is less than 2,382. So, it makes sense to use the words "is less than" or use the symbol that means "is less than."*

Talk About It

Guide Discussion Have students complete the Talk About It sentences with a partner. Remind them that if they need help with the meanings of these symbols, they can look back at Vocabulary in Context Picture It!

Your Turn

Guide Discussion Give students time to write their answers. Then have them work in small groups to share those answers.

Do You Understand?

The table shows the number of DVDs rented during three days.

Day	Number Rented
Friday	3,302
Saturday	2,382
Sunday	1,968

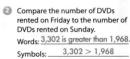

You can use words and symbols to compare the number of DVDs rented on Sunday to the number of DVDs rented on Saturday.

Words: 1,968 is less than 2,382.

Symbols: 1,968 < 2,382

1 Compare the number of DVDs rented on Saturday to the number of DVDs rented on Friday.

Words: 2,382 is less than 3,302.

Symbols: 2,382 < 3,302

2 Compare the number of DVDs rented on Friday to the number of DVDs rented on Sunday.

Words: 3,302 is greater than 1,968.

Symbols: 3,302 > 1,968

3 Going from top to bottom, the numbers in the table are written from greatest to least .

Talk About It 💬

Talk with a partner about each symbol.

4 The symbol < means ... is less than.

5 The symbol = means ... is equal to.

6 The symbol > means ... is greater than.

Your Turn ✏️

Choose any two numbers from the box. Compare them. Choose any three numbers in the box. Write them from least to greatest. Talk about your work with a group.

823	72
155	369
2,400	1,027

Leveled Language Proficiency

Students at each proficiency level should be able to perform the following tasks.

Listening/Speaking

Early Beginner Recognize a few vocabulary terms and follow very simple conversations with support. Repeat simple phrases, and use vocabulary terms to answer questions.

Beginner Follow simple directions. Recognize and use some vocabulary terms. Say individual terms and simple phrases, and repeat longer phrases and short sentences.

Early Intermediate Begin to follow more abstract discussion about vocabulary terms. Speak in phrases and simple sentences, showing an increasing understanding of lesson vocabulary.

Intermediate Understand abstract ideas; recognize vocabulary as individual terms and in the context of spoken sentences. Show an ability to express abstract ideas about vocabulary.

Advanced/Transitioning Understand complex sentence structures and follow abstract conversation involving lesson vocabulary. Speak on abstract topics, including those that involve lesson vocabulary, with few if any grammatical and syntactical errors.

Your Turn

The table shows how many pop, rock, and rap CDs were sold at a music store.

Kind of CD	Number Sold
Pop	5,066
Rock	7,921
Rap	4,370

Write the numbers in order from least to greatest.

<u>4,370</u> , <u>5,066</u> , <u>7,921</u>

Talk and Write About It

Complete the sentences about the numbers in your table.

Vocabulary			
compare	is greater than	equals	is less than
is equal to	order	least	greatest

① The number of pop CDs <u>is greater than</u> the number of rap CDs.

② The number of rap CDs <u>is less than</u> the number of rock CDs.

③ The number of rock CDs <u>is greater than</u> the number of pop CDs.

④ In the table, 7,921 is the <u>greatest</u> number.

⑤ The number of rap CDs <u>is equal to</u> 4,370.

Produce Language

Write about what you have learned about comparing and ordering numbers. Give examples. Use the vocabulary terms and symbols.

↻ Assess Understanding

Your Turn

Model Discuss the table and the types of music listed. Model how to read the numbers. *The first number is five thousand, sixty-six.* Call on volunteers to read the other numbers. Then have students work in pairs to write the numbers in order from least to greatest.

Talk and Write About It

On Their Own Have students work on their own to complete the sentences. Then have partners share their comparisons.

Produce Language

On Their Own Have students write what they have learned about the terms associated with comparing and ordering numbers.

Wrap Up

Table Talk Have students look back at the lesson's objectives. Allow time for them to reflect on what they have learned and then answer the essential question.

☑ **Learned** and applied vocabulary related to comparing and ordering numbers

☑ **Spoken** statements about comparing and ordering numbers

☑ **Written** statements about comparing and ordering numbers

Leveled Language Proficiency

Students at each proficiency level should be able to perform the following tasks.

Reading/Writing

Early Beginner Read some short, common words and easier vocabulary terms with visual support or help from a partner or adult. Copy terms and phrases from the board; write 1–2 vocabulary terms independently.

Beginner Read a growing number of everyday words and some lesson vocabulary terms. Use sentence starters and visual supports to write individual terms and phrases.

Early Intermediate Read most vocabulary terms in isolation or in context; read sentences made up of simple phonetically regular words and sight words. Write simple sentences with support to describe ideas and explain knowledge of vocabulary with some errors.

Intermediate Read lesson vocabulary both in and out of context, and read and follow simple directions. Read and understand some abstract ideas. Write in full sentences with some spelling and grammatical errors, using sentence starters as needed and including vocabulary as appropriate.

Advanced/Transitioning Read and write complete sentences, with very few errors and with minimal support, that contain concrete and abstract ideas related to lesson vocabulary.

Addition and Subtraction

Vocabulary Add, addition, addends, sum, plus, equals, total, subtract, subtraction, minus, difference, operations, symbols, regroup

Materials Index cards, place-value blocks (optional)

Math Background

- *Addition* is the process of combining quantities, called *addends*. Changing the order or the grouping of addends does not change the sum.

- *Subtraction* is the process of taking one quantity away from another. Order matters in subtraction.

Addition and Subtraction

Essential Question What words and symbols do you need to know in order to talk about addition and subtraction?

You Will
- Add two numbers with and without regrouping.
- Subtract two numbers with and without regrouping.
- Use symbols to write addition and subtraction sentences.
- Use math vocabulary to express addition and subtraction concepts.

Talk About It

Make an index card for each vocabulary term below. Place each card in one of three piles.

Pile 1 I know what this term means.
Pile 2 I have heard of this term, but I am not sure how it is used in math.
Pile 3 I have not heard of this term.

add	equals	difference
addition	total	operation
addends	subtract	regroup
sum	subtraction	symbols
plus	minus	

What do you know about each term? Explain, using the sentence starters for support.

I know … means …
I think … means …
I do not know what … means.

Your Turn
Look at the objectives listed under You Will at the top of the page. Working with a partner, predict what you are going to learn. Use the sentence starter for support.

I am going to learn about …

Addition and Subtraction 9

↻ Frontload the Lesson

Essential Question **What words and symbols do you need to know in order to talk about addition and subtraction?**

Talk About It

Build Background Explain the activity to students. As students sort their cards, read the terms aloud. Encourage them to tell what they know about the terms they place in piles 1 and 2.

↻ Content and Language

You Will

Model Read the objectives aloud and explain them in your own words. Use visual examples to support your explanations.

Your Turn

Guide Discussion Have students read the objectives. Discuss what these objectives mean to them.

Leveled Instruction

Early Beginner Early beginners may not use many English words in their responses. Encourage them to use gestures and pictures to communicate.

Beginner Have students partner with students of higher English language proficiency to complete activities. Expect short and simple sentences as responses.

Early Intermediate Encourage students to use sentence starters for support. Model using these sentence starters as needed.

Intermediate Encourage students to express their ideas without sentence starters, if possible. They should use complete sentences. Expect some grammatical mistakes.

Advanced/Transitioning Expect students to form sentences of increasing complexity. Have them use more advanced terms, and encourage them to try different sentence structures.

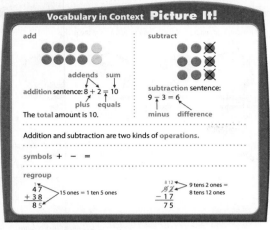

Academic Vocabulary

- Highlight the suffix *–tion* in *addition* and *subtraction*. Tell students that these suffixes turn the verbs *add* and *subtract* into nouns, *addition* and *subtraction*.

- Identify the prefix *re–* in *regroup*. Explain that *re–* means *again*, as in *rewrite*, *review*, and *remake*. So, *regroup* means to group again.

- Provide examples to distinguish the meaning of *sum* (quantity obtained by adding two or more numbers) from the various meanings of its homophone, *some*.

- Point out that while *difference* or *different* in everyday language means *not the same* or *not similar*, in math *difference* has a very specific meaning.

Additional resources for building and reinforcing vocabulary are provided on pages T37–T41.

Cultural Consideration

In many languages, especially Spanish, soccer is referred to as football (*fútbol*). This might cause some confusion for students when discussing the sports on page 11.

↻ Comprehensible Input

Guide students to understanding

Vocabulary in Context Picture It!

1. **Say the Term** Have students repeat, stressing each syllable. Then combine syllables and have students repeat.

2. **Introduce Meaning** Connect the term to the visual that illustrates it.

3. **Demonstrate** Use gestures and manipulatives to demonstrate. For example, when teaching the term *regroup,* use or draw place-value blocks to model the physical action of regrouping 1 ten as 10 ones.

4. **Apply** Have students demonstrate understanding with Talk About It.

Repeat the routine for each vocabulary term.

Remind students that they can review vocabulary terms for addition and subtraction on page 89 and record more terms as they learn them.

Talk About It

Guide Discussion Have students discuss the responses with a partner. Then provide this additional sentence completion, if time permits:

The answer to an addition problem is called the … sum.

Intervention

If students have difficulty distinguishing terms related to addition from those related to subtraction …

Then show them how to sort the cards related to these operations into two piles, one for addition and one for subtraction.

Your Turn

Guide Discussion Ask students to share their number sentences and their ideas about them for Your Turn.

↻ Language Production

Comprehension Support Talk about the information shown at the top of the page. Help students pronounce the names of the sports. Discuss the different sports and which sports some of your students enjoy. For the problems on this page, assume that each child plays only one sport. Ask questions to check understanding of the data, such as *How many children play football?* 324 or *158 children play which sport?* basketball

Model Before students complete the problems on their own, review 3-digit addition and subtraction with problems such as $218 + 127$ and $352 - 126$. Work through each step, using appropriate vocabulary terms and showing students how to record their work. Carefully discuss regrouping. For example, in the subtraction problem, explain: *I can't subtract 2 ones minus 6 ones. So I need to regroup the 5 tens and 2 ones as 4 tens and 12 ones.*

In Problem 1, guide students to understand that when they need to find how many *in all,* they add. Similarly, in Problem 2, when they need to find *how many more,* they subtract.

Talk About It

Guide Discussion Have students complete the Talk About It sentences with a partner. Remind them that if they need help with the terms, they can look back at Vocabulary in Context Picture It! In Exercise 5, suggest that students write the problem in vertical form. In that way, they will see that this problem requires regrouping before the ones can be subtracted.

Your Turn

Guide Discussion Invite students to plan their oral explanation by writing it down. Then have them discuss their work in pairs. Partners can record their work on copies of T44.

Do You Understand?

The number of children who play on sports teams at the park is shown below.

Baseball	Football	Soccer	Basketball
275 children	324 children	358 children	158 children

Complete each problem.

1 How many children play football and soccer in all?

$$\begin{array}{r} 324 \\ +358 \\ \hline \end{array}$$

In all, __682__ children play football and soccer.

2 How many more children play baseball than basketball?

$$\begin{array}{r} 275 \\ -158 \\ \hline \end{array}$$

__117__ more children play baseball than basketball.

Talk About It 💬
Talk with a partner about addition and subtraction. Complete the sentences.

3 To find the total number of children who play two sports, I … add.

4 To find the difference, I … subtract.

5 To subtract the ones in 275 minus 158, I need to … regroup.

Your Turn ✏️
Write two numbers. Each one should have three or four digits. Find the sum of your numbers. Then find the difference of your numbers. Tell a partner how you found each answer.

Leveled Language Proficiency

Students at each proficiency level should be able to perform the following tasks.

Listening/Speaking

Early Beginner Recognize some vocabulary terms and follow very simple conversations with support. Repeat simple phrases, and use vocabulary terms to answer questions.

Beginner Follow simple directions. Recognize vocabulary terms. Say terms and simple phrases, and repeat longer phrases and short sentences.

Early Intermediate Begin to follow more abstract discussions about vocabulary terms. Speak in phrases and simple sentences, showing an increasing understanding of lesson vocabulary.

Intermediate Understand abstract ideas; recognize vocabulary as individual terms and in the context of spoken sentences. Express abstract ideas about vocabulary.

Advanced/Transitioning Understand complex sentence structures; follow abstract conversations involving vocabulary. Speak on abstract topics, using vocabulary, with few errors.

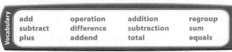

Think, Talk, and Write

Your Turn

Four children collect baseball cards.

Denise
360 cards

Julio
195 cards

Inez
234 cards

Henry
406 cards

1 Choose two of the children shown. Find the total number of baseball cards. *Answers will vary.*

2 Choose two other children. Find the difference in the number of baseball cards. *Answers will vary.*

Talk and Write About It

Complete the sentences about addition and subtraction.

Vocabulary			
add	operation	addition	regroup
subtract	difference	subtraction	sum
plus	addend	total	equals

3 When I subtract, I am finding the ___difference___ .

4 If the problem has a plus sign, I am using ___addition___ .

5 The symbol = means ___equals___ .

6 Breaking tens into ones is one way to ___regroup___ .

Produce Language

Write a set of instructions about how you find sums and differences. For support, use the vocabulary cards you made at the beginning of the lesson.

12 Lesson 3

Leveled Language Proficiency

Students at each proficiency level should be able to perform the following tasks.

Reading/Writing

Early Beginner Read some short, common words and easier vocabulary terms with visual support or help from a partner or adult. Copy terms from the board; write 1–2 vocabulary terms independently.

Beginner/Early Intermediate Read words and simple sentences with visual support or help from a partner or adult. Use sentence starters and visual supports to write words, phrases, and simple sentences.

Intermediate Read lesson vocabulary both in and out of context, and read and follow simple directions. Read and understand some abstract ideas. Write in full sentences with some errors, using sentence starters as needed.

Advanced/Transitioning Read and write complete sentences, with few errors and minimal support, that contain concrete and abstract ideas related to lesson vocabulary. Use sentence starters only as necessary.

↻ Assess Understanding

Your Turn

Model Clarify the word *collect* and talk about things people enjoy collecting. Have students read the number of baseball cards each child has. Model how to use some of the numbers to set up a problem. *If I want to know how many cards Julio and Inez have together, I have to add.* Write 195 + 234 and invite a volunteer to find the sum. Point to different parts of the problem and have students give words and sentences related to each one. Then have students generate their own addition and subtraction problems and record them on page 12.

Talk and Write About It

On Their Own Have students work on their own for ten minutes to complete the sentences. Then have partners share and compare their ideas.

Produce Language

On Their Own Have students write instructions for addition and subtraction. Suggest that they use sentence starters such as *First, you have to … Then you … Next, you … Finally, you …*

Wrap Up

Table Talk Have students look back at the lesson's objectives. Allow time for them to reflect on what they have learned and then answer the essential question.

☑ **Learned** and applied vocabulary related to addition and subtraction

☑ **Spoken** statements about addition and subtraction

☑ **Written** statements about addition and subtraction

Multiplication

Vocabulary Multiply, times, factors, product, multiplication, multiples, array, row, column

Materials Index cards

Math Background

- *Multiplication* is an operation used to combine equal groups. Changing the order or the grouping of the numbers multiplied, the *factors,* does not change the result, the *product.*

- An array is frequently used to model a multiplication sentence. The number of rows and the number of columns represent the factors, and the total number of elements is the product.

Frontload the Lesson

What words and symbols should you use when you discuss multiplication?

Essential Question

Talk About It

Build Background Have students tell what they already know about these terms related to multiplying numbers. Encourage them to describe real-world examples of multiplication or previous school experiences.

Content and Language

You Will

Model Read the objectives aloud and explain them in your own words. Use visual examples and symbols to support your explanations.

Your Turn

Guide Discussion Have students read the objectives and discuss what the objectives mean to them.

Multiplication

Essential Question What words and symbols should you use when you discuss multiplication?

You Will
- Use an array to model multiplication.
- Use math vocabulary to express multiplication concepts.

Talk About It

Make an index card for each vocabulary term below.

Place each card in one of three piles.

Pile 1 I know what this term means.
Pile 2 I have heard this term, but I am not sure how it is used in math.
Pile 3 I do not know this term.

multiply	multiplication
array	factor
product	times
multiple	row
column	

Explain what you know about these terms, using the sentence starters.

I know ... means ... in math.
I think ... means ...
I do not know what ... means.

Your Turn 💬
Look at the objectives listed under You Will at the top of the page. Working with a partner, predict what you are going to learn. Use the sentence starter for support.

I am going to learn about ...

Leveled Instruction

Early Beginner Early beginners may not use many English words in their responses. Encourage them to use gestures or pictures to communicate.

Beginner Have students partner with students of higher English language proficiency to complete activities. Expect short and simple sentences as responses.

Early Intermediate Encourage students to use sentence starters for support. Model using these sentence starters as needed.

Intermediate Encourage students to express their ideas without sentence starters if possible. They should use complete sentences. Expect some grammatical mistakes.

Advanced/Transitioning Expect students to form sentences of increasing complexity. Have them use more advanced terms, and encourage them to try different sentence structures.

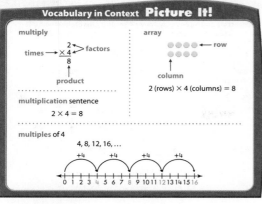

Vocabulary in Context **Picture It!**

multiply

times → $\times 4$ → factors (2)

8

↑ product

array

○ ○ ○ ○ ← row
○ ○ ○ ○

↑ column

2 (rows) × 4 (columns) = 8

multiplication sentence

2 × 4 = 8

multiples of 4

4, 8, 12, 16, …

+4 +4 +4 +4

0 1 2 3 4 5 6 7 8 9 10 11 12 13 14 15 16

Talk About It

Talk with a partner to complete the sentences.

1. The numbers multiplied to give a product are the … **factors.**
2. The answer in multiplication is the … **product.**
3. When you see the × symbol, you say … **times.**
4. A model with rows and columns is an … **array.**
5. 6, 12, 18, 24, 30, 36 are … of 6. **multiples**

Your Turn

Think about the new vocabulary terms.

• Write a multiplication sentence. Circle the factors. Underline the product.
• Choose any number from 2 to 9. List its first three multiples.

Share your answers with a partner.

Academic Vocabulary

• Distinguish the mathematical meaning of *times* from its various everyday meanings, such as the parts of a day—*i.e.,* hours, minutes.

• Distinguish the mathematical meaning of *factor* from its everyday meaning: a cause or event that brings about a result.

• Students may associate the term *product* with something they buy. Point out that in math *product* has a very specific meaning—the answer in a multiplication sentence.

• Make clear the differences between *array* and auditory similarities, such as *a ray* (narrow beam of light; part of a line with exactly one endpoint), and the name *Ray.*

Additional resources for building and reinforcing vocabulary are provided on pages T37–T41.

↻ Comprehensible Input

Guide students to understanding

Vocabulary in Context Picture It!

1. **Say the Term** Have students repeat, stressing each syllable. Then combine syllables and have students repeat.

2. **Introduce Meaning** Connect the term to the visual that illustrates it.

3. **Demonstrate** Use gestures and drawings to demonstrate. For example, when teaching the term *array*, draw an array or refer to the desks in the classroom, if they are arranged in an array. Point to the rows and say something like, *There are 5 rows in this array.* Point to the columns and say, *There are 6 columns in this array.*

4. **Apply** Have students demonstrate understanding with Talk About It.

Repeat the routine for each vocabulary term.

Remind students that they can review vocabulary terms for multiplication on page 90 and record more terms as they learn them.

Talk About It

Guide Discussion Have students discuss the responses with a partner. Then provide this additional sentence completion, if time permits:

8 × 3 = 24 is a … sentence. **multiplication**

Intervention

If students have difficulty distinguishing *multiply* and *multiple* …

Then have them practice listening by holding up cards for each term as you say it and provide examples.

Your Turn

Guide Discussion Ask students to share their responses to Your Turn.

Language Production

Comprehension Support Talk about things that are arranged in arrays, emphasizing vocabulary terms. For example, the tiles on a floor are probably an array. You can multiply the number of rows by the number of columns to find how many tiles cover a rectangular portion of the floor.

Model Explain how an array relates to multiplication. *I can see that the chairs are arranged in an array. There are 3 rows and 14 columns. I can multiply the number of rows, 3, by the number of columns, 14, to find the total number of chairs.* Guide students through the procedure of finding the product by breaking up the larger array into two smaller arrays. Have them provide the missing numbers.

Talk About It

Guide Discussion Have students complete the Talk About It sentences with a partner. Remind them that if they need help with the terms, they can look back at Vocabulary in Context Picture It!

Your Turn

Guide Discussion Encourage students to use vocabulary terms in their explanations.

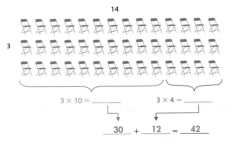

Do You Understand?

Students are putting on a play. They will set up 3 rows of chairs with 14 chairs in a row. That arrangement forms the array pictured below.

$$3 \times 14 = \text{total number of chairs}$$

To find the product, break up the array to make easier problems. Fill in the missing numbers.

$$3 \times 10 = \underline{\hphantom{00}} \qquad 3 \times 4 = \underline{\hphantom{00}}$$

$$\underline{\hphantom{0}30\hphantom{0}} + \underline{\hphantom{0}12\hphantom{0}} = \underline{\hphantom{0}42\hphantom{0}}$$

The students will use ___42___ chairs.

Talk About It 💬
Use multiplication terms to describe the problem. Complete the sentences.

1. A set of rows and columns is called an … array.
2. In the multiplication sentence 3 × 14 = 42, the … are 3 and 14. factors
3. In the multiplication sentence 3 × 14 = 42, the … is 42. product.

Your Turn ✏️
Write a few sentences that explain how you found the total number of chairs. Share your ideas with a group.

Leveled Language Proficiency

Students at each proficiency level should be able to perform the following tasks.

Listening/Speaking

Early Beginner Recognize a few vocabulary terms and follow very simple conversations with support. Repeat simple phrases, and use vocabulary terms to answer questions.

Beginner Follow simple directions. Recognize and use some vocabulary terms. Say individual terms and simple phrases, and repeat longer phrases and short sentences.

Early Intermediate Begin to follow more abstract discussion about vocabulary terms. Speak in phrases and simple sentences, showing an increasing understanding of lesson vocabulary.

Intermediate Understand abstract ideas; recognize vocabulary as individual terms and in the context of spoken sentences. Show an ability to express abstract ideas about vocabulary.

Advanced/Transitioning Understand complex sentence structures; follow abstract conversation involving lesson vocabulary. Speak on abstract topics, including those that involve lesson vocabulary, with few if any grammatical and syntactical errors.

Your Turn

How many chairs would the students use if they make 6 rows with 16 chairs in each row? Draw your array on the grid below.

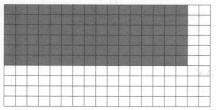

Write a multiplication sentence for your array.

<u> 6 </u> × <u> 16 </u> = <u> 96 </u>

The students would use <u> 96 </u> chairs.

Talk and Write About It

Complete the sentences about the problem.

Vocabulary			
multiply	multiplication	array	factors
product	columns	multiple	times

1 My array has 6 rows and 16 <u>columns</u> .

2 The number of rows and the number of columns in the array are the <u>factors</u> in my multiplication sentence.

3 The answer in my multiplication sentence is called the <u>product</u> .

Produce Language

Write about how to use arrays to show multiplication. For support, use the vocabulary cards you made at the beginning of the lesson.

Leveled Language Proficiency

Students at each proficiency level should be able to perform the following tasks.

Reading/Writing

Early Beginner Read some short, common words and easier vocabulary terms with visual support or help from a partner or adult. Copy terms and phrases from the board; write 1–2 vocabulary terms independently.

Beginner Read a growing number of everyday words and some lesson vocabulary terms. Use sentence starters and visual supports to write individual terms and phrases.

Early Intermediate Read most vocabulary terms in isolation or in context; read sentences of simple phonetically regular words and sight words. Write simple sentences with support to describe ideas and explain knowledge of vocabulary with some errors.

Intermediate Read lesson vocabulary both in and out of context, and follow simple directions. Read and understand some abstract ideas. Write in full sentences with some errors, using sentence starters as needed and including vocabulary as appropriate.

Advanced/Transitioning Read and write complete sentences, with very few errors and with minimal support, that contain concrete and abstract ideas related to lesson vocabulary.

↻ Assess Understanding

Your Turn

Model Draw a 4 × 8 grid on the board. Say, *In this array there are 4 rows and 8 columns.* Ask a volunteer to identify the two factors and the product. Then write the number sentence 4 × 8 = 32 below the array. Have students make the 6 × 16 array on the grid and write the related number sentence.

Talk and Write About It

On Their Own Have students work on their own for ten minutes to complete the sentences. Then have partners share and compare their arrays and their answers.

Produce Language

On Their Own Have students write what they have learned about the terms associated with multiplication. It might help if students begin by drawing an array.

Wrap Up

Table Talk Have students look back at the lesson's objectives. Allow time for them to reflect on what they have learned and then answer the essential question.

☑ **Learned** and applied symbols and vocabulary related to multiplication

☑ **Spoken** statements about multiplication

☑ **Written** statements about multiplication

Lesson 5

Division

Vocabulary Divide, division, dividend, divisor, divided by, quotient, remainder, divisible, fact family

Math Background

- *Division* is the process of determining the number of equal groups or the number in each group.
- The amount to divide is the *dividend;* the number by which an amount is divided is the *divisor;* the answer is the *quotient,* which may include a *remainder* expressed as a whole number, a fraction, or a decimal.
- Multiplication and division have an inverse relationship. Related multiplication and division facts can be grouped into *fact families.*

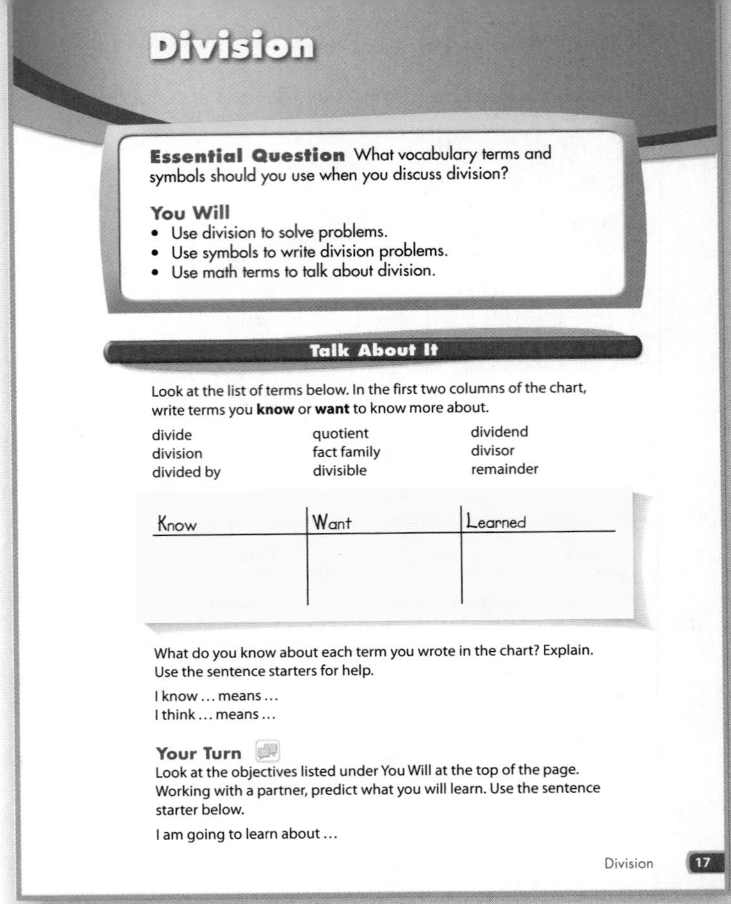
Division

Essential Question What vocabulary terms and symbols should you use when you discuss division?

You Will
- Use division to solve problems.
- Use symbols to write division problems.
- Use math terms to talk about division.

Talk About It

Look at the list of terms below. In the first two columns of the chart, write terms you **know** or **want** to know more about.

divide	quotient	dividend
division	fact family	divisor
divided by	divisible	remainder

Know	Want	Learned

What do you know about each term you wrote in the chart? Explain. Use the sentence starters for help.

I know … means …
I think … means …

Your Turn
Look at the objectives listed under You Will at the top of the page. Working with a partner, predict what you will learn. Use the sentence starter below.

I am going to learn about …

Division 17

Frontload the Lesson

Essential Question

What vocabulary terms and symbols should you use when you discuss division?

Talk About It

Build Background Have students say what they may already know about these division terms. (See page T43 for additional copies of the Know-Want-Learn chart.)

Content and Language

You Will

Model Read the objectives aloud and explain them in your own words. Use the symbols $\div$, $\overline{)}$, and $=$ to support your explanations.

Your Turn

Guide Discussion Have students read the objectives. Have them discuss what the objectives mean to them.

Leveled Instruction

Early Beginner Early beginners may not use many English words in their responses. Encourage them to use gestures to communicate. Allow students to draw pictures.

Beginner Have students partner with students of higher English language proficiency to complete activities. Expect short and simple sentences as responses.

Early Intermediate Encourage students to use sentence starters for support. Model using these sentence starters as needed.

Intermediate Encourage students to express their ideas without sentence starters if possible. They should use complete sentences. Expect some grammatical mistakes.

Advanced/Transitioning Expect students to form sentences of increasing complexity. Have them use a more varied English vocabulary, and encourage them to try different sentence structures.

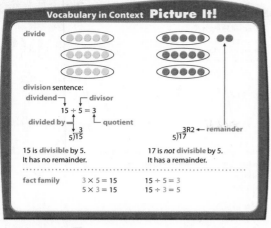

Vocabulary in Context **Picture It!**

divide

division sentence:

dividend $\longrightarrow$ $\longleftarrow$ divisor
$$15 \div 5 = 3$$
divided by $\longrightarrow$ $\longleftarrow$ quotient

$5\overline{)15}$ gives 3

$5\overline{)17}$ gives 3R2 $\longleftarrow$ remainder

15 is divisible by 5.
It has no remainder.

17 is *not* divisible by 5.
It has a remainder.

fact family | $3 \times 5 = 15$ | $15 \div 5 = 3$
$5 \times 3 = 15$ | $15 \div 3 = 5$

Talk About It

Talk with a partner to complete the sentences.

1. In $18 \div 6 = 3$, the number 3 is the ... quotient.
2. $6 \div 2 = 3$ and $2 \times 3 = 6$ are in the same ... fact family.
3. Six is ... by 2. divisible
4. In $37 \div 5$, the ... is 2. remainder

Your Turn

Write the rest of the fact family for $8 \times 7 = 56$. Label the parts of one
of the division sentences. Use as many vocabulary terms as you can.
Describe your answers with a partner.

Academic Vocabulary

- When discussing the term *remainder,* highlight
the word *remain,* which means *to stay* or *to be
left behind.* Model some division situations where
there are not enough objects to fairly share all
of them. To signal this, identify the number of
"leftovers."

- Help students notice that *divide, divided, division,*
and *divisible* are various forms of the same word.

- Point out that the facts in a *fact family* are related
to each other, just like a family of people.

Additional resources for building and reinforcing
vocabulary are provided on pages T37–T41.

Cultural Consideration

Some languages lack a /v/ sound. Speakers of
other languages, such as Spanish and Hungarian,
may substitute a /b/ or /w/ sound for /v/. Model
correct physical placement to help students form the
voiced labiodental fricative sound in *division* and
divide.

↻ Comprehensible Input

Guide students to understanding

Vocabulary in Context Picture It!

1. **Say the Term** Have students repeat,
stressing each syllable. Then combine
syllables and have students repeat.

2. **Introduce Meaning** Connect the term to
the visual that illustrates it.

3. **Demonstrate** Use gestures and models to
demonstrate. For example, when teaching
the term *division,* model moving objects
from a total quantity into same-size groups.
Highlight any *remainder* as leftovers you
push away from the equal groups.

4. **Apply** Have students demonstrate
understanding with Talk About It.

Repeat the routine for each vocabulary term.

Remind students that they can review
vocabulary terms for division on page 90 and
record more terms as they learn them.

Talk About It

Guide Discussion Have students discuss the
responses with a partner. Then provide this
additional sentence completion if time permits:

The number you divide by is the ... divisor.

Intervention

If students have difficulty distinguishing the
pronunciation of *division* from *divisible*...

Then have them tap out the syllables as you
slowly pronounce each term.

Your Turn

Guide Discussion Have student volunteers
share their number sentences. Ask them to point
out the parts of one of their division sentences.

↻ Language Production

Comprehension Support Talk about the division situation with students, applying the relevant vocabulary terms. Clarify that they are splitting the markers into 3 equal groups. In other words, they will divide by 3. Ask students to predict whether they think there will be a remainder in this situation, and to give their reasons.

Model Draw a simple sketch of the markers (short line segments) and cups on the board. Explain how to model the division: *I see 14 markers to start with. We will put an equal number of markers in each cup. I'll start by moving one marker into each cup.* Draw a marker in the first cup, and cross out one of the original markers. Repeat this for the next two cups. *I can keep drawing markers until I don't have enough to put one in each cup. If there are any markers left, I will draw them in the box. If I have some markers left over, I have a remainder.* Discuss the steps of the division algorithm shown for this division situation.

Talk About It

Guide Discussion Have students complete the Talk About It sentences with a partner. Remind them that if they need help with the terms, they can look back at Vocabulary in Context Picture It!

Your Turn

Guide Discussion After students plan their response, have them draw a picture and write their answer. If students have trouble generalizing, help them draw a simple picture showing 10 things divided into groups of 5. Then complete this sentence: *The number 10 is divisible by 5 because …*

There are 14 markers.
Divide the markers into 3 equal groups.
Draw them in the cups.
Draw any extras in the box.

Markers in each cup: __4__   Markers left over: __2__
So 14 ÷ 3 is __4__ with a remainder of __2__ .
Fill in the missing numbers.

$$3\overline{)14} \quad \begin{array}{r} 4\,R\,2 \\ \underline{-12} \\ 2 \end{array}$$

Talk About It 💬
Talk with a partner about division. Complete the sentences.
① I can make equal groups using … division.
② When I divide, the answer is the … quotient.
③ Fourteen is not divisible by 3, because there is a … remainder.
④ The ÷ symbol and the ⌐ symbol both mean … divided by.

Your Turn ✏️
What does *divisible* mean? Draw a picture and write a few sentences. Use the sentence starter for support. Share your paper with a partner.
A number is divisible if …

Leveled Language Proficiency

Students at each proficiency level should be able to perform the following tasks.

Listening/Speaking

Early Beginner Recognize a few vocabulary terms and follow very simple conversations with support. Repeat simple phrases, and use vocabulary terms to answer questions.

Beginner Follow simple directions. Recognize and use some vocabulary terms. Say simple phrases, and repeat longer phrases and short sentences.

Early Intermediate Begin to follow more abstract discussion about vocabulary terms. Speak in phrases and simple sentences.

Intermediate Understand abstract ideas; recognize vocabulary as individual terms and in the context of spoken sentences. Show an ability to express abstract ideas about vocabulary.

Advanced/Transitioning Understand complex sentence structures; follow abstract conversation involving lesson vocabulary. Speak on abstract topics, including those that involve lesson vocabulary.

Your Turn

Draw a picture of how to divide your class into groups of 4. Complete the division problem.

Number of students in class: _____

There are _____ groups.

4)‾‾‾

There are _____ students left over.

Talk and Write About It 💬 ✏️

Complete the sentences about the groups you made.

Vocabulary			
divide	division	divisible	dividend
quotient	remainder	fact family	divided by

1. To make groups of 4, I had to _____divide_____ .

2. In my division problem, the number of students in the class is the _____dividend_____ .

3. The number of leftover students is the _____remainder_____ .

4. If there is no remainder, the number of students is _____divisible_____ by 4.

Produce Language ✏️

Write the terms you learned about in this lesson in the third column of the chart on page 17. Write what you know about these terms. Use sentence starters from throughout the lesson for support.

Leveled Language Proficiency

Students at each proficiency level should be able to perform the following tasks.

Reading/Writing

Early Beginner Read some short, common words and easier vocabulary terms with visual support or help from a partner or adult. Copy terms from the board; write 1–2 vocabulary terms independently.

Beginner/Early Intermediate Read words and simple sentences with visual support or help from a partner or adult. Use sentence starters and visual supports to write words, phrases, and simple sentences.

Intermediate Read lesson vocabulary both in and out of context, and read and follow simple directions. Read and understand some abstract ideas. Write in full sentences with some errors, using sentence starters as needed.

Advanced/Transitioning Read and write complete sentences, with few errors and minimal support, that contain concrete and abstract ideas related to lesson vocabulary. Use sentence starters only as necessary.

↻ Assess Understanding

Your Turn

Model Provide the total number of students enrolled in your class by saying the number aloud and writing it in standard form on the board. Or for extra practice, count aloud with students to find the number of students present. Clarify that students will divide to find out how many groups of 4 can be formed. Guide students to create a simple but meaningful illustration. After students draw their pictures and write their division problems, revise and rework for other-size groups if time permits, or to ensure a remainder situation.

Talk and Write About It

On Their Own Have students work on their own for ten minutes to complete the statements. Then have partners share and compare their ideas.

Produce Language

On Their Own Have students complete the Know-Want-Learn chart from the beginning of the lesson. Have students write what they have learned about these terms and share their ideas with the class. They can refer to Vocabulary in Context Picture It! for support. If students have no new terms to add to column 3, ask them to write about several of the other terms in the lesson.

Wrap Up

Table Talk Have students look back at the lesson's objectives. Allow time for them to reflect on what they have learned and then answer the essential question.

☑ **Learned** and applied vocabulary related to division

☑ **Spoken** statements about division

☑ **Written** statements about division

Whole-Number Operations

Vocabulary Whole numbers, add, addition, plus, sum, subtract, subtraction, minus, difference, multiply, multiplication, times, product, divide, division, divided by, quotient, remainder, operations

Materials: Index cards

 Math Background

- The four common operations in mathematics are *addition*, *subtraction*, *multiplication*, and *division*.

- Whole numbers are the integers greater than or equal to zero. Whole numbers do not include fractions, decimals, or negative numbers.

Whole-Number Operations

Essential Question What vocabulary terms do you need to understand when you solve problems?

You Will
- Add, subtract, multiply, and divide to solve story problems.
- Use math vocabulary to talk about solving problems.

Talk About It

Copy each term from Vocabulary in Context on a card. As your teacher reads each term, create three piles of cards.

Pile 1 I know what this term means.
Pile 2 I have heard of this term, but I am not sure how it is used in math.
Pile 3 I have not heard of this term.

remainder

Explain what you know about these terms, using the sentence starters.

I know … means …
I think … means …
I do not know what … means.

Your Turn

Look at the objectives listed under You Will at the top of the page. Working with a partner, predict what you are going to learn. Use the sentence starter for support.

I am going to learn about …

♻ Frontload the Lesson

 What vocabulary terms do you need to understand when you solve problems?

Talk About It

Build Background Have students say what they may already know about these terms associated with whole-number operations.

♻ Content and Language

You Will

Model Read the objectives aloud and explain them in your own words. Use real-life examples and math symbols to support your explanations.

Your Turn

Guide Discussion Have students read the objectives. Have them discuss what the objectives mean to them.

Leveled Instruction

Early Beginner Early beginners may not use many English words in their responses. Encourage them to use gestures and pictures to communicate.

Beginner Have students partner with students of higher English language proficiency to complete activities. Expect short and simple sentences as responses.

Early Intermediate Encourage students to use sentence starters for support. Model using these sentence starters as needed.

Intermediate Encourage students to express their ideas without sentence starters if possible. They should use complete sentences. Expect some grammatical mistakes.

Advanced/Transitioning Expect students to form sentences of increasing complexity. Have them use more advanced terms, and encourage them to try different sentence structures.

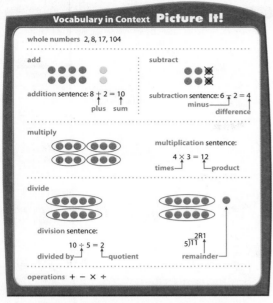

whole numbers 2, 8, 17, 104

add

subtract

addition sentence: 8 + 2 = 10
plus sum

subtraction sentence: 6 − 2 = 4
minus
difference

multiply

multiplication sentence:
4 × 3 = 12
times product

divide

division sentence:
10 ÷ 5 = 2
divided by quotient

2R1
5)11
remainder

operations + − × ÷

Talk About It

Talk with a partner to complete the sentences.

1. 8, 41, and 170 are all … whole numbers.
2. To find how many more things are in one group than another, use … subtraction.
3. If a number divides evenly, there is no … remainder.
4. If things are in equal groups, you can … to find the total number. multiply (or add)

Your Turn

Write a number sentence. Tell your partner about it. Use as many vocabulary terms as you can.

Academic Vocabulary

- Provide examples to distinguish the more common medical meaning of *operation* from the math meaning as an arithmetic process: addition, subtraction, multiplication, or division.

- *Whole* may be confused with *hole*. Draw a picture of a hole in the ground or point to a hole. Draw a figure and gesture to show whole vs. part.

- Give examples to distinguish the meaning of *sum* (quantity obtained by adding two or more numbers) from the various meanings of its homophone, *some*.

- Point out that while *difference* or *different* in everyday language means *not the same* or *not similar*, in math *difference* has a very specific meaning: the answer to a subtraction problem.

Additional resources for building and reinforcing vocabulary are provided on pages T37–T41.

↻ Comprehensible Input

Guide students to understanding

Vocabulary in Context Picture It!

1. **Say the Term** Have students repeat, stressing each syllable. Then combine syllables and have students repeat.

2. **Introduce Meaning** Connect the term to the visual that illustrates it.

3. **Demonstrate** Use gestures and visuals to demonstrate. Use counters or other small objects to convey the meaning of *addition*. Show a group of 7 counters and a group of 5 counters. Push them together as you explain that addition means joining, or combining, two or more groups. Have the class help you write a number sentence for the situation, 7 + 5 = 12.

4. **Apply** Have students demonstrate understanding with Talk About It.

Repeat the routine for each vocabulary term.

Remind students that they can review vocabulary terms for the operations on pages 89–90 and record more terms as they learn them.

Talk About It

Guide Discussion Have students discuss the responses with a partner. Then provide this additional sentence completion, if time permits:

If you need to split some things into equal groups, you can use … division.

Intervention

If students have difficulty remembering which terms correspond to a particular operation …

Then help them sort some of their vocabulary cards into one pile for addition, one for subtraction, one for multiplication, and one for division.

Your Turn

Guide Discussion Ask students to share their number sentences and tell how they described them to their partner.

↻ Language Production

Comprehension Support Read and talk about each problem with students. Clarify any unfamiliar words or situations. Explain to students that they will need to represent each problem with a simple drawing, choose the correct operation, write the number sentence, and give the answer.

Model Work through Problem 1. As you discuss it, draw the diagram on the board. *The problem tells me that a fourth-grade class has 92 students. This big bar represents those 92 students. The smaller bars represent the two parts that make up the 92 students, the girls and the boys. I know one part: there are 47 girls. I have to find the other part. I'll write a question mark to show that I don't know, yet, the number of boys.* Have students complete the problem and then work on the other ones.

Talk About It

Guide Discussion Have students complete the Talk About It sentences with a partner. Remind them that if they need help with the terms, they can look back at Vocabulary in Context Picture It!

Your Turn

Guide Discussion Give students time to plan and write their answer. Then have them read their writing in a small group. Partners can record their work on copies of T44.

Do You Understand?

Read the problem. Draw a picture. Decide whether you should add, subtract, multiply, or divide. Write a number sentence and give the answer. The first problem is started for you.

	Problem	Picture	Number Sentence and Answer
1	A fourth-grade class has 92 students. 47 are girls. How many are boys?	92 students / 47 girls / ? boys	$92 - 47 = \underline{45}$ $\underline{45}$ boys
2	The Art Club is making 15 banners. Four gold stars are needed for each one. How many gold stars does the Art Club need?	Drawings will vary.	$15 \times 4 = 60$ 60 gold stars
3	A gym class has 42 students. How many teams of 6 can be made?	Drawings will vary.	$42 \div 6 = 7$ 7 teams
4	There are 240 blue balloons and 175 red balloons at the school picnic. In all, how many balloons are there?	Drawings will vary.	$240 + 175 = 415$ 415 balloons

Talk About It 💬
Complete the sentences to tell about the problems.
5 To solve Problem 1, I needed to ... subtract.
6 To solve Problem 2, I needed to ... multiply (or add).
7 To solve Problem 3, I needed to ... divide.
8 To solve Problem 4, I needed to ... add.

Your Turn ✏️
Choose one of the problems. Write a few sentences about how you solved it.

Leveled Language Proficiency

Students at each proficiency level should be able to perform the following tasks.

Listening/Speaking

Early Beginner Recognize a few vocabulary terms and follow very simple conversations with support. Repeat simple phrases, and use vocabulary terms to answer questions.

Beginner Follow simple directions. Recognize and use vocabulary terms. Say terms and short phrases, and repeat longer phrases and short sentences.

Early Intermediate Begin to follow more abstract discussion about vocabulary terms and math ideas. Speak in phrases and simple sentences, showing an increasing understanding of lesson vocabulary.

Intermediate Understand abstract ideas; recognize vocabulary as individual terms and in the context of spoken sentences. Show an ability to express abstract ideas about vocabulary.

Advanced/Transitioning Understand complex sentence structures; follow abstract conversation involving lesson vocabulary. Speak on abstract topics involving lesson vocabulary with few errors.

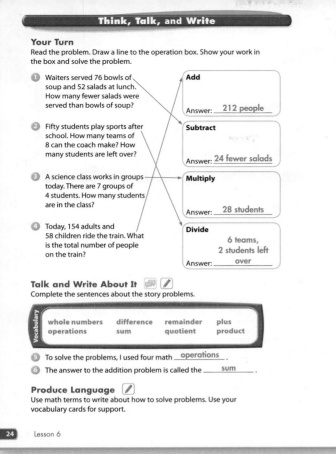

Your Turn

Read the problem. Draw a line to the operation box. Show your work in the box and solve the problem.

1 Waiters served 76 bowls of soup and 52 salads at lunch. How many fewer salads were served than bowls of soup?

2 Fifty students play sports after school. How many teams of 8 can the coach make? How many students are left over?

3 A science class works in groups today. There are 7 groups of 4 students. How many students are in the class?

4 Today, 154 adults and 58 children ride the train. What is the total number of people on the train?

Add

Answer: _212 people_

Subtract

Answer: _24 fewer salads_

Multiply

Answer: _28 students_

Divide

6 teams, 2 students left over

Answer: _____

Talk and Write About It

Complete the sentences about the story problems.

Vocabulary

| whole numbers | difference | remainder | plus |
| operations | sum | quotient | product |

5 To solve the problems, I used four math ___operations___ .

6 The answer to the addition problem is called the ___sum___ .

Produce Language

Use math terms to write about how to solve problems. Use your vocabulary cards for support.

24   Lesson 6

Leveled Language Proficiency

Students at each proficiency level should be able to perform the following tasks.

Reading/Writing

Early Beginner Read some words and vocabulary terms with visual support or help. Copy terms and phrases; write 1–2 terms independently.

Beginner Read a growing number of everyday words and some lesson vocabulary terms. Use sentence starters and visual supports to write individual terms and phrases.

Early Intermediate Read most vocabulary terms in isolation or in context; read simple sentences. Write simple sentences with support to describe ideas and explain knowledge of vocabulary with some errors.

Intermediate Read lesson vocabulary both in and out of context, and follow simple directions. Write in full sentences with some errors, using sentence starters as needed and including vocabulary.

Advanced/Transitioning Read and write complete sentences, with minimal support, that contain concrete and abstract ideas related to lesson vocabulary.

↻ Assess Understanding

Your Turn

Model Make clear that students should show their work in the appropriate box. Encourage them to write number sentences and/or draw a diagram to help them solve the problem. As needed, read and work through the problems with students to support understanding. Have partners work together.

Talk and Write About It

On Their Own Have students work on their own for ten minutes to complete the sentences. Then have partners share and compare their answers to the sentence completions.

Produce Language

On Their Own Have students write what they have learned about the terms associated with using whole-number operations to solve problems. Remind them to refer to sentence starters throughout the lesson if they need help.

Wrap Up

Table Talk Have students look back at the lesson's objectives. Allow time for them to reflect on what they have learned and then answer the essential question.

☑ **Learned** and applied vocabulary related to solving problems that involve whole-number operations

☑ **Spoken** statements about solving problems that involve whole-number operations

☑ **Written** statements about solving problems that involve whole-number operations

Factors and Multiples

Vocabulary Array, row, column, multiple, divisible, factor, composite number, even number, odd number, prime number

Materials Index cards, grid paper, tiles, red and blue pencils

Math Background

- A *prime number* is a counting number with exactly two different factors. (13 is a prime number. $1 \times 13 = 13$) A counting number with more than two factors is a *composite number*. (4 is a composite number. $1 \times 4 = 4$ and $2 \times 2 = 4$)

- The number 1 is neither prime nor composite because 1 is its *only* factor.

- When x divides y, we can say that x is a divisor of y and a *factor* of y, and that y is a *multiple* of x and is *divisible* by x.

Frontload the Lesson

Essential Question

How do you explain factors and multiples?

Talk About It

Build Background Read the terms aloud. Have students tell what they already know about some of these terms.

Content and Language

You Will

Model Read the objectives aloud and explain them in your own words. Use visual examples and models to support your explanations.

Your Turn

Guide Discussion Have students read the objectives and tell what the objectives mean to them.

Essential Question How do you explain factors and multiples?

You Will
- Use models to show factors and multiples.
- Learn the difference between prime and composite numbers.
- Use math vocabulary to talk about factors and multiples.

Talk About It

Rate these mathematical terms according to the following scale:

1. I do not know this term.
2. I have heard this term, but I do not know how to use it in math.
3. I understand this term and know how to use it in math.

_____ factor	_____ even number
_____ divisible	_____ odd number
_____ multiple	_____ array
_____ prime number	_____ row
_____ composite number	_____ column

What do you know about each term? Explain, using the sentence starters for support.

I do not know what … means.
I know … means …
I think … means …

Your Turn 💬
Look at the objectives listed under You Will at the top of the page. Working with a partner, predict what you are going to learn. Use the sentence starter for support.

I am going to learn about …

Leveled Instruction

Early Beginner Early beginners may not use many words in their responses. Encourage them to use gestures and pictures to communicate.

Beginner Have students partner with students of higher English language proficiency to complete activities. Expect short and simple sentences as responses.

Early Intermediate Encourage students to use sentence starters for support. Model using these sentence starters as needed.

Intermediate Encourage students to express their ideas without sentence starters, if possible. They should use complete sentences. Expect some grammatical mistakes.

Advanced/Transitioning Expect students to form sentences of increasing complexity. Have them use more advanced terms, and encourage them to try different sentence structures.

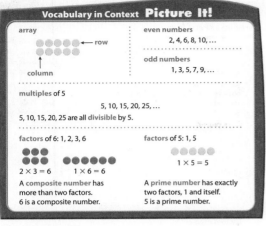

Vocabulary in Context Picture It!

array
row
column

even numbers
2, 4, 6, 8, 10, …

odd numbers
1, 3, 5, 7, 9, …

multiples of 5
5, 10, 15, 20, 25, …
5, 10, 15, 20, 25 are all **divisible** by 5.

factors of 6: 1, 2, 3, 6
$2 \times 3 = 6$ $1 \times 6 = 6$
A **composite number** has more than two factors. 6 is a composite number.

factors of 5: 1, 5
$1 \times 5 = 5$
A **prime number** has exactly two factors, 1 and itself. 5 is a prime number.

Talk About It

Talk with a partner. Complete the sentences.
1. A number with more than two factors is a … composite number.
2. A prime number is … only by 1 and itself. divisible
3. The numbers 4, 6, 8, and 10 are all … of 2. multiples
4. The numbers 3, 7, 9, 15, and 19 are all … odd numbers.

Your Turn

Think about the new vocabulary terms that describe numbers. On what date of the month were you born? Describe the kind of number it is. Use as many of the new terms as you can. Share your answers with a partner.

Academic Vocabulary

- Tell students there is more than one meaning for the term *prime*. Remind them that a *prime* number has exactly two factors, 1 and itself. Explain that *prime* can also mean valuable, first, or important, as in *prime location, prime meridian,* or *prime time.*

- Differentiate the mathematical meaning of *odd* as in *odd number* (every second counting number, starting with 1), from its everyday meaning (strange; irregular).

- Point out the similarities between *multiple* and *multiply.* Explain that when you multiply, the answer is a multiple of both factors. Note that in everyday language, *multiple* can mean "many."

Additional resources for building and reinforcing vocabulary are provided on pages T37–T41.

↻ Comprehensible Input

Guide students to understanding

Vocabulary in Context Picture It!

1. **Say the Term** Have students repeat, stressing each syllable. Then combine syllables and have students repeat.

2. **Introduce Meaning** Connect the term to the visual that illustrates it.

3. **Demonstrate** Use models and examples to demonstrate. For example, on a calendar or other kind of numbered grid, you can easily point out factors, multiples, odd, even, prime, and composite numbers. As you point out a number, model how the new terms are used to describe it. *9 is a composite number. It is divisible by 1, 3, and 9.*

4. **Apply** Have students demonstrate understanding with Talk About It.

Repeat the routine for each vocabulary term.

Remind students that they can review vocabulary terms for multiplication and division on page 90 and record more terms as they learn them.

Talk About It

Guide Discussion Have students discuss the responses with a partner. Then provide this additional sentence completion, if time permits:

A number divisible by 2 must be an …
even number.

Intervention

If students have difficulty distinguishing *odd numbers* from *prime numbers* …

Then list the first fifteen odd numbers on the board. Have students hold up either their odd number card or prime number card or both as you say each number aloud. For odd numbers that are *not* prime, ask students to name their factors.

Your Turn

Guide Discussion Ask students to share their numbers and ideas.

↻ Language Production

Comprehension Support Talk about the sheet of stamps with students. Explain that its rows and columns form an array. Discuss the other arrays shown in the second problem. For Problem 3, students can use grid paper or tiles.

Model Read the problems with students. Help them work through the problems. *The array of stamps has 5 rows. One row has 3 stamps. Two rows have ... Now let's look at all the ways to make a sheet of 15 stamps.*

Talk About It

Guide Discussion Have students complete the Talk About It sentences with a partner. Remind them that if they need help with the terms, they can look back at Vocabulary in Context Picture It!

Your Turn

Guide Discussion Partners can record their work on copies of T44. If they choose the same number, have them compare their descriptions.

Do You **Understand?**

Benito has a sheet of 15 stamps. They are arranged in an array.

1. How many stamps are in 1 row? __3__
   2 rows? __6__   3 rows? __9__
   4 rows? __12__   5 rows? __15__

2. The drawings below show all the different possible arrays for 15 stamps. They can help you find the factors of 15.

1 × 15

3 × 5   5 × 3   15 × 1

List the factors of 15: __1, 3, 5, 15__

3. Use tiles or grid paper to show different possible sheets of 13 stamps.
   List the factors of 13: __1, 13__

Talk About It 💬
Complete the sentences.
4. The answers to Problem 1 are all ... of 3. **multiples**
5. Since 15 has more than two factors, 15 is a ... **composite number.**
6. Since 13 has exactly 2 factors, 13 is a ... **prime number.**
7. 13 and 15 are both ... **odd numbers.**

Your Turn ✏️
Choose a number between 10 and 20. Write a few sentences to describe that number in different ways. Share your ideas with a partner.

Leveled Language Proficiency

Students at each proficiency level should be able to perform the following tasks.

Listening/Speaking

Early Beginner Recognize a few vocabulary terms and follow simple conversations with support. Use vocabulary terms to answer questions.

Beginner Recognize and use some vocabulary terms. Say individual terms and simple phrases, and repeat longer phrases and short sentences.

Early Intermediate Begin to follow more abstract discussion about vocabulary terms. Speak in phrases and simple sentences, showing an increasing understanding of lesson vocabulary.

Intermediate Understand abstract ideas; recognize vocabulary as individual terms and in the context of spoken sentences. Show an ability to express abstract ideas about vocabulary.

Advanced/Transitioning Follow abstract conversation involving lesson vocabulary. Speak on abstract topics, using lesson vocabulary, with few errors.

Your Turn

A hundred chart is a 10 × 10 array.

① On the chart, draw
- **red** ☐ around multiples of 9.
- **blue** ◯ around ten prime numbers.
- **×** on numbers divisible by 11.
- △ on five composite numbers between 50 and 70.

1	2	3	4	5	6	7	8	9	10
11	12	13	14	15	16	17	18	19	20
21	22	23	24	25	26	27	28	29	30
31	32	33	34	35	36	37	38	39	40
41	42	43	44	45	46	47	48	49	50
51	52	53	54	55	56	57	58	59	60
61	62	63	64	65	66	67	68	69	70
71	72	73	74	75	76	77	78	79	80
81	82	83	84	85	86	87	88	89	90
91	92	93	94	95	96	97	98	99	100

② How many numbers have ☐?
___11___

③ How many numbers have ×?
___9___

Talk and Write About It

Complete the sentences about factors and multiples.

> **Vocabulary**
>
> factor   composite number   odd number   multiple
> divisible   prime number   even number   array

④ The number 74 is an ___even number___ .

⑤ The number 49 is an ___odd number___ .

⑥ A number with five factors is a ___composite number___ .

⑦ Four is a factor of 28. So 28 is ___divisible___ by 4.

Produce Language

Write about what you have learned about ways to describe numbers. Use at least five terms. Also use examples. Use your vocabulary cards for support.

Leveled Language Proficiency

Students at each proficiency level should be able to perform the following tasks.

Reading/Writing

Early Beginner Read some short, common words and easier vocabulary terms with help. Copy terms and phrases from the board.

Beginner Read a growing number of everyday words and some lesson vocabulary terms. Use sentence starters and visual supports to write individual terms and phrases.

Early Intermediate Read most vocabulary terms in and out of context; read sentences made up of simple phonetically regular words and sight words. Write simple sentences with support.

Intermediate Read and understand some abstract ideas. Write in full sentences with some errors, using sentence starters as needed and including vocabulary as appropriate.

Advanced/Transitioning Read and write complete sentences, with very few errors and with minimal support, that contain concrete and abstract ideas.

↻ Assess Understanding

Your Turn

Model Help students understand the tasks they must complete on this page. Talk about patterns they can locate in the hundred chart to help them identify some of the numbers they need to mark. Be sure students understand that some numbers may be marked in more than one way if they fit more than one description.

Talk and Write About It

On Their Own Have students work on their own for ten minutes to complete the sentences. Then have partners share and compare their answers to the sentence completions.

Produce Language

On Their Own Have students write what they have learned about the terms associated with factors and multiples.

Wrap Up

Table Talk Have students look back at the lesson's objectives. Allow time for them to reflect on what they have learned and then answer the essential question.

- ☑ **Learned** and applied vocabulary related to factors and multiples
- ☑ **Spoken** statements about factors and multiples
- ☑ **Written** statements about factors and multiples

Lesson 8

Decimal Notation

Vocabulary Digit, decimal, decimal point, dollar, dime, penny, cent, place value, tenths, hundredths

Materials Dollars, dimes, pennies

Math Background

- A *decimal* is written with a decimal point placed between the ones and tenths places to signal where the whole number ends and the decimal portion begins. Typically, if the decimal represents a quantity less than 1, a zero is written in the ones place as a placeholder. For example: 0.71

- Money can be used as a model for decimal place values, where a dollar represents 1 whole, dimes represent tenths, and pennies represent hundredths.

Essential Question What words and symbol should you use to read and write decimals?

You Will
- Use coins and bills to represent decimal place-value concepts.
- Read, name, and write decimals.
- Use math vocabulary to express decimal notation.

Talk About It

Rate these mathematical terms according to the following scale.

1. I have never heard of this term before.
2. I have heard this term, but I do not know how to use it in math.
3. I understand this term and know how to use it in math.

_____ digit	_____ place value
_____ decimal	_____ penny
_____ decimal point	_____ cent
_____ dollar	_____ tenths
_____ dime	_____ hundredths

What do you know about each term? Explain, using the sentence starters for support.

I do not know what . . . means.
I think . . . means . . .
I know . . . means . . .

Your Turn
Look at the objectives under You Will at the top of the page. Working with a partner, predict what you are going to learn. Use the sentence starter for support.

I am going to learn about . . .

 Frontload the Lesson

 What words and symbol should you use to read and write decimals?

(Essential Question)

Talk About It

Build Background Have students tell what they already know about these terms that describe decimals and money amounts.

Content and Language

You Will

Model Read the objectives aloud and explain them in your own words. Use dollars, dimes, and pennies to visually support your explanations.

Your Turn

Guide Discussion Have students read the objectives and discuss what the objectives mean to them

Leveled Instruction

Early Beginner Early beginners may not use many words in their responses. Encourage them to use gestures and pictures to communicate.

Beginner Have students partner with students of higher English language proficiency to complete activities. Expect short and simple sentences as responses.

Early Intermediate Encourage students to use sentence starters for support. Model using these sentence starters as needed.

Intermediate Encourage students to express their ideas without sentence starters, if possible. They should use complete sentences. Expect some grammatical mistakes.

Advanced/Transitioning Expect students to form sentences of increasing complexity. Have them use more advanced terms, and encourage them to try different sentence structures.

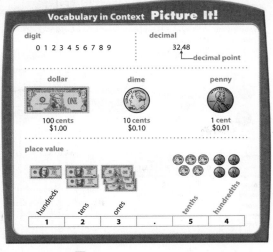

Vocabulary in Context **Picture It!**

digit

0 1 2 3 4 5 6 7 8 9

decimal

32.48

decimal point

dollar

100 cents
$1.00

dime

10 cents
$0.10

penny

1 cent
$0.01

place value

hundreds	tens	ones	.	tenths	hundredths
1	2	3	.	5	4

Talk About It

Talk with a partner to complete the sentences.

1. The dot in a decimal is called the ... decimal point.
2. Pennies are hundredths of a ... dollar.
3. A tenth of a dollar is the same as a ... dime.
4. The number 2.04 has three ... digits.
5. The number 0.58 has an 8 in the ... place. hundredths

Your Turn

Write about the dollar amount, $6.89. Use as many vocabulary terms as you can. Tell your ideas to a partner.

Academic Vocabulary

- Distinguish the meaning of *cent* (penny) from the meaning of its homophones *sent* (past tense of *send*) and *scent* (odor). Focus on the differences in spelling. Note the Latin origin of *cent,* and help students to read other words that have *cent* as a root (centimeter, century, centipede, etc.).

- Model with gestures to make clear the difference between *point* (show with a finger) and a decimal *point,* a dot-like mark used to separate the ones place from the tenths place in a decimal. Also, distinguish between decimal points and *periods,* which end sentences.

Additional resources for building and reinforcing vocabulary are provided on pages T37–T41.

Cultural Consideration

Keep in mind that students from most other countries may be more familiar with decimals than their American classmates. This is because the metric system of measures is based on decimal notation.

The many different uses of point in English might be confusing to some English language learners. In Spanish, *Punto de* ... gives the listener a clear understanding of what kind of point the speaker is referring to.

↻ Comprehensible Input

Guide students to understanding

Vocabulary in Context Picture It!

1. **Say the Term** Have students repeat, stressing each syllable. Then combine syllables and have students repeat.

2. **Introduce Meaning** Connect the term to the visual that illustrates it.

3. **Demonstrate** Use a place-value chart to support how to say numbers with decimals. For example, for 123.54 say *one hundred twenty-three and fifty-four hundredths.* Emphasize the word *and* for the decimal point.

4. **Apply** Have students demonstrate understanding with Talk About It.

Repeat the routine for each vocabulary term.

Talk About It

Guide Discussion Have students discuss the responses with a partner. Then provide this additional sentence completion, if time permits:

One dollar is made up of one hundred ... **cents (or pennies).**

Intervention

If students have difficulty distinguishing between *tens/tenths* and between *hundreds/hundredths,*

Then say these terms clearly and in random order while students hold up number cards that read 10, 0.1, 100, or 0.01.

Your Turn

Guide Discussion Discuss the dollar sign ($) and explain that $6.89 means six dollars and eighty-nine cents. Ask students to share their ideas about $6.89.

Decimal Notation

↻ Language Production

Comprehension Support Talk about the groups of money shown at the top of the page. Help students identify each coin. Then discuss the connection between place values in the chart, and the corresponding unit of money. *This place is for the number of pennies each person has. It takes 100 pennies to make a dollar, so we call this the* hundredths *place.* Continue with the other columns.

Model Work through the example given in the table for Eva. *Eva has 5 pennies. Pennies go in the hundredths place.* Explain that there are zeros in the ones and tenths place because there are no dollars or dimes. *This number has no tenths, so we write 0 in the tenths place. This number has no whole number part, so we write zero in the ones place.*

Talk About It

Guide Discussion Have students complete the Talk About It sentences with a partner.

Your Turn

Guide Discussion Invite students to plan their ideas by drawing and labeling a decimal place-value chart. Partners can record their work on copies of T44. Then have them share their answers.

Do You Understand?

Write how much money each person has in the place-value chart. Then write the decimal in word form.

	Eva	Dale	Marc	Tyra

	tens	ones		tenths	hundredths
Eva		0	·	0	5
Dale		0	.	2	3
Marc		1	.	4	0
Tyra	1	0	.	1	2

Word Form

five hundredths

twenty-three hundredths

one and forty hundredths (or one and four tenths)

ten and twelve hundredths

Talk About It 🗨
How is money related to decimals? Complete the sentences to explain.
1. For both money and decimals, we write a dot called a … decimal point.
2. A dime is one … of a dollar. tenth
3. A penny is one … of a dollar. hundredth
4. $10.12 is the same as 10 dollars and 12 hundredths of another … dollar.

Your Turn ✏
Make up three decimals. Use ones, tenths, and hundredths in each number. Write the words you say to read each number aloud. Read your decimals to a partner.

Leveled Language Proficiency

Students at each proficiency level should be able to perform the following tasks.

Listening/Speaking

Early Beginner Recognize a few vocabulary terms and follow very simple conversations with support. Repeat simple phrases, and use vocabulary terms to answer questions.

Beginner Follow simple directions. Recognize and use some vocabulary terms. Say individual terms and simple phrases, and repeat longer phrases and short sentences.

Early Intermediate/Intermediate Begin to follow and take part in more abstract discussion about vocabulary terms in spoken phrases and sentences. Show an ability to express abstract ideas about target vocabulary.

Advanced/Transitioning Understand complex sentence structures; follow abstract conversations involving lesson vocabulary. Speak on abstract topics, including those that involve lesson vocabulary, with few if any grammatical and syntactical errors.

Your Turn

Finish the signpost. Write each town. Write its distance as a decimal. Use the data below.

Town	Distance in Miles
Arno	three and four tenths
Brilla	eight and seven tenths
Cody	seventy-eight hundredths
Drew	seven and five hundredths
Edna	four and three tenths

Arno 3.4
Brilla 8.7
Cody 0.78
Drew 7.05
Edna 4.3

Talk and Write About It

Complete the sentences about the decimals you wrote.

Vocabulary

digits	decimals	tenths	dime
dollar	decimal point	hundredths	penny

1. The numbers I wrote on the signs are called ___decimals___ .

2. The dot between the ones place and tenths place is called the ___decimal point___ .

3. The decimal for Cody has a 7 in the ___tenths___ place.

4. The decimal for Edna has two ___digits___ .

Produce Language

Think about how place value helps you understand decimals. Write about how tenths and tens are different. Write about how hundreds and hundredths are different. Draw a place-value chart to help you explain.

Leveled Language Proficiency

Students at each proficiency level should be able to perform the following tasks.

Reading/Writing

Early Beginner Read some short, common words and easier vocabulary terms, if given visual support or help from a partner or adult. Copy terms and phrases from the board; write 1–2 vocabulary terms independently.

Beginner Read a growing number of everyday words and some lesson vocabulary terms. Use sentence starters and visual supports to write individual terms and phrases.

Early Intermediate/Intermediate Read most lesson vocabulary in isolation and in context; read sentences composed of phonetically regular words and sight words, including directions. Write full sentences with support to describe ideas and explain vocabulary with some spelling and grammatical errors. Read and understand some abstract ideas.

Advanced/Transitioning With minimal support, read and write full sentences, with few errors, that contain concrete and abstract ideas related to lesson vocabulary. Use sentence starters only as necessary.

↻ Assess Understanding

Your Turn

Model Discuss the kind of information a signpost gives, and how to interpret it. Clarify that all distances given are measured in miles from that signpost. Be sure students write each distance in standard decimal notation.

Talk and Write About It

On Their Own Have students work on their own to complete the sentences. Then have partners share and compare their answers.

Produce Language

On Their Own Have students write what they have learned about decimals.

Wrap Up

Table Talk Have students look back at the lesson's objectives. Allow time for them to reflect on what they have learned and then answer the essential question.

☑ **Learned** and applied vocabulary related to decimal notation

☑ **Spoken** statements about decimal notation

☑ **Written** statements about decimal notation

Estimation

Vocabulary Estimation, about, round, estimate, nearest ten, nearest hundred, exact, reasonable, unreasonable

 Math Background

- Estimation comes in many forms, from "guesstimates," (how many marbles in a jar), to computational estimation—finding an approximate answer to a computation.

- Computational estimation techniques include rounding to the nearest ten, hundred, thousand, and so on.

Frontload the Lesson

 Essential Question What vocabulary do you need to understand to discuss estimation?

Talk About It

Build Background Explain how to use the Know-Want-Learned chart. (See page T43 for additional copies.) Have students tell what they already know about the terms they wrote in the first two columns.

Content and Language

You Will

Model Read the objectives aloud and explain them in your own words. Use examples to support your explanations.

Your Turn

Guide Discussion Have students read the objectives and discuss what the objectives mean to them.

Estimation

Essential Question What vocabulary do you need to understand to discuss estimation?

You Will
- Use place-value concepts to round numbers and money amounts.
- Talk about reasonable and unreasonable estimates.
- Use math vocabulary to discuss estimation.

Talk About It

Look at the list of terms below. In the first two columns of the chart, write terms you **know** or **want** to know more about.

estimate	unreasonable	about
estimation	round	nearest ten
reasonable	nearest hundred	exact

Know	Want	Learned

Tell what you know about each term.

I know the term …
I want to learn …

Your Turn
Look at the objectives listed under You Will. Working with a partner, predict what you are going to learn. Use the sentence starter for support.

I am going to learn about …

Estimation   33

Leveled Instruction

Early Beginner Students may not use many words in their responses. Invite them to use gestures to respond or to answer "Yes" or "No."

Beginner Have students partner with students of higher English language proficiency to complete activities. Expect short and simple sentences as responses.

Early Intermediate Encourage students to use sentence starters for support. Model using these sentence starters as needed.

Intermediate Encourage students to express their ideas without sentence starters, if possible. They should use complete sentences. Expect some mistakes.

Advanced/Transitioning Expect students to form sentences of increasing complexity. Have them use more advanced terms, and encourage them to try different sentence structures.

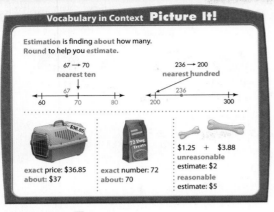

Vocabulary in Context Picture It!

Estimation is finding **about** how many.
Round to help you **estimate**.

67 → 70
nearest ten

67
60   70   80

236 → 200
nearest hundred

236
200   300

exact price: $36.85
about: $37

exact number: 72
about: 70

$1.25 + $3.88
unreasonable
estimate: $2
reasonable
estimate: $5

Talk About It
Talk with a partner to complete the sentences.
1. Estimate to find ... how many. about
2. You can round to help you ... estimate.
3. The large bone has the ... price of $3.88. exact
4. An estimate that seems about right is ... reasonable.
5. An estimate that seems much too high or low is ... unreasonable.

Your Turn
Choose three terms from the chart above. Use your own words to tell
your partner what each term means.

34   Lesson 9

Academic Vocabulary

- Explain that *estimate* is both a noun and a verb.
  Distinguish between the two pronunciations.
  Model for students that the noun form of *estimate*
  has the accent on the first syllable and has a short
  i sound in the last syllable. Then model saying the
  verb form, which has a long *a* sound in the last
  syllable.

- Distinguish between *round* as a verb, as in "round
  the number," and as an adjective, as in "a circle
  is round."

- Point out that the word *about* has multiple
  meanings. Students might read a story and tell
  what it is about. In math, *about* means "close to."

- Take the opportunity to highlight the prefix *un-*
  (not) in *unreasonable*. Show other words in which
  un- reverses the meaning of the base word.

Additional resources for building and reinforcing
vocabulary are provided on pages T37–T41.

↻ Comprehensible Input
Guide students to understanding

Vocabulary in Context Picture It!

1. **Say the Term** Have students repeat,
   stressing each syllable. Then combine
   syllables and have students repeat.

2. **Introduce Meaning** Connect the term to
   the visual that illustrates it.

3. **Demonstrate** Use gestures, visuals, and
   actions to demonstrate. As you discuss
   nearest ten or *nearest hundred,* demonstrate
   the concept of *nearest* (closest). Have
   volunteers identify the student, desk, closet,
   and so on, nearest to him or her.

4. **Apply** Have students demonstrate
   understanding with Talk About It.

Repeat the routine for each vocabulary term.

Talk About It

Guide Discussion Have students discuss the
responses with a partner. Then provide this
additional sentence completion, if time permits:

When you round 573 to 600, you have
rounded to the ... **nearest hundred.**

Intervention

If students confuse the two pronunciations
of *estimate* (long *a,* verb) and *estimate*
(short *i,* noun) ...

Then say both forms of *estimate* as students
repeat them. Then ask students to use the correct
form as you point to it in the Vocabulary In
Context Picture It! definitions.

Your Turn

Guide Discussion Ask students to share their
terms and ideas.

Estimation

↻ Language Production

Comprehension Support Help students pronounce the name of each pet item pictured. Clarify its use, as needed. Then ask questions to check understanding, such as: *What is the price of the leash?* Or *Which item costs $4.29?*

Model Read the directions and work through Problem 1 with students. *I find the prices under the pictures. Then I think about which dollar is closest. The dog bowl has an exact price of $4.29. Is that nearer to $4 or to $5? Halfway between is $4.50, so I round $4.29 to $4.* Guide students through the other items.

If students ask how to round a "halfway" number, such as $4.50, tell them to round it up to $5. They will practice rounding "halfway" numbers in math class.

Talk About It

Guide Discussion Have students complete the Talk About It sentences with a partner. Remind them that if they need help with the terms, they can look back at Vocabulary in Context Picture It! As needed, provide additional examples.

Your Turn

Guide Discussion Suggest that students write the name of each item, the exact cost, and the rounded cost. Then have them add the rounded prices to estimate the total cost. Have them work in small groups and use vocabulary terms to explain their work.

Do You Understand?

See what is on sale at the pet store.

bowl $4.29   leash $9.75   toy $1.77   bed $23.25

Round each price to the nearest dollar.

1. The dog bowl costs about ___$4___ .
2. The leash costs about ___$10___ .
3. The toy costs about ___$2___ .
4. The dog bed costs about ___$23___ .

Find each estimate.

5. Two toys cost about ___$4___ .
6. You buy a bowl and a leash. You pay about ___$14___ .
7. The pet store has 58 dog bowls. About how many is that? Round to the nearest ten.

   About ___60___ dog bowls
8. The pet store has 217 leashes. About how many is that? Round to the nearest hundred.

   About ___200___ leashes

Talk About It 💬
What terms help you talk about estimation? Complete the sentences.

9. Round to the nearest dollar to ... a price. **estimate**
10. An estimate close to the exact answer is ... **reasonable.**
11. If 43 is rounded to 40, it is rounded to the ... **nearest ten.**

Your Turn ✏️
Choose any three items pictured above. Estimate the total cost. Talk about your work with your group.

Estimation   35

Leveled Language Proficiency

Students at each proficiency level should be able to perform the following tasks.

Listening/Speaking

Early Beginner Recognize a few vocabulary terms and follow very simple conversations with support. Repeat simple phrases, and use vocabulary terms to answer questions.

Beginner Follow simple directions. Recognize and use some vocabulary terms. Say individual terms and simple phrases. Repeat longer phrases and short sentences.

Early Intermediate/Intermediate Begin to follow and take part in more abstract discussions about vocabulary terms. Express abstract ideas about target vocabulary.

Advanced/Transitioning Understand complex sentence structures; follow abstract conversations using lesson vocabulary. Speak on abstract topics, including those that involve lesson vocabulary, with few errors.

Your Turn

Give each item at the party store an exact price, such as $3.71.

Mask $ _____   Teeth $ _____   Hat $ _____   Balloon $ _____

Round your prices to the nearest dollar. **Answers will vary; check rounded prices.**

1. A mask costs about _____ .
2. Teeth cost about _____ .
3. A hat costs about _____ .
4. A balloon costs about _____ .

Find each estimate.

5. Teeth and a balloon cost about _____ .
6. Last month, the party store sold 575 hats and 238 masks. About how many more hats were sold than masks? Round each number to the nearest hundred. Then subtract.

About ___400___ more hats

Talk and Write About It

Complete the sentences about estimation.

Vocabulary			
estimate	round	nearest ten	unreasonable
reasonable	about	exact	nearest hundred

7. Estimation helps you find a ___reasonable___ answer.
8. An estimate does not give the ___exact___ answer.

Your Turn

Write the terms you learned about in this lesson in the third column of the chart on page 33. Write what you have learned about these terms. Use sentence starters from throughout the lesson for support.

36   Lesson 9

Leveled Language Proficiency

Students at each proficiency level should be able to perform the following tasks.

Reading/Writing

Early Beginner Read some short, common words and easier vocabulary terms, with visual support or help. Copy terms and phrases from the board; write 1–2 vocabulary terms independently.

Beginner Read a growing number of everyday words and some lesson vocabulary terms. Use sentence starters and visual supports to write individual terms and phrases.

Early Intermediate/Intermediate Read most lesson vocabulary in isolation and in context; read sentences composed of phonetically regular words and sight words, including directions. Write full sentences with support to describe ideas and explain vocabulary with some errors.

Advanced/Transitioning With minimal support, read and write full sentences, with few errors, that contain concrete and abstract ideas related to lesson vocabulary. Use sentence starters only as necessary.

⟳ Assess Understanding

Your Turn

Model Help students identify each item pictured and discuss the missing prices. *I see that the items have no prices. I need to write a price for each one. An exact price has dollars and cents. I'll give the mask an exact price of $3.71. What price would you give it?* After students provide the prices for the items, have them complete the problems on the page.

Talk and Write About It

On Their Own Have students work on their own to complete the sentences. Then have partners share and compare their ideas.

Produce Language

On Their Own Have students review the chart on page 33. In the third column, have them write the terms they learned in this lesson. Then have them write what they have learned about these terms. If some students did not need to add any terms to the third column, have them write about any three or four vocabulary terms.

Wrap Up

Table Talk Have students look back at the lesson's objectives. Allow time for them to reflect on what they have learned and then answer the essential question.

☑ **Learned** and applied vocabulary related to estimation

☑ **Spoken** statements about estimation

☑ **Written** statements about estimation

Fractions and Decimals

Vocabulary Fraction, numerator, denominator, mixed number, decimal, decimal point, equivalent, number line

Materials Number line, decimal and fraction number cards

Math Background

- To convert a fraction to a decimal, find an equivalent fraction with a denominator of 100, then write that fraction as a decimal: $\frac{3}{4} = \frac{75}{100} = 0.75$. Or, divide the numerator by the denominator: $\frac{3}{4} = 3 \div 4 = 0.75$. The latter method is useful when the denominator is not a factor of 100.

Fractions and Decimals

Essential Question What words and symbols do you need to understand to work with fractions and decimals?

You Will
- Learn that fractions and decimals can name the same amount.
- Find equivalent fractions and decimals.
- Use math vocabulary to show how fractions and decimals are related.

Talk About It

Rate these mathematical terms according to the following scale.

1 I do not know this term.
2 I have heard this term, but I do not know how to use it in math.
3 I understand this term and know how to use it in math.

_____ decimal   _____ decimal point
_____ fraction   _____ equivalent
_____ mixed number   _____ numerator
_____ number line   _____ denominator

Explain what you know about these terms, using the sentence starters.

I do not know what … means.
I think … means …
I know … means …

Your Turn
Look at the objectives listed under You Will. Working with a partner, predict what you are going to learn. Use the sentence starter for support.

I am going to learn about …

Frontload the Lesson

What words and symbols do you need to understand to work with fractions and decimals?

Talk About It

Build Background Have students tell what they already know about these terms that describe fractions and how fractions and decimals relate.

Content and Language

You Will

Model Read the objectives aloud and explain them in your own words. Use decimal and fraction number cards to support your explanations.

Your Turn

Guide Discussion Have students read the objectives and explain what the objectives mean to them.

Leveled Instruction

Early Beginner Early beginners may not use many words in their responses. Encourage them to use gestures and pictures to communicate.

Beginner Have students partner with students of higher English language proficiency to complete activities. Expect short and simple sentences as responses.

Early Intermediate Encourage students to use sentence starters for support. Model using these sentence starters as needed.

Intermediate Encourage students to express their ideas without sentence starters, if possible. They should use complete sentences. Expect some grammatical mistakes.

Advanced/Transitioning Expect students to form sentences of increasing complexity. Have them use a more varied English vocabulary and encourage them to try different sentence structures.

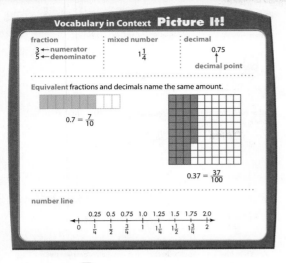

Vocabulary in Context **Picture It!**

fraction	mixed number	decimal
$\frac{3}{5}$ ←numerator ←denominator	$1\frac{1}{4}$	0.75 ↑ decimal point

Equivalent fractions and decimals name the same amount.

$0.7 = \frac{7}{10}$

$0.37 = \frac{37}{100}$

number line

0.25 0.5 0.75 1.0 1.25 1.5 1.75 2.0

0 $\frac{1}{4}$ $\frac{1}{2}$ $\frac{3}{4}$ 1 $1\frac{1}{4}$ $1\frac{1}{2}$ $1\frac{3}{4}$ 2

Talk About It

Talk with a partner to complete the sentences.

1. Decimals and fractions that name the same amount are ... equivalent.
2. The top number in a fraction is called the ... numerator.
3. The bottom number in a fraction is called the ... denominator.
4. 3.07 is a ... decimal.
5. $5\frac{1}{2}$ is a ... mixed number.

Your Turn

Look at these numbers: 0.3 and $\frac{3}{10}$.

Use vocabulary terms to tell your partner about these numbers. You may use drawings to support your explanation.

Academic Vocabulary

- Write the terms *equal* and *equivalent,* and circle the initial three letters. Help students pronounce each word after you. Tell them that *equivalent* means *equal* in amount, value, or meaning, as ten pennies is equivalent to one dime, and five tenths is equivalent to one half. Write examples using the equal sign.

- Distinguish the meaning of *mixed* (as in mixed number) from its everyday meanings (stirred together or different). Discuss the meaning of *mix* in *trail mix.* Then point out that a mixed number is formed by a *mix* of a whole-number part and a fraction part.

Additional resources for building and reinforcing vocabulary are provided on pages T37–T41.

↻ Comprehensible Input

Guide students to understanding

Vocabulary in Context Picture It!

1. **Say the Term** Have students repeat, stressing each syllable. Then combine syllables and have students repeat.

2. **Introduce Meaning** Connect the term to the visual that illustrates it.

3. **Demonstrate** Use a grid or a number line to highlight *equivalent* fractions and decimals. For example, point out that both one fourth and 0.25 represent the same amount on the grid or are the same distance from zero on the number line. Therefore, they name the same amount.

4. **Apply** Have students demonstrate understanding with Talk About It.

Repeat the routine for each vocabulary term.

Talk About It

Guide Discussion Have students discuss the responses with a partner. Then provide this additional sentence completion, if time permits:

A mixed number is made up of a whole number and a ... fraction.

Intervention

If students have difficulty recalling which fraction term is the *numerator* or *denominator* ...

Then display the following visual cue on the board or bulletin board for reference:

Numerator   Think: *u* for UP
Denominator   Think: *d* for DOWN

Your Turn

Guide Discussion Ask students to share their ideas with a partner. You may wish to have them talk about how they can use a grid or a number line to show that the numbers are equivalent.

↻ Language Production

Comprehension Support Discuss the picture at the top of the page. Talk about bus stops, a bus station, and about how far a kilometer is. (It is a little more than half a mile.) Help students read the direction lines. Model how to pronounce the street names in the first column of the table. Clarify that *km* means *kilometer* and that each distance starts at the bus station and ends at a street. Ask questions to check understanding, such as: *What names are in the* Bus Stop *column?* Or *What will you write in the empty columns?*

Model Discuss the row for Apple Lane. Say: *Apple Lane is the first stop the bus makes. Apple Lane is at a point named by the fraction $\frac{8}{10}$ and the decimal 0.8. Each number is written in its place in the table. Since $\frac{8}{10}$ is equivalent to $\frac{4}{5}$, you can write that for the fraction.* Guide students through the other rows.

Talk About It

Guide Discussion Have students complete the Talk About It sentences with a partner. Remind them that if they need help with the terms, they can look back at Vocabulary in Context Picture It!

Your Turn

Guide Discussion Have students discuss their solution in small groups. Listen for the term *equivalent* as they talk about the numbers.

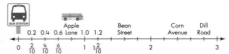

The number line shows bus stops. The distances are given in kilometers.

How many kilometers is it from the bus station to each stop? The first one is done for you.

Bus Stop	Fraction	Decimal
Apple Lane	$\frac{8}{10}$ or $\frac{4}{5}$ km	0.8 km
Bean Street	$1\frac{6}{10}$ or $1\frac{3}{5}$ km	1.6 km
Corn Avenue	$2\frac{4}{10}$ or $2\frac{2}{5}$ km	2.4 km
Dill Road	$2\frac{8}{10}$ or $2\frac{4}{5}$ km	2.8 km

Talk About It 🗨

What terms help you describe fractions and decimals? Complete the sentences to explain.

1. The dot in 2.6 is called the … decimal point.
2. The decimal 3.5 and the mixed number $3\frac{1}{2}$ are … equivalent.
3. In the fraction $\frac{2}{10}$, 2 is the … numerator.
4. In the fraction $\frac{7}{8}$, 8 is the … denominator.

Your Turn ✏️

Look in the box. Two numbers name the same amount. Circle them both. Use vocabulary terms to write about these numbers. Share your work with your group.

$2\frac{50}{100}$	2.14
$2\frac{3}{4}$	2.25
$2\frac{2}{5}$	(2.50)

Leveled Language Proficiency

Students at each proficiency level should be able to perform the following tasks.

Listening/Speaking

Early Beginner Recognize a few vocabulary terms and follow very simple conversations with support. Repeat simple phrases, and answer yes/no and choice questions.

Beginner Follow simple directions. Recognize and use some vocabulary terms. Say terms and short phrases; repeat longer phrases and short sentences.

Early Intermediate/Intermediate Begin to follow and take part in more abstract discussions about vocabulary terms. Express abstract ideas about target vocabulary.

Advanced/Transitioning Understand complex sentence structures; follow abstract conversations involving lesson vocabulary. Justify explanations and speak on abstract topics, including those that involve lesson vocabulary, with few errors.

Your Turn

The numbers along this bicycle path stand for distances in miles. Write the missing fraction or decimal in each box.

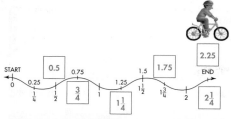

Talk and Write About It

Complete the sentences about fractions and decimals.

Vocabulary

fraction	mixed number	denominator	equivalent
decimal	number line	numerator	decimal point

1. Numbers can be shown in order along a ___number line___.

2. In the fraction $\frac{2}{3}$, the 3 is the ___denominator___.

3. $5\frac{1}{3}$ is a ___mixed number___.

4. 0.75 and $\frac{3}{4}$ are ___equivalent___.

Produce Language

Write about how fractions and decimals can name the same amount. Give examples on a number line or use the bicycle path pictured above. Use as many vocabulary terms as you can.

Leveled Language Proficiency

Students at each proficiency level should be able to perform the following tasks.

Reading/Writing

Early Beginner Read some short, common words and easier vocabulary terms, with visual support or help. Copy terms and phrases from the board.

Beginner Read a growing number of everyday words and some lesson vocabulary terms. Use sentence starters and visual supports to write terms and phrases.

Early Intermediate/Intermediate Read most lesson vocabulary in isolation and in context; read sentences composed of phonetically regular words and sight words. Read and understand some abstract ideas. Write full sentences with support to describe ideas and explain vocabulary with some errors.

Advanced/Transitioning With minimal support, read and write full sentences, with few errors, that contain concrete and abstract ideas related to lesson vocabulary. Use sentence starters only as necessary.

↻ Assess Understanding

Your Turn

Model Talk about the number line with students, making clear that the distances from the start of the path are shown as fractions and as decimals. Clarify that for the End point, students write the distance as a fraction *and* as its equivalent decimal. Help students complete the first box. Then have them complete the rest of the boxes independently and discuss their results with a partner.

Talk and Write About It

On Their Own Have students work on their own for ten minutes to complete the sentences. Then have partners share and compare their ideas.

Produce Language

On Their Own Have students write what they have learned about how fractions and decimals relate. Encourage them to use a number line to support their explanation. Alternatively, you might want to have students show shaded grids to support their explanations.

Wrap Up

Table Talk Have students look back at the lesson's objectives. Allow time for them to reflect on what they have learned and then answer the essential question.

☑ **Learned** and applied vocabulary related to fractions and decimals

☑ **Spoken** statements about fractions and decimals

☑ **Written** statements about fractions and decimals

Patterns

Vocabulary Patterns, repeating patterns, repeat, addition pattern, subtraction pattern, rule, multiplication pattern, division pattern

Materials Index cards, color counters (optional), colored pencils or markers

Math Background

- *Repeating patterns* are commonly found in decorative art and music. Sometimes the set of repeating elements is referred to as a *pattern unit*.

- Changing patterns include addition, subtraction, multiplication, and division patterns, though they are not limited to these. Changing patterns are defined by their first element and a *rule*.

Patterns

Essential Question What words will help you explain patterns?

You Will
- Understand repeating patterns.
- Understand addition, subtraction, multiplication, and division patterns.
- Use math vocabulary to describe and continue patterns.

Talk About It

Make an index card for each vocabulary term below. Place each card in one of three piles.

Pile 1: I know what this term means.
Pile 2: I have heard of this term, but I am not sure how it is used in math.
Pile 3: I have not heard of this term.

pattern	division pattern	rule
repeating pattern	repeat	multiplication pattern
addition pattern	subtraction pattern	

What do you know about each term? Explain, using the sentence starters for support.

I know … means …
I think … means …
I do not know what … means.

Your Turn

Look at the objectives under You Will at the top of the page. Working with a partner, predict what you are going to learn. Use the sentence starter for support.

I am going to learn about …

Frontload the Lesson

Essential Question

What words will help you explain patterns?

Talk About It

Build Background As students sort the cards, read the terms aloud. Have students tell what they know about the terms they placed in the first two piles.

Content and Language

You Will

Model Read the objectives aloud and explain them in your own words. Use visual examples to support your explanations.

Your Turn

Guide Discussion Have students read the objectives and tell what the objectives mean to them.

Leveled Instruction

Early Beginner Early beginners may not use many words in their responses. Encourage them to use pictures, manipulatives, and gestures to communicate, or answer yes/no questions.

Beginner Have students partner with students of higher English language proficiency to complete activities. Expect oral responses of short phrases and simple sentences.

Early Intermediate Encourage students to use sentence starters for support. Model using the sentence starters as needed.

Intermediate Encourage students to express their ideas without sentence starters, if possible, using full sentences. Expect some grammatical mistakes.

Advanced/Transitioning Expect students to form written and spoken sentences of greater complexity. Have them use a more varied English vocabulary and try varied sentence structures.

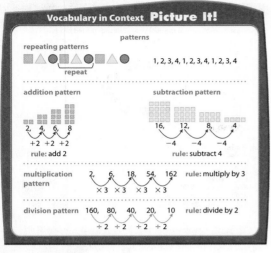

Vocabulary in Context Picture It!

patterns

repeating patterns

1, 2, 3, 4, 1, 2, 3, 4, 1, 2, 3, 4

repeat

addition pattern

2, 4, 6, 8
+2 +2 +2
rule: add 2

subtraction pattern

16, 12, 8, 4
−4 −4 −4
rule: subtract 4

multiplication pattern

2, 6, 18, 54, 162
×3 ×3 ×3 ×3
rule: multiply by 3

division pattern 160, 80, 40, 20, 10
÷2 ÷2 ÷2 ÷2
rule: divide by 2

Talk About It

Talk with a partner. Complete the sentences.

1. The pattern 6, 2, 5, 6, 2, 5, 6, 2, 5 is called a … repeating pattern.
2. In the pattern in Problem 1, the first three numbers … repeat.
3. In the pattern 3, 6, 9, 12, 15, the … is "add 3." rule
4. A pattern with the rule "subtract 2" is a … subtraction pattern.
5. A pattern with the rule "multiply by 5" is a … multiplication pattern.

Your Turn

Write or draw an example of a repeating pattern. Then write an example of an addition pattern. Talk about your patterns with a partner.

42   Lesson 11

Academic Vocabulary

- Discuss patterns students find in daily life: sewing patterns used to cut fabric to make clothing; rhythmic patterns in music; or a repeating design on wrapping paper or fabric.

- Clarify that in this context, a *rule* describes how to go from one number to another in a pattern. It explains how the pattern works, as soccer rules explain and govern that game.

- Note that *repeat* is used as a verb, noun, and adjective (*repeating*) in this lesson. Help students become familiar with all three usages.

Additional resources for building and reinforcing vocabulary are provided on pages T37–T41.

Cultural Consideration

Visual patterns are familiar elements in the art and design of many cultures. African and Asian fabric designs and Arabic mosaic tiles are some examples.

↻ Comprehensible Input

Guide students to understanding

Vocabulary in Context Picture It!

1. **Say the Term** Have students repeat, stressing each syllable. Then combine syllables and have students repeat.

2. **Introduce Meaning** Connect the term to the visual that illustrates it.

3. **Demonstrate** Use counters or number lines to model different kinds of patterns. For example, use a number line with curved arrows to show a skip-counting pattern such as 3, 6, 9, 12. Help students express the rule.

4. **Apply** Have students demonstrate understanding with Talk About It.

Repeat the routine for each vocabulary term.

Remind students that they can review vocabulary terms for the four operations on pages 89 and 90 and record more terms as they learn them.

Talk About It

Guide Discussion Have students discuss the responses with a partner. Then provide this additional sentence completion, if time permits:

A pattern with the rule "divide by 4" is a … division pattern.

Intervention

If students have trouble naming addition, subtraction, multiplication, and division patterns …

Then write examples of patterns on the board and point to each. Emphasize the connection between the rule and the first word of each type of pattern.

Your Turn

Guide Discussion Ask volunteers to share their patterns and describe them for Your Turn.

↻ Language Production

Comprehension Support Help students understand the words *necklace* and *beads*. Show students that there are 3 different types of beads on the necklace: red, blue, and yellow. Some students might need help with the names of colors. Review the words *circle* and *square* to help students talk about the patterns in Problems 2 and 3. Draw examples of each.

Model Ask students to look for a pattern in the necklace. *The first beads are red. There are 2 red beads.* Write 2 on the board. Continue counting the next group of blue beads, and so on, until a repeating number pattern emerges. For Problems 2 and 3 show students how the visuals match the numbers. Then discuss how they change. *Each number of circles is two fewer than the one before. So, the rule is to subtract 2.* In Problems 4 and 5, encourage students to think about what can be added, subtracted, multiplied, or divided to get from any number to the next.

Talk About It

Guide Discussion Have students complete the Talk About It sentences with a partner. Remind them that if they need help with the terms, they can look back at Vocabulary in Context Picture It!

Your Turn

Guide Discussion Give students a few minutes to write about the letter pattern. Then have them share their ideas with a partner.

Do You Understand?

1. What is the pattern in the necklace? Start with the red beads. Count how many of each color. Write the pattern with numbers.

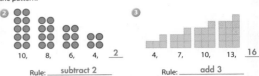

2, 3, 1, 2, 3, 1, 2, 3, 1

Find the rule for these patterns. Then find the next number in the pattern.

2. 10, 8, 6, 4, __2__

Rule: __subtract 2__

3. 4, 7, 10, 13, __16__

Rule: __add 3__

4. 55, 50, 45, 40, __35__

Rule: __subtract 5__

5. 10, 20, 40, 80, __160__

Rule: __multiply by 2__

Talk About It

Complete the sentences about patterns.

6. The pattern made by the necklace is a ... repeating pattern.

7. The pattern in Problem 2 is a ... subtraction pattern.

8. The pattern in Problem 5 is a ... multiplication pattern.

9. To find the next number in the pattern in Problem 4, I first find the ... rule.

Your Turn

Look at this pattern of letters.

A A B C A A B C A A B C A A B C

Write a few sentences about the pattern. Tell what kind of pattern it is. Describe the pattern to your partner.

Patterns   43

Leveled Language Proficiency

Students at each proficiency level should be able to perform the following tasks.

Listening/Speaking

Early Beginner Recognize a few vocabulary terms and follow very simple conversations with support. Repeat simple phrases, and use vocabulary terms to answer questions.

Beginner Follow simple directions. Recognize and use some vocabulary terms. Say individual terms and simple phrases, and repeat longer phrases and short sentences.

Early Intermediate/Intermediate Begin to follow and take part in more abstract discussion about vocabulary terms in spoken phrases and sentences. Show an ability to express abstract ideas about target vocabulary.

Advanced/Transitioning Understand complex sentence structures; follow abstract conversations involving lesson vocabulary. Speak on abstract topics, including those that involve lesson vocabulary, with few if any grammatical and syntactical errors.

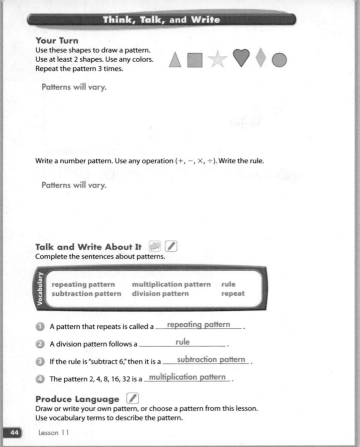

Your Turn
Use these shapes to draw a pattern.
Use at least 2 shapes. Use any colors.
Repeat the pattern 3 times.

Patterns will vary.

Write a number pattern. Use any operation (+, −, ×, ÷). Write the rule.

Patterns will vary.

Talk and Write About It
Complete the sentences about patterns.

Vocabulary
| repeating pattern | multiplication pattern | rule |
| subtraction pattern | division pattern | repeat |

1 A pattern that repeats is called a ___repeating pattern___ .

2 A division pattern follows a ___rule___ .

3 If the rule is "subtract 6," then it is a ___subtraction pattern___ .

4 The pattern 2, 4, 8, 16, 32 is a ___multiplication pattern___

Produce Language
Draw or write your own pattern, or choose a pattern from this lesson.
Use vocabulary terms to describe the pattern.

44   Lesson 11

Leveled Language Proficiency

Students at each proficiency level should be able to perform the following tasks.

Reading/Writing

Early Beginner Read some short, common words and easier vocabulary terms, if given visual support or help from a partner or adult. Copy terms and phrases from the board; write 1–2 vocabulary terms independently.

Beginner Read a growing number of everyday words and some lesson vocabulary terms. Use sentence starters and visual supports to write individual terms and phrases.

Early Intermediate/Intermediate Read most lesson vocabulary in isolation and in context; read sentences composed of phonetically regular words and sight words, including directions. Write full sentences with support to describe ideas and explain vocabulary with some spelling and grammatical errors. Read and understand some abstract ideas.

Advanced/Transitioning With minimal support, read and write full sentences, with few errors, that contain concrete and abstract ideas related to lesson vocabulary. Use sentence starters only as necessary.

↻ Assess Understanding

Your Turn

Model Name the shapes that can be used to create a pattern. Help students understand the task. *I have to make up a pattern using shapes. I have to use at least two different shapes. That means I can use two shapes, or I can use more than two. I can use any colors.* Then have students do the activity independently.

Talk and Write About It

On Their Own Have students work with a partner to complete the sentences.

Produce Language

On Their Own Remind students that they can look back at Vocabulary in Context Picture it! for examples of the patterns discussed in the lesson.

Wrap Up

Table Talk Have students look back at the lesson's objectives. Allow time for them to reflect on what they have learned and then answer the essential question.

☑ **Learned** and applied vocabulary related to patterns

☑ **Spoken** statements about patterns

☑ **Written** statements about patterns

Lesson 12

Patterns in Tables

Vocabulary Pattern, number pattern, table, input, output, rule

Math Background

- Tables are a convenient way to record numerical information. The tables in this lesson are *input/output* tables. Such a table can be shown horizontally (as in the lesson) or vertically.

- Not all tables exhibit numerical patterns, but when they do, a rule can be used to relate the number you start with, the *input*, to the number that results, the *output*.

Frontload the Lesson

Essential Question What vocabulary terms will help you explain patterns in tables?

Talk About It

Build Background Have students tell what they already know about terms they list in the first two columns of the Know-Want-Learn chart. (See page T43 for additional copies of the chart.)

Content and Language

You Will

Model Read the objectives aloud and explain them in your own words. Use models and tables to visually support your explanations.

Your Turn

Guide Discussion Have students read the objectives and explain what the objectives mean to them.

Patterns in Tables

Essential Question What vocabulary terms will help you explain patterns in tables?

You Will
- Explore number patterns in tables.
- Find the rule and missing numbers in an input/output table.
- Use math vocabulary to discuss patterns in tables.

Talk About It

Look at the list of terms below. In the first two columns of the chart, write terms you **know** or **want** to know more about.

| pattern | rule | input |
| output | table | number pattern |

Know	Want	Learned

Tell what you know about each term.

I know the term …
I want to learn …

Your Turn
Look at the objectives under You Will at the top of the page. Working with a partner, predict what you are going to learn. Use the sentence starter for support.

I am going to learn about …

Patterns in Tables   45

Leveled Instruction

Early Beginner Early beginners may not use many words in their responses. Encourage them to use gestures, pictures, and yes/no responses to communicate.

Beginner Have students partner with students of higher English language proficiency to complete activities. Expect short and simple sentences as responses.

Early Intermediate Encourage students to use sentence starters for support. Model using these sentence starters as needed.

Intermediate Encourage students to express their ideas without sentence starters. They should use complete sentences. Expect some mistakes.

Advanced/Transitioning Expect students to form sentences of increasing complexity. Have them use a more varied English vocabulary, and encourage them to try different sentence structures.

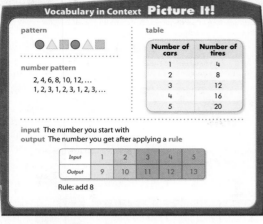

pattern	table	
● ▲ ■ ● ▲ ■		

number pattern

2, 4, 6, 8, 10, 12, …

1, 2, 3, 1, 2, 3, 1, 2, 3, …

Number of cars	Number of tires
1	4
2	8
3	12
4	16
5	20

input The number you start with
output The number you get after applying a **rule**

Input	1	2	3	4	5
Output	9	10	11	12	13

Rule: add 8

Talk About It

Talk with a partner to complete the sentences.

① Numbers and other information can be shown in a … table.

② The number you start with in a table is the … input.

③ What you do to change an input number is the … rule.

④ The number you get after using a rule is the … output.

Your Turn

Describe the following to your partner. Try to use all of the vocabulary terms.

Number of nickels	Number of pennies
1	5
2	10
3	15
4	20
5	25

46   Lesson 12

Academic Vocabulary

- Discuss the everyday meaning of *table* (a piece of furniture) and the mathematical meaning (an organized way to show numerical information).

- Compare the common meanings of the noun *rule* (a statement or law meant to guide how people act; guidelines to follow in a game) with its mathematical meaning in number patterns.

- Use a container to demonstrate *in* and *out*. Then tie this to a discussion of *input* and *output*.

Additional resources for building and reinforcing vocabulary are provided on pages T37–T41.

↻ Comprehensible Input

Guide students to understanding

Vocabulary in Context Picture It!

1. **Say the Term** Have students repeat, stressing each syllable. Then combine syllables and have students repeat.

2. **Introduce Meaning** Connect the term to the visual that illustrates it.

3. **Demonstrate** When you discuss *table*, draw a variety of tables on the board. If possible, show examples from newspapers or books.

4. **Apply** Have students demonstrate understanding with Talk About It.

Repeat the routine for each vocabulary term.

Talk About It

Guide Discussion Have students discuss the responses with a partner. Then provide this additional sentence completion, if time permits:

The numbers in an input/output table might show a … **pattern.**

Intervention

If students confuse input and output numbers …

Then connect *input* with *put in*. Next, draw a "function machine" that looks like a funnel (with the wider opening at the top). Write + 3 on the machine as the rule. Show the number 1 near the larger opening of the funnel, ready to go in. Label it *input*. Show the resulting number 4, labeled *output,* coming out the smaller end of the funnel. Then connect *output* with *put out*.

Your Turn

Guide Discussion Ask students to share their descriptions of the table. Note that all the vocabulary terms can be applied.

↻ Language Production

Comprehension Support Discuss *tiles*. Point to them in your classroom if there are any on the floor or wall. Talk about the tile pattern at the top of the page. Help students see how the pictures and the table describe the same pattern: one using shapes, the other using numbers. Discuss the shape names *triangles* and *hexagons*. Draw examples of each. Ask questions to check understanding, such as: *How many triangles are needed for 2 hexagons?* Or *When the input is 3, what is the output?*

Model Before students complete the table on their own, suggest that they write the number of hexagons and the number of triangles under each new stage of the tile pattern. For the third stage, say: *I see that there are 3 hexagons and 9 triangles. I can write that under the picture, and I can also record it in the table.*

Talk About It

Guide Discussion Have students complete the Talk About It sentences with a partner. Remind them that if they need help with the terms, they can look back at Vocabulary in Context Picture It!

Your Turn

Guide Discussion Have students work in pairs to share their answers and to explain their reasoning.

Do You Understand?

Marta is making a floor tile pattern. Every time she puts down 1 hexagon ⬡, she puts down 3 triangles △ around it.

1 hexagon   2 hexagons
3 triangles 6 triangles

Marta uses a table to show the number of hexagons and the number of triangles. Write the missing numbers in the table.

⬡ (Input)	1	2	3	4	5	6	7	8
△ (Output)	3	6	9	12	15	18	21	24

Talk About It 💬
Complete the sentences.

1 The number of hexagons and the number of triangles is written in a … table.

2 The number of hexagons is the input, and the number of triangles is the … output.

3 In this table, "multiply by 3" is the … rule.

Your Turn 💬
Explain to your partner how you could find the next four input and output numbers in the table.

Leveled Language Proficiency

Students at each proficiency level should be able to perform the following tasks.

Listening/Speaking

Early Beginner Recognize a few vocabulary terms and follow very simple conversations with support. Repeat simple phrases and use vocabulary terms to answer questions.

Beginner Follow simple directions. Recognize and use some vocabulary terms. Say individual terms and simple phrases, and repeat longer phrases and short sentences.

Early Intermediate/Intermediate Begin to follow and take part in more abstract discussions about vocabulary terms and math ideas in spoken phrases and sentences. Show an ability to express abstract ideas about target vocabulary.

Advanced/Transitioning Understand complex sentence structures; follow abstract conversations involving lesson vocabulary. Speak on abstract topics, including those that involve lesson vocabulary, with few, if any, errors.

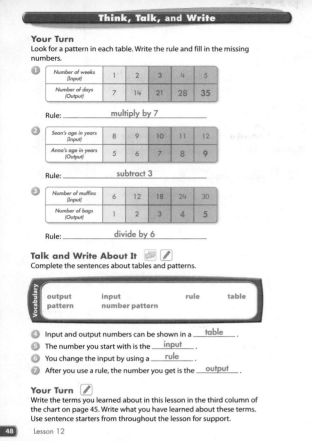

Your Turn

Look for a pattern in each table. Write the rule and fill in the missing numbers.

1

Number of weeks (Input)	1	2	3	4	5
Number of days (Output)	7	14	21	28	35

Rule: _____ multiply by 7 _____

2

Sean's age in years (Input)	8	9	10	11	12
Anna's age in years (Output)	5	6	7	8	9

Rule: _____ subtract 3 _____

3

Number of muffins (Input)	6	12	18	24	30
Number of bags (Output)	1	2	3	4	5

Rule: _____ divide by 6 _____

Talk and Write About It

Complete the sentences about tables and patterns.

> **Vocabulary**
>
> output   input   rule   table
> pattern   number pattern

4 Input and output numbers can be shown in a ___table___ .

5 The number you start with is the ___input___ .

6 You change the input by using a ___rule___ .

7 After you use a rule, the number you get is the ___output___ .

Your Turn

Write the terms you learned about in this lesson in the third column of the chart on page 45. Write what you have learned about these terms. Use sentence starters from throughout the lesson for support.

48   Lesson 12

↻ Assess Understanding

Your Turn

Model Discuss the first table. *I see that the table shows the number of weeks for the input and the number of days for the output. For 1 week, there are 7 days. For 2 weeks, there are 14 days. For 3 weeks, there are 21 days. Does anyone see a pattern, yet? Does that help you find the rule? How can you use the rule to find the missing number of days for 4 weeks? For 5 weeks?*

Talk and Write About It

On Their Own Have students work on their own to complete the sentences. Then have partners share and compare their answers.

Produce Language

On Their Own Have students complete the Know-Want-Learn chart from the beginning of the lesson. Have students write what they have learned about these terms and share their ideas in a group. If some students have no new terms to add to column 3, ask them to write about any three or four terms in the lesson.

Wrap Up

Table Talk Have students look back at the lesson's objectives. Allow time for them to reflect on what they have learned and then answer the essential question.

☑ **Learned** and applied vocabulary related to patterns and tables

☑ **Spoken** statements about patterns and tables

☑ **Written** statements about patterns and tables

Leveled Language Proficiency

Students at each proficiency level should be able to perform the following tasks.

Reading/Writing

Early Beginner Read some short, common words and easier vocabulary terms, if given visual support or help from a partner or adult. Copy terms and phrases from the board; write 1–2 vocabulary terms independently.

Beginner Read a growing number of everyday words and some lesson vocabulary terms. Use sentence starters and visual supports to write individual terms and phrases.

Early Intermediate/Intermediate Read and understand some complex sentences. Write full sentences with support to describe ideas and explain vocabulary, with some errors.

Advanced/Transitioning With minimal support, read and write full sentences, with few errors, that contain concrete and abstract ideas related to lesson vocabulary.

Variables and Equations

Vocabulary Equation, equal sign, equals, is equal to, inverse operations, solve, value, missing number, solution, variable

Math Background

- An *equation* is a number sentence that includes an equal sign, numbers (or symbols that represent them), and usually one or more operations.

- A *variable* is used to represent an unknown quantity in an equation. A variable can be a symbol, shape, or letter.

- Two operations are *inverses* if they "undo" each other. For example, addition and subtraction are *inverse operations*: subtracting 6 is the inverse of adding 6.

Frontload the Lesson

Essential Question

What words and symbols should you use when you work with equations and variables?

Talk About It

Build Background Have students tell what they already know about these terms that describe equations and variables.

Content and Language

You Will

Model Read the objectives aloud and explain them in your own words. Use models and examples to visually support your explanations.

Your Turn

Guide Discussion Have students read the objectives and tell what the objectives mean to them.

Essential Question What words and symbols should you use when you work with equations and variables?

You Will
- Understand and discuss what variables and equations are.
- Solve equations with missing numbers.
- Use math vocabulary to describe variables and equations.

Talk About It

Rate these mathematical terms according to the following scale:

1. I do not know this term.
2. I have heard this term, but I do not know how to use it in math.
3. I understand this term and know how to use it in math.

_____ variable	_____ equation
_____ is equal to	_____ missing number
_____ inverse operations	_____ value
_____ solution	_____ equals
_____ solve	_____ equal sign

Use the sentence starters to talk about the terms.

I know … means …
I think … means …
I do not know what … means.

Your Turn
Look at the objectives under You Will at the top of the page. Working with a partner, predict what you are going to learn. Use the sentence starter for support.

I am going to learn about …

Leveled Instruction

Early Beginner Early beginners may not use many words in their responses. Encourage them to use gestures to communicate.

Beginner Have students partner with students of higher English language proficiency to complete activities. Expect short and simple sentences as responses.

Early Intermediate Encourage students to use sentence starters for support. Model using these sentence starters as needed.

Intermediate Encourage students to express their ideas without sentence starters, if possible. Have them use complete sentences. Expect some grammatical mistakes.

Advanced/Transitioning Expect students to form sentences of increasing complexity. Encourage them to use more advanced terms, and to try different sentence structures.

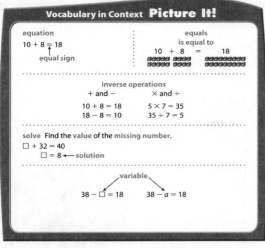

Vocabulary in Context **Picture It!**

equation	equals
$10 + 8 = 18$	is equal to
↑ equal sign	$10 + 8 = 18$

inverse operations

+ and −	× and ÷
$10 + 8 = 18$	$5 × 7 = 35$
$18 − 8 = 10$	$35 ÷ 7 = 5$

solve Find the **value** of the **missing number**.

$□ + 32 = 40$
$□ = 8 ←$ **solution**

variable

$38 − □ = 18$ $\quad$ $38 − a = 18$

Talk About It 🗨

Talk with a partner. Complete the sentences.

1. You can say that $3 × 6 = 18$ is a number sentence or an … **equation**.
2. You can use a shape or letter for the … **missing number**.
3. Addition and subtraction are … **inverse operations**.
4. The answer to an equation is the … **solution**.
5. In $n × 42 = 126$, n is the … **variable**.

Your Turn ✏

Think about the new vocabulary terms.

- Write an addition equation. Use a as the variable.
- Have your partner solve your equation.
- Use vocabulary terms to discuss your partner's work.

Academic Vocabulary

- Link the terms *equal* and *equation* by showing that an equation is a number sentence in which equal amounts appear on either side of an = sign. Write and pronounce both terms as you point to the letters *equa-*, and have students repeat the pronunciations.

- Explain the relationship between *solve* and *solution*. Show students that when you *solve* a problem, the answer is the *solution*. Highlight the common letters *sol*. Clarify that in the words *solve* and *solution* there is no relation to the Spanish word *sol*, which means *sun*.

- Explain that variables are often lower-case letters. Caution students not to confuse the commonly used variable x and the multiplication symbol ×.

Additional resources for building and reinforcing vocabulary are provided on pages T37–T41.

↻ Comprehensible Input

Guide students to understanding

Vocabulary in Context Picture It!

1. **Say the Term** Have students repeat, stressing each syllable. Then combine syllables and have students repeat.

2. **Introduce Meaning** Connect the term to the visual that illustrates it.

3. **Demonstrate** Write different simple equations to show how variables represent missing numbers, and to clarify the meanings of key terms. For example, write $□ ÷ 4 = 6$ and $y − 4 = 5$. Model how to read each equation and identify the variable.

4. **Apply** Have students demonstrate understanding with Talk About It.

Repeat the routine for each vocabulary term.

Remind students that they can review vocabulary terms for the four operations on pages 89 and 90 and record more terms as they learn them.

Talk About It

Guide Discussion Have students discuss the responses with a partner. Then provide this additional sentence completion if time permits:

An equation states that two amounts are … **equal.**

Intervention

If students confuse *variable* and *value* …

Then model the pronunciation of each word while tapping its syllables. Students will hear that *value* has two syllables, while *variable* has four.

Your Turn

Guide Discussion Ask students to share their equations and solutions. Have small groups of students practice using vocabulary terms as they discuss their classmates' equations and solutions.

Variables and Equations

⟳ Language Production

Comprehension Support Read the problems with students. Guide students through the steps that help them find the unknown quantity. Help students see that they can write and solve an equation to find the missing number. Ask questions to check understanding, such as: *What do you need to find out in the first problem?* Or *What information is missing in the second problem?*

Model Work through Problem 1 with students. *I see there are 3 vans. There are 24 students in them. But we don't know how many students are in each van. This looks like a multiplication problem. The square stands for the missing number. 3 times what number equals 24? What's the inverse operation for multiplication? How can that help you solve the equation?* You might need to pause and remind students that *3 times what number* means the same thing as *3 multiplied by what number.*

Talk About It

Guide Discussion Have students complete the Talk About It sentences with a partner. Remind them that if they need help with the terms, they can look back at Vocabulary in Context Picture It!

Your Turn

Guide Discussion Have partners work with other pairs to share and compare their explanations.

Use equations to solve the problems.

① Each van has the same number of students. How many students are in each van?

24 students in all

What number do you need to find?
  the number of students in each van

The equation for this problem is $3 \times \square = 24$
The value of $\square$ is __8__ .
There are __8__ students in each van.

② There are 57 students in this group. 33 are boys. How many are girls?

33 boys and ? girls

What number do you need to find?
  the number of girls

The equation for this problem is $33 + g = 57$
The value of g is __24__ .
There are __24__ girls.

57 students in all

Talk About It 💬
Complete the sentences about solving equations. Discuss your answers with a partner.

③ Multiplication and division are … operations. inverse
④ You can show a missing number with a … variable.
⑤ You solve an equation by finding the … of the variable. value

Your Turn ✏️
Explain how you can use inverse operations to solve one of the equations above. Use the sentence starters for help.

The operation in the equation is …
The inverse operation is …
To solve the equation, I …

Variables and Equations **51**

Leveled Language Proficiency

Students at each proficiency level should be able to perform the following tasks.

Listening/Speaking

Early Beginner Recognize a few vocabulary terms and follow very simple conversations with support. Repeat simple phrases, and use vocabulary terms to answer questions.

Beginner Follow simple directions. Recognize and use some vocabulary terms. Say individual terms and simple phrases, and repeat longer phrases and short sentences.

Early Intermediate/Intermediate Begin to follow and take part in more abstract discussion about vocabulary terms in spoken phrases and sentences. Show an ability to express abstract ideas about target vocabulary.

Advanced/Transitioning Understand complex sentence structures; follow abstract conversations involving lesson vocabulary. Speak on abstract topics, including those that involve lesson vocabulary, with few if any grammatical and syntactical errors.

Your Turn

Use a variable to solve the problem. How many pencils are in the box?

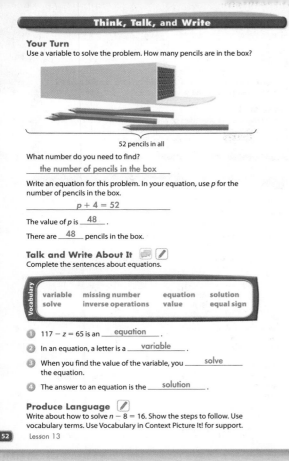

52 pencils in all

What number do you need to find?

the number of pencils in the box

Write an equation for this problem. In your equation, use *p* for the number of pencils in the box.

$$p + 4 = 52$$

The value of *p* is ___48___ .

There are ___48___ pencils in the box.

Talk and Write About It 💬 ✏️

Complete the sentences about equations.

Vocabulary

variable	missing number	equation	solution
solve	inverse operations	value	equal sign

① $117 - z = 65$ is an ___equation___ .

② In an equation, a letter is a ___variable___ .

③ When you find the value of the variable, you ___solve___ the equation.

④ The answer to an equation is the ___solution___ .

Produce Language ✏️

Write about how to solve $n - 8 = 16$. Show the steps to follow. Use vocabulary terms. Use Vocabulary in Context Picture It! for support.

Leveled Language Proficiency

Students at each proficiency level should be able to perform the following tasks.

Reading/Writing

Early Beginner Read some short, common words and easier vocabulary terms, with help. Copy terms and phrases from the board; write a few vocabulary terms independently.

Beginner Read a growing number of commonly used words and some lesson vocabulary terms. Use sentence starters and visual supports to write individual terms and phrases.

Early Intermediate/Intermediate Read most lesson vocabulary in isolation and in context; read sentences composed of phonetically regular words and sight words. Write sentences with support to describe ideas and explain vocabulary, with some errors.

Advanced/Transitioning With minimal support, read and write complete sentences, with few errors, that contain concrete and abstract ideas related to lesson vocabulary.

🔄 Assess Understanding

Your Turn

Model Read the directions and the problem with students. Then say: *To find how many pencils are in the box, use the variable* p *and write an equation.* Have students solve the problem, offering support as needed.

Talk and Write About It

On Their Own Have students work on their own for ten minutes to complete the statements. Then have partners share and compare their ideas.

Produce Language

On Their Own Have students use the given equation to write what they have learned about variables and equations.

Wrap Up

Table Talk Have students look back at the lesson's objectives. Allow time for them to reflect on what they have learned and then answer the essential question.

☑ **Learned** and applied vocabulary related to variables and equations

☑ **Spoken** statements about variables and equations

☑ **Written** statements about variables and equations

Lesson 14

Lines and Angles

Vocabulary Point, line, line segment, ray, intersecting lines, perpendicular lines, parallel lines, angle, vertex, acute angle, right angle, obtuse angle, straight angle

Math Background

- *Intersecting lines* have one point in common. *Parallel lines* have no points in common. *Perpendicular lines* intersect to form four right angles.

- All *angles* can be measured in degrees (°). *Right angles* measure exactly 90°. *Acute angles* measure less than 90°, *obtuse angles* measure between 90° and 180°, and *straight angles* measure exactly 180°.

Frontload the Lesson

Essential Question — What vocabulary terms should you use to describe lines and angles?

Talk About It

Build Background Have students tell what they already know about these terms that describe lines and angles.

Content and Language

You Will

Model Read the objectives aloud and explain them in your own words. Use diagrams and gestures to support your explanations.

Your Turn

Guide Discussion Have students read the objectives and discuss what the objectives mean to them.

Lines and Angles

Essential Question What vocabulary terms should you use to describe lines and angles?

You Will
- Recognize the properties of lines and angles.
- Recognize special angles and special pairs of lines.
- Use math vocabulary to describe lines and angles.

Talk About It

Rate these mathematical terms according to the following scale.

1. I have never heard of this term before.
2. I have heard this term, but I do not know how to use it in math.
3. I understand this term and know how to use it in math.

_____ line	_____ ray
_____ intersecting lines	_____ point
_____ line segment	_____ perpendicular lines
_____ parallel lines	_____ vertex
_____ angle	_____ right angle
_____ acute angle	_____ obtuse angle
_____ straight angle	

Explain what you know about each term, using the sentence starters.

I do not know what … means.
I know … means …
I think … means …

Your Turn
Look at the objectives under You Will at the top of the page. Working with a partner, predict what you are going to learn. Use the sentence starter for support.

I am going to learn about …

Leveled Instruction

Early Beginner Early beginners may not use many words in their responses. Encourage them to use gestures and pictures to communicate.

Beginner Have students partner with students of higher English language proficiency to complete activities. Expect short and simple sentences as responses.

Early Intermediate Encourage students to use sentence starters for support. Model using these sentence starters as needed.

Intermediate Encourage students to express their ideas without sentence starters, if possible. Have them use complete sentences. Expect some grammatical mistakes.

Advanced/Transitioning Expect students to form sentences of increasing complexity. Encourage them to use more advanced terms, and to try different sentence structures.

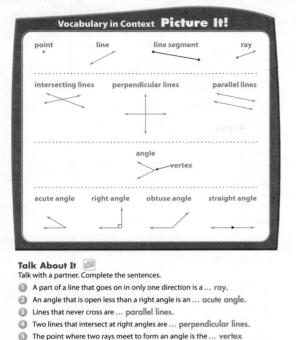

Academic Vocabulary

- Relate *intersecting lines* to streets that intersect. Refer students to the map on page 55, to local streets near the school, and to halls within your school building. Discuss busy intersections near your school.

- Point out that the plural of *vertex* is *vertices* and model how to pronounce it: with the accent on the first syllable. Inform students that *-cies* often forms the plural of words that end in /x/.

- Distinguish the everyday meaning of *point* (a location; an exact time; a unit of scoring; a gesture) with its mathematical meaning (location in a plane; where lines cross or meet).

Additional resources for building and reinforcing vocabulary are provided on pages T37–T41.

Cultural Consideration

Invite students to bring in street maps of the towns or cities in which they were born. Alternatively, a student might bring in a map of the capital city in their native country. Have students identify different kinds of lines and angles on it.

↻ Comprehensible Input
Guide students to understanding

Vocabulary in Context Picture It!

1. **Say the Term** Have students repeat, stressing each syllable. Then combine syllables and have students repeat.

2. **Introduce Meaning** Connect the term to the visual that illustrates it.

3. **Demonstrate** Point out examples of *line segments, intersecting* and *parallel lines,* and different kinds of *angles* in the classroom.

4. **Apply** Have students demonstrate understanding with Talk About It.

Repeat the routine for each vocabulary term.

Talk About It

Guide Discussion Have students discuss their responses with a partner. Then provide this additional sentence completion, if time permits:

An angle that is opened up all the way and looks like a line is a … **straight angle.**

Intervention

If students confuse *parallel* and *perpendicular* …

Then highlight the parallel /ll/ as a hint built into the spelling of the word itself.

Your Turn

Guide Discussion Ask students to share their drawings and descriptions of them.

Language Production

Comprehension Support Talk about the street map. Read together the names of the streets and buildings pictured. Invite volunteers to "finger walk" the map by going, for example, from Mark Street to Hill Street. Ask questions to check understanding, such as: *Where does Hill Street end?* Or *What angles do you see at intersections?*

Model Help students move around the map. Say: *I see that State Street crosses three streets. Starting at the top of the map, it crosses Pine Street. Then it crosses Mark Street, then Bird Street. It does not cross Hill Street because that street ends at Bird Street.* Check that students understand the match-up for *right angle.*

Talk About It

Guide Discussion Have students complete the Talk About It sentences with a partner. Remind them that if they need help with the terms, they can check the descriptions of the streets and angles or look back at Vocabulary in Context Picture It!

Your Turn

Guide Discussion Have partners work in small groups. Ask them to share their drawings and to explain them to members of the group.

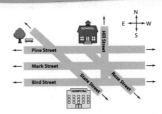

Do You Understand?

Match each term with what it describes on the map. The first one is done for you.

right angle   Bird Street and Pine Street

parallel lines   The angle where the hospital is

perpendicular lines   The angle where the park is

obtuse angle   The angle where the school is

acute angle   Mark Street and Hill Street

Talk About It
Complete the sentences that describe lines or angles.

1. State Street and Rose Street look like ... *parallel lines.*
2. Where Pine Street and Hill Street intersect is a ... *right angle.*
3. Pine Street and Hill Street look like ... *perpendicular lines.*
4. A line that goes in only one direction is a ... *ray.*

Your Turn
Add to the map.

- Draw a new street parallel to Bird Street.
- Draw a new street perpendicular to Bird Street.

Talk about your work with a partner.

Leveled Language Proficiency

Students at each proficiency level should be able to perform the following tasks.

Listening/Speaking

Early Beginner Recognize a few vocabulary terms and follow very simple conversations with support. Repeat simple phrases, and use vocabulary terms to answer questions.

Beginner Follow simple directions. Recognize and use some vocabulary terms. Say individual terms and simple phrases, and repeat longer phrases and short sentences.

Early Intermediate/Intermediate Begin to follow and take part in more abstract discussions about vocabulary terms in spoken phrases and sentences. Show an ability to express abstract ideas about target vocabulary.

Advanced/Transitioning Understand complex sentence structures; follow abstract conversations involving lesson vocabulary. Speak on abstract topics, including those that involve lesson vocabulary, with few, if any, grammatical and syntactical errors.

Your Turn

Draw a street map with 6 streets. Name the streets.

Be sure your map has:

- intersecting streets
- parallel streets
- perpendicular streets
- acute angles
- obtuse angles

Talk to a partner about your map. Use vocabulary terms to point out the special lines and angles in your drawing.

Talk and Write About It

Complete the sentences about your map.

Vocabulary

| parallel lines | intersecting lines | right angles |
| perpendicular lines | lines | obtuse angles |

1. Streets that never cross look like ___parallel lines___ .
2. Streets that cross look like ___intersecting lines___ .
3. The angles made by perpendicular lines are ___right angles___ .

Produce Language

Identify the kinds of lines and angles you can see in your classroom. Write to describe them. Use Vocabulary in Context Picture It! for support.

56 Lesson 14

Leveled Language Proficiency

Students at each proficiency level should be able to perform the following tasks.

Reading/Writing

Early Beginner Read some short, common words and easier vocabulary terms, if given visual support or help from a partner or adult. Copy terms and phrases from the board; write a few vocabulary terms independently.

Beginner Read a growing number of commonly used words and some lesson vocabulary terms. Use sentence starters and visual supports to write individual terms and phrases.

Early Intermediate/Intermediate Read most lesson vocabulary in isolation and in context; read sentences composed of phonetically regular words and sight words, including directions. Write full sentences, with support, to describe ideas and explain vocabulary with some spelling and grammatical errors. Read and understand some abstract ideas.

Advanced/Transitioning With minimal support, read and write complete sentences, with few errors, that contain concrete and abstract ideas related to lesson vocabulary. Use sentence starters only as needed.

Assess Understanding

Your Turn

Model Draw a simple map on the board with two perpendicular streets that intersect. Name them A Street and B Street. Say: *I want to add a new street that does not intersect with A Street. Where could I draw it?* Invite a volunteer to direct you. Draw several more streets and have students describe pairs of them. Then ask volunteers to identify the angles at the intersections of some of the streets. Have students draw their own maps, working in pairs or on their own. Highlight the need to include each of the five bulleted items.

Talk and Write About It

On Their Own Have students work for ten minutes to complete their maps and their sentences. Then have partners share and compare their ideas.

Produce Language

On Their Own Have students write what they have learned about lines and angles and the terms that define and describe them, using examples in the classroom.

Wrap Up

Table Talk Have students look back at the lesson's objectives. Allow time for them to reflect on what they have learned and then answer the essential question.

☑ **Learned** and applied vocabulary related to lines and angles

☑ **Spoken** statements about lines and angles

☑ **Written** statements about lines and angles

Shapes

Vocabulary Shapes, polygons, triangle, side, angle, quadrilateral, pentagon, hexagon, octagon, equilateral triangle, isosceles triangle, scalene triangle, right triangle, acute triangle, obtuse triangle, square, rectangle, rhombus, parallelogram, trapezoid

Materials Shapes Four Corner Activity (pages 91–93), scissors, glue, rulers

Math Background

- Polygons are closed figures with straight sides. Shapes with curves, such as circles, are not polygons.

Frontload the Lesson

Essential Question What vocabulary terms do you use when you discuss shapes?

Talk About It

Build Background Read aloud the steps in the Four Corner Activity. Post the following terms in each corner of the room: (1) *rectangle,* (2) *rhombus,* (3) *trapezoid,* (4) *triangle.* Have students work in pairs to complete the activity. Ask for volunteers to say what they know about each term.

Content and Language

You Will

Model Read the objectives aloud and explain them in your own words.

Your Turn

Guide Discussion Have students read the objectives. Discuss what these objectives mean to them.

Shapes

Essential Question What vocabulary terms do you use when you discuss shapes?

You Will
- Recognize the attributes of shapes.
- Compare and contrast polygons, quadrilaterals, and triangles.
- Use math vocabulary to describe shapes.

Talk About It

Tear out the Shapes Four Corners Activity sheet on pages 91–92. Then cut out the activity cards on page 93.

Work with a partner.

Each corner of the room shows the name of a shape.

Step 1 Go to a corner of the room. On the activity sheet, write the name of the shape.

Step 2 Look at the shapes on the activity cards. Find 2 cards that match the name of the shape in the box. Paste them in the box.

Repeat Steps 1 and 2 for each corner of the room.

What do you know about the names of the shapes you wrote in each box? Use the sentence starters for support.

I know … means …
I think … means …
I do not know what … means.

Your Turn
Look at the objectives under You Will at the top of the page. Working with a partner, predict what you are going to learn. Use the sentence starter for support.

I am going to learn about …

Shapes **57**

Leveled Instruction

Early Beginner Have students partner with students of higher language proficiency to complete the activities. Use gestures, drawings, and simple phrases to help students understand the concepts of the lesson.

Beginner Have students partner with students of higher English language proficiency to complete activities. Expect short and simple phrases as responses.

Early Intermediate Encourage students to use sentence starters for support. Model using these sentence starters as needed.

Intermediate Encourage students to express their ideas without sentence starters, if possible. Have them use complete sentences. Expect some grammatical mistakes.

Advanced/Transitioning Expect students to produce detailed answers with minimal assistance. Students should partner with students of lower level language proficiency to support them in completing activities.

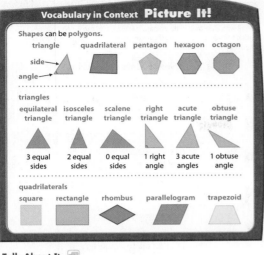

Shapes can be polygons.

triangle   quadrilateral   pentagon   hexagon   octagon

side →
angle →

triangles

| equilateral triangle | isosceles triangle | scalene triangle | right triangle | acute triangle | obtuse triangle |

3 equal sides | 2 equal sides | 0 equal sides | 1 right angle | 3 acute angles | 1 obtuse angle

quadrilaterals

square   rectangle   rhombus   parallelogram   trapezoid

Talk About It

Talk with a partner. Complete the sentences.

1. A triangle has 3 … sides.
2. Any polygon with 4 sides is a … quadrilateral.
3. Every quadrilateral with 4 equal sides is a … rhombus.

Your Turn

Write ways to remember the terms for different figures. List terms that are hard to say. Talk about your ideas in a small group.

↻ Comprehensible Input

Guide students to understanding

Vocabulary in Context Picture It!

1. **Say the Term** Have students repeat, stressing each syllable. Then combine syllables and have students repeat.

2. **Introduce Meaning** Connect the term to the visual that illustrates it.

3. **Demonstrate** Find classroom objects or photos in books and magazines that represent the different geometric figures discussed in the lesson. Point to features of these figures, such as right angles or equal sides.

4. **Apply** Have students demonstrate understanding with Talk About It.

Repeat the routine for each vocabulary term.

Talk About It

Guide Discussion Have students discuss the responses with a partner. Then provide this additional sentence completion, if time permits:

A triangle with 1 obtuse angle is called an … obtuse triangle.

Intervention

If students confuse the terms *equilateral* and *quadrilateral* …

Then emphasize the prefixes as you slowly articulate each term.

Your Turn

Guide Discussion Review some of the terms needed to describe the properties of various quadrilaterals, such as *parallel lines* (or parallel sides) and *right angle*. Encourage students to use these terms to compare and contrast two quadrilaterals. Ask students to share their ideas for remembering the names of figures for Your Turn.

Academic Vocabulary

- Be sure students understand that a *shape* is a flat figure. *Polygons* are just those shapes that have straight sides. Circles and hearts are shapes, but they are not polygons. *Shape* is also an attribute of an object, as in the *shape of a garden*.

- As you model how to say *rhombus*, point out that the *h* is silent.

- Write the terms *equilateral* and *equal* on the board. Guide students to notice similarities in them, and predict what an equilateral triangle is.

- Highlight the numerical prefixes *poly-*, *tri-*, *quad-*, *pent-*, *hex-*, and *oct-* in words that name polygons according to how many sides. Display labeled pictures of common objects that use some of these prefixes, such as *octopus* and *tricycle*.

Additional resources for building and reinforcing vocabulary are provided on pages T37–T42.

Cultural Consideration

Be aware that there are various definitions of *trapezoid*. Students schooled outside of the United States might have learned some properties of the trapezoid that are different from what they are learning in their math class here.

↻ Language Production

Comprehension Support Focus students on the example. Explain that there is often more than one term that can be used to describe a shape. Discuss why each term written describes the first shape pictured.

Model Before students complete the problems, say: *I have to think carefully about the shape pictured. I can ask myself questions to help me choose vocabulary terms. Is the shape a polygon? How many sides does it have? What is the name of a polygon that has that number of sides? Is it a special type of quadrilateral or triangle?*

Talk About It

Guide Discussion Have students complete the Talk About It sentences with a partner. Remind them that if they need help with the terms, they can look back at Vocabulary in Context Picture It!

Your Turn

Guide Discussion Partners can record their work on copies of T44. Then have partners share and discuss their answers.

Do You Understand?

Work with a partner. Write as many names as you can for each shape using the vocabulary terms shown on page 58. The example is done for you.

polygon, quadrilateral, trapezoid

1. polygon, triangle, right triangle, scalene triangle

2. polygon, hexagon

3. polygon, triangle, obtuse triangle, isosceles triangle

4. polygon, quadrilateral, parallelogram, rectangle, square

5. polygon, octagon

6. polygon, triangle, acute triangle, equilateral triangle

7. polygon, quadrilateral, parallelogram, rectangle

Talk About It 💬
Complete the sentences that describe figures.

8. Stop signs have 8 sides, so they are … octagons.

9. An equilateral triangle has 3 … sides. equal

10. A polygon with 5 sides is a … pentagon.

Your Turn ✏️
Choose two quadrilaterals. Write how they are alike and how they are different. Draw a picture of each one. Share your work with a partner.

Shapes   59

Leveled Language Proficiency

Students at each proficiency level should be able to perform the following tasks.

Listening/Speaking

Early Beginner Recognize a few vocabulary terms and follow very simple conversations with support. Repeat simple phrases, and use vocabulary terms to answer questions.

Beginner Follow simple directions. Recognize and use some vocabulary terms. Say individual terms and simple phrases, and repeat longer phrases and short sentences.

Early Intermediate/Intermediate Begin to follow and take part in more abstract discussions about vocabulary terms and math ideas in spoken phrases and sentences. Show an ability to express abstract ideas about target vocabulary.

Advanced/Transitioning Understand complex sentence structures; follow abstract conversations involving lesson vocabulary. Speak on abstract topics, including those that involve lesson vocabulary, with few if any errors.

Your Turn

Design a polygon picture. Draw it on grid paper. Use a ruler to help you draw straight sides. Use at least 7 different shapes. Label the shapes.

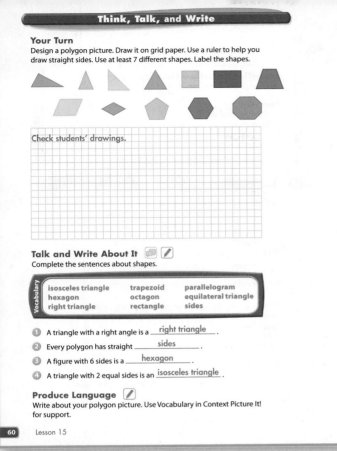

Check students' drawings.

Talk and Write About It 💬 ✏️

Complete the sentences about shapes.

Vocabulary		
isosceles triangle	trapezoid	parallelogram
hexagon	octagon	equilateral triangle
right triangle	rectangle	sides

① A triangle with a right angle is a __right triangle__.

② Every polygon has straight ___sides___.

③ A figure with 6 sides is a __hexagon__.

④ A triangle with 2 equal sides is an __isosceles triangle__.

Produce Language ✏️

Write about your polygon picture. Use Vocabulary in Context Picture It! for support.

Leveled Language Proficiency

Students at each proficiency level should be able to perform the following tasks.

Reading/Writing

Early Beginner Read some short, common words and easier vocabulary terms with support. Copy terms and phrases from the board; write a few vocabulary terms independently.

Beginner Read a growing number of commonly used words and some lesson vocabulary terms. Use sentence starters and visual supports to write individual terms and phrases.

Early Intermediate/Intermediate Read most lesson vocabulary in isolation and in context. Write full sentences with support to describe ideas and explain vocabulary, with some errors. Read and understand some abstract ideas.

Advanced/Transitioning With minimal support, read and write complete sentences, with few errors, that contain concrete and abstract ideas related to lesson vocabulary.

↻ Assess Understanding

Your Turn

Model Encourage students to be creative in planning a polygon picture. You may suggest that they create a geometric design, or draw a representative figure, such as a building, animal, or robot. Demonstrate creating one. Clarify that the overall image should be made of at least 7 different polygons that they have studied. Remind students that *at least 7* means 7 or more than 7. The polygons can appear in any size and orientation on the grid.

Talk and Write About It

On Their Own Have students work on their own to complete the sentences. Then have partners share and compare their ideas.

Produce Language

On Their Own Have students write what they have learned about shapes and the terms that define and describe them.

Wrap Up

Table Talk Have students look back at the lesson's objectives. Allow time for them to reflect on what they have learned and then answer the essential question.

☑ **Learned** and applied vocabulary related to shapes

☑ **Spoken** statements about shapes

☑ **Written** statements about shapes

Lesson 16

Transformations and Symmetry

Vocabulary Transformations, flip, reflection, turn, rotation, slide, translation, congruent, symmetry, lines of symmetry

Materials Index cards, Quarter-Inch Grid paper (page 95)

 Math Background

- *Reflections* (*flips*), *rotations* (*turns*), and *translations* (*slides*) are examples of *transformations*.

- A figure has *symmetry* if it can be "folded" to create perfect matching *(congruent)* halves. That "fold line" is called the *line of symmetry*.

Frontload the Lesson

Essential Question How can you describe transformations and symmetry?

Talk About It

Build Background Have students tell what they already know about these terms that describe transformations and symmetrical figures.

Content and Language

You Will

Model Read the objectives aloud and explain them in your own words. Use visual examples to support your explanations.

Your Turn

Guide Discussion Have students read the objectives and discuss what these objectives mean to them.

Transformations and Symmetry

Essential Question How can you describe transformations and symmetry?

You Will
- Flip, turn, and slide figures.
- Recognize congruence and symmetry.
- Use math vocabulary to describe transformations and symmetry.

Talk About It

Make an index card for each vocabulary term below. Place each card in one of three piles.

Pile 1: I know what this term means.
Pile 2: I have heard this term, but I am not sure how it is used in math.
Pile 3: I have not heard of this term.

reflection	rotation	translation
flip	turn	slide
transformation	symmetry	line of symmetry
congruent		

What do you know about each term? Explain, using the sentence starters for support.

I know … means …
I think … means …
I do not know what … means.

Your Turn
Look at the objectives under You Will at the top of the page. Working with a partner, predict what you are going to learn. Use the sentence starter for support.

I am going to learn about …

Leveled Instruction

Early Beginner Encourage students to use gestures to communicate. Allow students to include pictures in their responses.

Beginner Have students partner with students of higher English language proficiency to complete activities. Expect short and simple sentences as responses.

Early Intermediate Encourage students to use sentence starters for support. Model using these sentence starters as needed.

Intermediate Encourage students to express their ideas without sentence starters, if possible. Have them use complete sentences. Expect some grammatical mistakes.

Advanced/Transitioning Expect students to form sentences of increasing complexity. Encourage them to use more advanced terms and to try different sentence structures.

Vocabulary in Context **Picture It!**

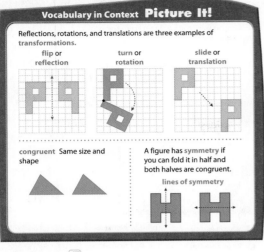

Reflections, rotations, and translations are three examples of transformations.

flip or reflection   turn or rotation   slide or translation

congruent Same size and shape

A figure has **symmetry** if you can fold it in half and both halves are congruent.

lines of symmetry

Talk About It
Talk with a partner. Complete the sentences.
1. Figures that are the same size and shape are … congruent.
2. Another term for slide is … translation.
3. Another term for rotation is … turn.
4. If halves of a figure match when the figure is folded, the fold is a … line of symmetry.

Your Turn
The letter E has one line of symmetry. Draw it. Write how you knew where to draw the line. Tell how to know you are correct.

62   Lesson 16

↻ Comprehensible Input
Guide students to understanding

Vocabulary in Context Picture It!

1. **Say the Term** Have students repeat, stressing each syllable. Then combine syllables and have students repeat.

2. **Introduce Meaning** Connect the term to the visual that illustrates it.

3. **Demonstrate** Use gestures, physical models, or body movements for each transformation. Make simple paper cutouts of hearts or snowflakes to model lines of symmetry and the congruent halves that the lines of symmetry determine.

4. **Apply** Have students demonstrate understanding with Talk About It.

Repeat the routine for each vocabulary term.

Talk About It

Guide Discussion Have students discuss the responses with a partner. Then provide this additional sentence completion, if time permits:

Another term for a flip is a … **reflection.**

Intervention

If students confuse the terms *translation* and *transformation* …

Then pronounce each term syllable by syllable, emphasizing the differences in the middles of each word.

Your Turn

Guide Discussion Ask students to share their drawings and written work for Your Turn.

Academic Vocabulary

- Make connections between the everyday meanings of *flip, turn,* and *slide* and their mathematical meanings as transformations. For instance, discuss that after going down a playground *slide,* the person is the same size, faces the same direction, is in the same sitting position, but is in a different location.

- Use a hand mirror to model the idea of *mirror image* as you link it to *reflection.*

Additional resources for building and reinforcing vocabulary are provided on pages T37–T41.

Cultural Consideration

Display a variety of representative examples of the use of symmetry and transformations in the designs of rugs, pottery, tiles, and works of fine art produced by different cultures.

↻ Language Production

Comprehension Support Discuss how the letters are made up of connecting squares, as on a grid. Some students may be more successful using the simpler terms *flip, turn,* and *slide* over the more formal ones. Allow them to return to page 62 for help, as needed. Help them work through the page, and encourage discussion, gesturing, and interaction.

Model To guide students' thinking, say: *Each letter in Problems 1–4 is moved to a new position. I know that a figure can flip, turn, or slide. If it looks flipped over, I'll write* flip *or* reflection. *If it looks like it is turning, I'll write* turn *or* rotation. *If it looks like it is sliding in a straight line, I'll write* slide *or* translation.

Talk About It

Guide Discussion Have students complete the Talk About It sentences with a partner. Remind them to look back at Vocabulary in Context Picture It! if they need help with the terms.

Your Turn

Guide Discussion Have students use the grid paper provided on page 95. Ask students to share their transformations in a small group, and discuss their answers with others.

These letters were made with connecting squares. Here are L, P, J, and F.

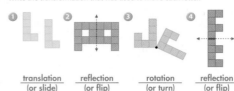

Write the transformation that was used to move each letter.

① ② ③ ④

translation (or slide) reflection (or flip) rotation (or turn) reflection (or flip)

Look at the transformation of each letter.

⑤ What changed? ___position or place___

⑥ What stayed the same? ___size and shape___

⑦ The letter before the transformation and the letter after the transformation are ___congruent___ .

Talk About It
Complete the sentences about transformations and symmetry.

⑧ Another term for a flip is a … reflection.

⑨ Both halves of a symmetric figure are … congruent.

⑩ Reflections, rotations, and translations are examples of … transformations.

Your Turn ✏
Tear out the grid paper on page 95. Write your initials in capital letters. Draw and label three transformations of each letter. Use vocabulary terms to describe what you did.

Transformations and Symmetry   **63**

Leveled Language Proficiency

Students at each proficiency level should be able to perform the following tasks.

Listening/Speaking

Early Beginner Recognize a few vocabulary terms and follow very simple conversations with support. Repeat simple phrases, and use vocabulary terms to answer questions.

Beginner Follow simple directions. Recognize and use some vocabulary terms. Say individual terms and simple phrases, and repeat longer phrases and short sentences.

Early Intermediate/Intermediate Begin to follow and take part in more abstract discussions about vocabulary terms in spoken phrases and sentences. Show an ability to express abstract ideas about target vocabulary.

Advanced/Transitioning Understand complex sentence structures; follow abstract conversations involving lesson vocabulary. Speak on abstract topics, including those that involve lesson vocabulary, with few, if any, errors.

Your Turn

"Mirror" is a reflection game. Get a partner and a pencil.

Each player uses one side of the "mirror."

Work together to make a symmetric **M.**

Take turns. Fill in a square on your side. Then your partner fills in the square on the other side to make a reflection.

Two reflections are shown in blue to help you get started.

MIRROR

Talk and Write About It 📣 ✏️

Complete the sentences about transformations and symmetry.

Vocabulary			
reflection	rotation	translation	flip
transformation	congruent	line of symmetry	turn

① Both sides of a symmetric figure are _____congruent_____ .

② Moving figures are _____transformations_____ .

③ Another term for *turn* is _____rotation_____ .

④ The purple line in "Mirror" is a _____line of symmetry_____ .

Produce Language ✏️

Write to tell what you have learned about transformations and symmetry. Use as many vocabulary terms as you can.

Leveled Language Proficiency

Students at each proficiency level should be able to perform the following tasks.

Reading/Writing

Early Beginner Read some short, common words and easier vocabulary terms with support. Copy terms and phrases from the board; write a few vocabulary terms independently.

Beginner Read a growing number of commonly used words and some lesson vocabulary terms. Use sentence starters and visual supports to write individual terms and phrases.

Early Intermediate/Intermediate Read most lesson vocabulary in isolation and in context; read sentences comprised of phonetically regular words and sight words, including directions. Write full sentences with support to describe ideas and explain vocabulary with some errors.

Advanced/Transitioning With minimal support, read and write complete sentences, with few errors, that contain concrete and abstract ideas related to lesson vocabulary.

↻ Assess Understanding

Your Turn

Model Read the directions with students. Demonstrate how partners play "Mirror" by starting a mirror-like design with a volunteer. Model using mathematical terms as you select, shade, and reflect grid boxes. After students have completed the game on one partner's grid, you can have them play again on the other partner's grid. This time, have them use different colors, thereby requiring reflections to show correct placement and color. Or have them determine another symmetric letter and use that one in the game. When students have completed a game, they can carefully tear out the page, fold it along the symmetry line, and hold it up to the light to check that all of the reflections were drawn correctly.

Talk and Write About It

On Their Own Have students work on their own to complete the statements. Then have partners share and compare their ideas.

Produce Language

On Their Own Have students write what they have learned about transformations and symmetry and the terms that define and describe them.

Wrap Up

Table Talk Have students look back at the lesson's objectives. Allow time for them to reflect on what they have learned and then answer the essential question.

☑ **Learned** and applied vocabulary related to transformations and symmetry

☑ **Spoken** statements about transformations and symmetry

☑ **Written** statements about transformations and symmetry

Measurement

Vocabulary Customary units, length, inch (in.), foot (ft), yard (yd), mile (mi), ruler, yardstick, metric units, millimeter (mm), centimeter (cm), meter (m), kilometer (km), meterstick, weight, mass, ounce (oz), pound (lb), ton (T), gram (g), kilogram (kg), pan balance

Materials Rulers showing inches and centimeters, yardsticks, metersticks; pan balances and weights

Math Background

- Mass, the amount of matter that an object contains, is measured in metric units (grams). Weight, the pull of gravity on an object, is measured in customary units.

Measurement

Essential Question What vocabulary terms should you use to discuss measurement?

You Will
- Understand how to measure length, weight, and mass.
- Learn about measurement tools and some units of measure.
- Use math vocabulary to describe measurement concepts.

Talk About It

Rate these mathematical terms according to the following scale.

1. I have never heard of this term before.
2. I have heard this term, but I do not know how to use it in math.
3. I understand this term and know how to use it in math.

_____ length	_____ ruler	_____ yardstick
_____ mass	_____ pan balance	_____ metric units
_____ inch (in.)	_____ customary units	_____ meter (m)
_____ foot (ft)	_____ ounce (oz)	_____ centimeter (cm)
_____ pound (lb)	_____ weight	_____ gram (g)
_____ kilogram (kg)	_____ yard (yd)	_____ millimeter (mm)
_____ mile (mi)	_____ kilometer (km)	_____ meterstick

What do you know about each term? Explain, using the sentence starters for support.

I do not know what … means.
I think … means …
I know that … means …

Your Turn
Look at the objectives under You Will at the top of the page. Working with a partner, predict what you are going to learn. Use the sentence starter for support.

I am going to learn about …

Measurement **65**

↻ Frontload the Lesson

What vocabulary terms should you use to discuss measurement?

Talk About It

Build Background Have students tell what they already know about these measurement terms.

↻ Content and Language

You Will

Model Read the objectives aloud and explain them in your own words. Use a ruler, yardstick, and pan balance to support your explanations.

Your Turn

Guide Discussion Have students read the objectives and discuss what these objectives mean to them.

Leveled Instruction

Early Beginner Partner early beginners with students at higher proficiency levels so they may provide added support. Expect single words, gestures, and simple responses as answers.

Beginner/Early Intermediate Expect phrases and simple sentences from these students when they are answering questions, especially when sentence starters are provided.

Intermediate Students should be able to complete activities with minimal assistance. Expect phrases and simple sentences in answering questions and joining discussions. Provide immediate feedback so students can self-correct.

Advanced/Transitioning Students should produce detailed answers with minimal assistance. They can offer students at lower proficiency levels support and assistance.

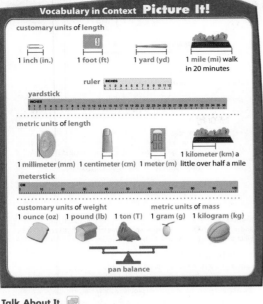

Vocabulary in Context Picture It!

customary units of length

1 inch (in.) 1 foot (ft) 1 yard (yd) 1 mile (mi) walk in 20 minutes

ruler

yardstick

metric units of length

1 millimeter (mm) 1 centimeter (cm) 1 meter (m) 1 kilometer (km) a little over half a mile

meterstick

customary units of weight **metric units of mass**

1 ounce (oz) 1 pound (lb) 1 ton (T) 1 gram (g) 1 kilogram (kg)

pan balance

Talk About It

Talk with a partner. Complete the sentences.

1. Use a ruler to measure … **length.**
2. Use a pan balance to measure mass or … **weight.**
3. A 4th-grade student might be 5 … tall. **feet**

Your Turn

What units of measure and measurement tools do you use at home? How do you use them? Write your ideas. Share them in a small group.

66 Lesson 17

Academic Vocabulary

- Be sure students understand that units of *length* are used to tell how *long* (or *tall, wide, thick*) an object is, units of *weight* are used to tell how *heavy* an object is, and units of *mass* are used to tell how much *matter* is in an object.

- Distinguish the everyday meaning of *foot* (body part with toes) from its measurement meaning. Clarify that *feet* is the plural of foot.

- Contrast the everyday meaning of *yard* (plot of land by a house) with its measurement meaning.

- Differentiate between the meanings of the homophones *weigh* and *way*, and *weight* and *wait*.

- Explain what abbreviations are and give some examples from everyday use, such as *Mr.* for *mister*. Point out that the abbreviation for *inch* (*in.*) is the only one with a period in this lesson.

Additional resources for building and reinforcing vocabulary are provided on pages T37–T41.

Cultural Consideration

Foreign-born students may be more familiar with metric measures than with customary ones.

↻ Comprehensible Input

Guide students to understanding

Vocabulary in Context Picture It!

1. **Say the Term** Have students repeat, stressing each syllable. Then combine syllables and have students repeat.

2. **Introduce Meaning** Connect the term to the visual that illustrates it.

3. **Demonstrate** Show actual rulers, yardsticks, metersticks, and a pan balance to help students understand the new terms. Point out calibrations in inches, centimeters, ounces or pounds, grams or kilograms, if possible.

4. **Apply** Have students demonstrate understanding with Talk About It.

Repeat the routine for each vocabulary term.

Talk About It

Guide Discussion Have students discuss the responses with a partner. Then provide this additional sentence completion, if time permits:

A metric unit of mass that is used when measuring very small objects is … **gram.**

Intervention

If students confuse *foot* and *feet* …

Then hold up one 12-inch ruler as you say *one foot.* Then hold up two rulers next to each other and say *two feet.*

Your Turn

Guide Discussion Ask volunteers to share their answers and discussions.

Measurement

↻ Language Production

Comprehension Support Point to the picture of the pan balance. Explain that a pan balance is sometimes called a *balance scale*. Then identify what is in the picture: *I see a pan balance with a nickel in one pan. The abbreviation* g *stands for* grams, *so there are 5 grams on the other pan. Grams are a metric measure of mass. The pan balance is measuring the mass of the nickel. The pans are balanced, so 5 grams is the mass of the nickel.*

After students have answered the questions about the length of the pencil, explain that they will now do a hands-on task measuring lengths. Provide students with 1-foot rulers for measuring in inches and/or centimeters.

Model Before students measure, say (as you demonstrate): *Let's practice using a ruler. First I find the 0 end of my ruler. I line it up with one end of my pencil. Then I look to see where the other end of the pencil reaches on the ruler. I find the inch (or centimeter) mark nearest that end. That is the length of my pencil.* Review rounding to the nearest inch (or centimeter), as needed. If students have a ruler that measures both inches and centimeters, have them measure using the other unit next.

Similarly, show students how to measure the weight or mass of an object using a pan balance.

Talk About It

Guide Discussion Have students complete the Talk About It sentences with a partner. Remind them that if they need help with the terms, they can look back at Vocabulary in Context Picture It!

Your Turn

Guide Discussion Have partners talk about their experience measuring. Ask them to share their responses with other students.

The unit of measure used by the pan balance is ___grams___ .

The pan balance is measuring the ___mass___ of a nickel.

The unit of measure used by the ruler is ___inches___ .

The ruler is measuring the ___length___ of the pencil.

Measure these objects: your pen or pencil, an eraser, your book, and a piece of paper. Tell whether you are measuring length or weight, what tool you are using, and the unit of measure. Check students' answers.

Talk About It 🗨
Complete the sentences about measurement.

1. You measure weight on a … pan balance.
2. Distances on a road map will probably show miles or … kilometers.
3. Metric units of mass include grams and … kilograms.
4. The term for how heavy you are is your … weight.

Your Turn ✏
Write about using a ruler or meterstick to measure length. Use as many vocabulary terms as you can. Talk about your ideas with a partner.

Leveled Language Proficiency

Students at each proficiency level should be able to perform the following tasks.

Listening/Speaking

Early Beginner Recognize a few vocabulary terms and follow very simple conversations with support. Repeat simple phrases, and use vocabulary terms to answer questions.

Beginner Follow simple directions. Recognize and use some vocabulary terms. Say individual terms and simple phrases, and repeat longer phrases and short sentences.

Early Intermediate/Intermediate Begin to follow and take part in more abstract discussions about vocabulary terms in spoken phrases and sentences. Show an ability to express abstract ideas about target vocabulary.

Advanced/Transitioning Understand complex sentence structures; follow abstract conversations involving lesson vocabulary. Speak on abstract topics, including those that involve lesson vocabulary, with few, if any, grammatical and syntactical errors.

Your Turn

Work with a partner. Help each other measure using both customary and metric units.

How long is your ear? _____ Check students' answers.

How long is your arm? _____

How long is your shoe? _____

How long is your foot? _____

How far is your knee from the floor? _____

How long is your thumb? _____

How thick is your thumb? _____

How wide is your smile? _____

How long is your arm from elbow to fingertips? _____

How long is your arm from shoulder to elbow? _____

How wide is your hand? _____

How wide is your hand if you stretch it? _____

Talk and Write About It 💬 ✏️

Complete the sentences about measurement.

Vocabulary			
mass	pounds	grams	pan balance
ounces	centimeters	weight	inches
miles	kilometers	length	yards

1. You might weigh a large animal in ____pounds____ or tons.

2. A thumb might be 2 ____centimeters____ thick.

3. A pan balance measures weight or ____mass____ .

Produce Language ✏️

Write what you learned about measurement. Tell about measuring yourself. Use sentence starters from throughout the lesson for support.

Leveled Language Proficiency

Students at each proficiency level should be able to perform the following tasks.

Reading/Writing

Early Beginner Read some short, common words and easier vocabulary terms, if given visual support or help from a partner or adult. Copy terms and phrases from the board; write a few vocabulary terms independently.

Beginner Read a growing number of commonly used words and some lesson vocabulary terms. Use sentence starters and visual supports to write individual terms and phrases.

Early Intermediate/Intermediate Read most lesson vocabulary in isolation and in context; read sentences composed of phonetically regular words and sight words, including directions. Write full sentences with support to describe ideas and explain vocabulary with some spelling and grammatical errors. Read and understand some abstract ideas.

Advanced/Transitioning With minimal support, read and write complete sentences, with few errors, that contain concrete and abstract ideas related to lesson vocabulary. Use sentence starters only as needed.

↻ Assess Understanding

Your Turn

Model Provide 1-foot rulers with inches and/or centimeters, yardsticks, or metersticks. Discuss the meaning of various measurements on your own body to help students understand the everyday vocabulary (e.g., *long, knee, thumb, elbow*). Model how to find and record measurements in both customary and metric units. Encourage students to communicate as they work, and to record measurements as they go.

Talk and Write About It

On Their Own Have students work on their own for ten minutes to complete the sentences. Then have partners share and compare their ideas.

Produce Language

On Their Own Have students write what they have learned about measurement and the terms that define and describe them.

Wrap Up

Table Talk Have students look back at the lesson's objectives. Allow time for them to reflect on what they have learned and then answer the essential question.

☑ **Learned** and applied vocabulary related to measurement

☑ **Spoken** statements about measurement

☑ **Written** statements about measurement

Lesson 18

Converting Units of Measure

Vocabulary Convert, unit of measure, length, customary units, foot/feet, inch, yard, metric units, meter, centimeter, millimeter, kilometer, weight, pound, ounce, mass, kilogram, gram

Materials Index cards, rulers showing inches and centimeters, yardstick, meterstick, balance and weights (optional)

Math Background

- Divide to express smaller units of measure as larger units. Multiply to express larger units of measure as smaller ones.

Converting Units of Measure

Converting Units of Measure

Essential Question How can you use vocabulary terms to talk about converting units of measure?

You Will
- Convert customary units of length and weight.
- Convert metric units of length and mass.
- Use math vocabulary to describe measurement concepts.

Talk About It

Copy each term from Vocabulary in Context on a card. As your teacher reads each term, create three piles of cards.

1. Place terms that you know in **Pile 1.**
2. Place terms that you have heard but are not sure what they mean in **Pile 2.**
3. Place terms that you do not know in **Pile 3.**

What do you know about each term? Explain, using the sentence starters for support.

I know … means …
I think … means …
I do not know what … means.

Your Turn
Look at the objectives under You Will at the top of the page. Working with a partner, predict what you are going to learn. Use the sentence starter for support.

I am going to learn about …

inch

gram

convert

Frontload the Lesson

How can you use vocabulary terms to talk about converting units of measure?

Talk About It

Build Background Have students tell what they know about how units of measurement are related.

Content and Language

You Will

Model Read the objectives aloud and explain them in your own words. Use a ruler, yardstick, meterstick, and balance to support your explanations.

Your Turn

Guide Discussion Have students read the objectives and discuss what these objectives mean to them.

Leveled Instruction

Early Beginner Use gestures and a few English words to communicate.

Beginner Provide short and simple sentences as responses. Would benefit from partnering with students of higher English language proficiency to complete activities.

Early Intermediate Construct sentences using sentence starters and modeling of these sentence starters for support.

Intermediate Use complete sentences and express their ideas without sentence starters.

Advanced/Transitioning Form sentences of increasing complexity. Use more advanced sentence structures.

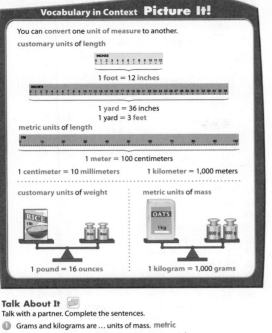

You can convert one unit of measure to another.

customary units of length

1 foot = 12 inches

1 yard = 36 inches
1 yard = 3 feet

metric units of length

1 meter = 100 centimeters

1 centimeter = 10 millimeters   1 kilometer = 1,000 meters

customary units of weight

RICE
1 lb   8oz 8oz

1 pound = 16 ounces

metric units of mass

OATS
1 kg   500 g 500 g

1 kilogram = 1,000 grams

Talk About It

Talk with a partner. Complete the sentences.

1. Grams and kilograms are ... units of mass. **metric**
2. Ounces and pounds are customary units of ... **weight.**
3. Three feet is equal to one ... **yard.**
4. One meter is equal to 100 ... **centimeters.**

Your Turn

Describe to a partner how you would convert 5 meters to centimeters.

70   Lesson 18

Academic Vocabulary

- Distinguish the everyday meaning of *customary* (what is usually done; according to custom) with its meaning as a system of measurement.

- Clarify the meanings of the Latin prefixes *kilo-* (one thousand) and *centi-* (hundredth) that precede metric measurements. Model the correct pronunciation of kilo (kē′ lō).

- Differentiate between two meanings of the word *pound* (to hit with a heavy blow; crush) and in math (a customary unit of weight equal to 16 ounces).

- Point out the difference between *scale* as a measurement tool and *scale* as the numbers on a graph.

- Display a table that provides measurement words and their abbreviations.

Additional resources for building and reinforcing vocabulary are provided on pages T37–T41.

↻ Comprehensible Input

Guide students to understanding

Vocabulary in Context Picture It!

1. **Say the Term** Have students repeat, stressing each syllable. Then combine syllables and have students repeat.

2. **Introduce Meaning** Connect the term to the visual that illustrates it.

3. **Demonstrate** Model the relationship among inches, feet, and yards by aligning three rulers along a yardstick. Also, point out the centimeter calibrations on a meterstick to help students visualize how a centimeter compares in size to a meter.

4. **Apply** Have students demonstrate understanding with Talk About It.

Repeat the routine for each vocabulary term.

Talk About It

Guide Discussion Have students discuss their responses with a partner. Then provide this additional sentence completion, if time permits:

One pound equals sixteen ... **ounces.**

Intervention

If students confuse the terms *ounces* and *inches* ...

Then slowly pronounce each term, exaggerating the medial /s/ or /ch/ sound, and have students repeat.

Your Turn

Guide Discussion Ask students to share their responses for Your Turn.

↻ Language Production

Comprehension Support Help students use the correct abbreviation, noting that it is the same for both the singular and plural form of the unit: foot or feet is *ft*, inch/inches is *in.*, ounce or ounces is *oz*. Emphasize that only the abbreviation for inch has a period at the end of it. Clarify that students will not need to mix metric and customary units in this lesson.

Model Before students make the conversions, say: *To convert units of measure, I use what I know about how the units compare. Twelve inches is equal to 1 foot, so 24 inches must be more than one foot. I know that 2 × 12 = 24, so 24 inches is equal to 2 feet.*

You may wish to discuss a general principle which students will learn in math class: When you convert from larger to smaller units, you need more of the smaller units, so you multiply; when you convert from smaller to larger units, you need fewer of the larger units, so you divide.

Talk About It

Guide Discussion Have students complete the Talk About It sentences with a partner. Remind them that if they need help with the terms, they can refer to the charts they completed on this page, or look back at Vocabulary in Context Picture It!

Your Turn

Guide Discussion Have partners talk about how they answered the questions about Kenji's height. Ask them to share their responses and solution methods with other students.

Do You Understand?

Work together to fill in each chart. Include the abbreviations.

Convert Customary Units of Measure

1 foot (ft) = 12	inches (in.)
3 feet (ft) = 1	yard (yd)
1 yard (yd) = 36	inches (in.)
1 pound (lb) = 16	ounces (oz)

Convert Metric Units of Measure

1 kilogram (kg) = 1,000	grams (g)
1 centimeter (cm) = 10	millimeters (mm)
1 meter (m) = 100	centimeters (cm)
1 kilometer (km) =1,000	meters (m)

Convert.

1. 12 in. = 1 ft, so 24 in. = __2 ft__ .
2. 3 ft = 1 yd, so 12 ft = __4 yd__ .
3. 1 lb = 16 oz, so 4 lb = __64 oz__ .
4. 1 kg = 1,000 g, so 3 kg = __3,000 g__ .
5. 100 cm = 1 m, so 600 cm = __6 m__ .
6. 1 cm = 10 mm, so 5 cm = __50 mm__ .
7. 1,000 m = 1 km, so 10,000 m = __10 km__ .

Talk About It 🗨
Complete the sentences about converting units of measure.

8. One meter equals 100 … centimeters.
9. I can convert 1 yard to either feet or … inches.
10. 4 kilograms is the same mass as 4,000 … grams.
11. 32 ounces is the same weight as 2 … pounds.

Your Turn ✏️
Kenji is 5 feet tall. Write about how to convert his height to inches. Tell if Kenji is taller or shorter than 2 yards. Talk about your answer with a partner.

Leveled Language Proficiency

Students at each proficiency level should be able to perform the following tasks.

Listening/Speaking

Early Beginner Recognize a few vocabulary terms and follow very simple conversations with support. Repeat simple phrases, and use vocabulary terms to answer questions.

Beginner Follow simple directions. Recognize and use some vocabulary terms. Say individual terms and simple phrases, and repeat longer phrases and short sentences.

Early Intermediate/Intermediate Begin to follow and take part in more abstract discussions about vocabulary terms in spoken phrases and sentences. Show an ability to express abstract ideas about target vocabulary.

Advanced/Transitioning Understand complex sentence structures; follow abstract conversations involving lesson vocabulary. Speak on abstract topics, including those that involve lesson vocabulary, with few if any grammatical and syntactical errors.

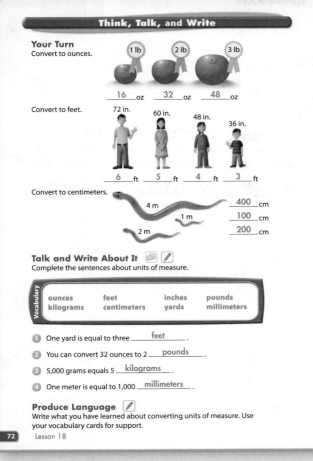

Think, Talk, and Write

Your Turn
Convert to ounces.

1 lb — __16__ oz
2 lb — __32__ oz
3 lb — __48__ oz

Convert to feet.

72 in. — __6__ ft
60 in. — __5__ ft
48 in. — __4__ ft
36 in. — __3__ ft

Convert to centimeters.

4 m — __400__ cm
1 m — __100__ cm
2 m — __200__ cm

Talk and Write About It
Complete the sentences about units of measure.

Vocabulary			
ounces	feet	inches	pounds
kilograms	centimeters	yards	millimeters

1. One yard is equal to three __feet__ .
2. You can convert 32 ounces to 2 __pounds__ .
3. 5,000 grams equals 5 __kilograms__ .
4. One meter is equal to 1,000 __millimeters__ .

Produce Language
Write what you have learned about converting units of measure. Use your vocabulary cards for support.

72   Lesson 18

Leveled Language Proficiency

Students at each proficiency level should be able to perform the following tasks.

Reading/Writing

Early Beginner Read some short, common words and easier vocabulary terms, if given visual support or help from a partner or adult. Copy terms and phrases from the board; write a few vocabulary terms independently.

Beginner Read a growing number of commonly used words and some lesson vocabulary terms. Use sentence starters and visual supports to write individual terms and phrases.

Early Intermediate/Intermediate Read most lesson vocabulary in isolation and in context; read sentences composed of phonetically regular words and sight words, including directions. Write full sentences with support to describe ideas and explain vocabulary with some spelling and grammatical errors. Read and understand some abstract ideas.

Advanced/Transitioning With minimal support, read and write complete sentences, with few errors, that contain concrete and abstract ideas related to lesson vocabulary. Use sentence starters only as needed.

↻ Assess Understanding

Your Turn

Model Before students begin, go over the abbreviations used in the activity. Ask them to tell the unit represented by each abbreviation, what you measure using that unit, and whether the unit is a customary or metric unit. Students will convert from pounds to ounces, from inches to feet, and from meters to centimeters. Model how to do one of the conversions. Invite students to communicate as they work, to look at rulers, yardsticks, and metersticks for visual clues, and to refer to the conversion tables they completed for Do You Understand?

Talk and Write About It

On Their Own Have students work on their own for ten minutes to complete the sentences. Then have partners share and compare their ideas.

Produce Language

On Their Own Have students write what they have learned about converting units of measure in the metric and customary systems.

Wrap Up

Table Talk Have students look back at the lesson's objectives. Allow time for them to reflect on what they have learned and then answer the essential question.

☑ **Learned** and applied vocabulary related to converting units of measure

☑ **Spoken** statements about converting units of measure

☑ **Written** statements about converting units of measure

Lesson 19

Perimeter and Area

Vocabulary Perimeter, distance, dimensions, width, length, area, unit, square unit, square centimeter, square inch, square foot, square meter, irregular figure

Materials Index cards, grid paper, Inch Tiles (page 97), scissors

Math Background

- The perimeter of a polygon is the sum of the lengths of its sides. For a rectangle with dimensions *l* and *w*, $P = 2l + 2w$.

- To find the area of a polygon, determine the number of square units needed to fill it. For a rectangle with dimensions *l* and *w*, $A = l \times w$.

- An *irregular figure*, as used in this lesson, is a region formed by conjoined rectangles.

Frontload the Lesson

Essential Question

How do you talk about perimeter and area?

Talk About It

Build Background Have students tell what they already know about perimeter and area.

Content and Language

You Will

Model Read the objectives aloud and explain them in your own words. Use visual examples to support your explanations.

Your Turn

Guide Discussion Have students read the objectives and discuss what the objectives mean to them.

Essential Question How do you talk about perimeter and area?

You Will
- Understand perimeter and area.
- Find the perimeter and area of rectangles and irregular figures.
- Use math vocabulary to describe perimeter and area.

Talk About It

Make an index card for each vocabulary term below. Place each card in one of three piles.

Pile 1: I know what this term means.
Pile 2: I have heard this term, but I do not know how to use it in math.
Pile 3: I have not heard this term.

dimensions

dimensions	irregular figure	square centimeter
square unit	perimeter	width
distance	unit	length
square inch	square meter	
square foot	area	

What do you know about each term? Explain, using the sentence starters for support.

I know that … means …
I think that … means …
I do not know what … means.

Your Turn ✏
Look at the objectives under You Will at the top of the page. Working with a partner, predict what you are going to learn. Use the sentence starter for support.

I am going to learn about … .

Leveled Instruction

Early Beginner Early beginners may not use many English words in their responses. Encourage them to use gestures, pictures, and yes/no responses to communicate.

Beginner Have students partner with students of higher English language proficiency to complete activities. Expect short, simple sentences as responses.

Early Intermediate Encourage students to use sentence starters for support. Model using these sentence starters as needed.

Intermediate Encourage students to express their ideas without sentence starters, if possible. Have them use complete sentences. Expect some grammatical mistakes.

Advanced/Transitioning Expect students to form sentences of increasing complexity. Encourage them to try different sentence structures.

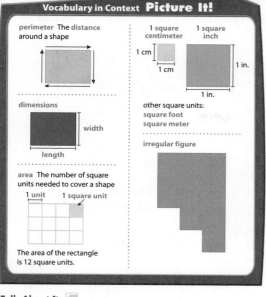

Vocabulary in Context **Picture It!**

perimeter The distance around a shape

dimensions

width

length

area The number of square units needed to cover a shape

1 unit   1 square unit

The area of the rectangle is 12 square units.

1 square centimeter   1 square inch

1 cm

1 cm

1 in.

1 in.

other square units: square foot square meter

irregular figure

Talk About It

Talk with a partner to complete the sentences.

1. The perimeter of a figure is the ... around it. **distance**
2. To find the area inside a figure, you can count the ... **square units.**
3. Length and width are two ... **dimensions.**

Your Turn

Write what perimeter means. Write what area means. Tell a partner about your ideas. Then, explain how you could find the perimeter and area of the top of your desk.

74   Lesson 19

Academic Vocabulary

- Students have probably heard *area* used to refer to a particular place. Your classroom might have a reading *area*, or your city or town might have a historical *area*. Be sure students know the difference between this use of the word and the term *area* that refers to a measurement.

- The following words are cognates with Spanish, and should be easy for some students to understand: *distance*, *perimeter*, and *dimensions*.

- *Irregular* means not regular or not the usual. Show students that an *irregular figure* is not the typical rectangle or square. It is often formed, though, by joining two or more common shapes to make a new one.

- Relate the words *length/long* and *width/wide* and point out how the spelling changes in examples, such as "How *long* is the rectangle?" and "What is the rectangle's *length*?" Explain that *length* and *width* can refer to either set of sides of a rectangle.

Additional resources for building and reinforcing vocabulary are provided on pages T37–T41.

↻ Comprehensible Input

Guide students to understanding

Vocabulary in Context Picture It!

1. **Say the Term** Have students repeat, stressing each syllable. Then combine syllables and have students repeat.

2. **Introduce Meaning** Connect the term to the visual that illustrates it.

3. **Demonstrate** Use gestures and models to show the meaning of area and perimeter. For example, run your hand all the way around the border of a picture to show its perimeter. Cover the picture to show its area as the space within the border.

4. **Apply** Have students demonstrate understanding with Talk About It.

Repeat the routine for each vocabulary term.

Talk About It

Guide Discussion Have students discuss their responses with a partner. Then provide this additional sentence completion, if time permits:

How long means what is the ... **length?**

Intervention

If students confuse *length* and *width* ...

Then clarify that the longer side is generally called the length.

Your Turn

Guide Discussion Ask students to share their ideas with a partner for Your Turn.

↻ Language Production

Comprehension Support Students should cut out the tiles on page 97. Explain that each tile has sides that are 1 inch long. Help students understand what it means to cover something with tiles. Edges should align, but not overlap, and corners should touch.

Model Once students have covered the drawing, help them understand how to use the tiles to find the area and perimeter. *I want to find the perimeter. I know that the sides of each tile are 1 inch long. I can count the sides of the tiles on the edge of the drawing until I go all the way around.* Encourage students to count the sides along the edge carefully. For area, guide students to count the tiles.

Talk About It

Guide Discussion Have students complete the Talk About It sentences with a partner. Remind them that if they need help with the terms, they can look back at Vocabulary in Context Picture It!

Your Turn

Guide Discussion Have partners find the area and perimeter of each other's rectangles. Encourage them to explain their reasoning.

Do You Understand?

Cut out the square tiles on page 97. The drawing below shows the bedroom in a doll house. Cover the bedroom with the tiles. Find the area and perimeter of the bedroom.

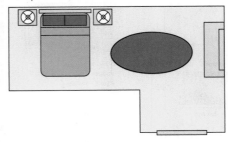

1. Each tile has a length 1 __inch__ long.
2. The perimeter of the bedroom is __16 inches__ .
3. Each tile has an area of 1 __square inch__ .
4. The area of the bedroom is __12 square inches__ .
5. A figure shaped like the doll house bedroom is an __irregular figure__ .

Talk About It 💬
Complete the sentences.
6. Measure area using ... square units.
7. Perimeter is the ... around a figure. distance
8. A square unit that is smaller than a square inch is a ... square centimeter.
9. A square unit that is bigger than a square inch is a ...
square foot (or square meter).

Your Turn 💬
Make a rectangle out of square tiles. With a partner, take turns telling about the area and perimeter of the rectangle.

Leveled Language Proficiency

Students at each proficiency level should be able to perform the following tasks.

Listening/Speaking

Early Beginner Recognize a few vocabulary terms and follow very simple conversations with support. Repeat simple phrases, and use vocabulary terms to answer questions.

Beginner Follow simple directions. Recognize and use some vocabulary terms. Say individual terms and simple phrases, and repeat longer phrases and short sentences.

Early Intermediate/Intermediate Begin to follow and take part in more abstract discussions about vocabulary terms in spoken phrases and sentences. Show an ability to express abstract ideas about target vocabulary.

Advanced/Transitioning Understand complex sentence structures; follow abstract conversations involving lesson vocabulary. Speak on abstract topics, including those that involve lesson vocabulary, with few if any grammatical and syntactical errors.

Your Turn

Draw a doll house room on the grid below.

1. Draw a room in the shape of a rectangle.
2. What are the dimensions of the room? Write the length and width.
3. Find the perimeter and area of the room.

1 cm
1 cm

Talk and Write About It

Complete the sentences about perimeter and area.

Vocabulary			
length	width	area	square unit
distance	irregular figure	perimeter	dimensions

4. The distance around a figure is the ___perimeter___ .
5. The number of square units inside a figure is the ___area___ .
6. Length and width are two ___dimensions___ .
7. A figure that has an L shape is an ___irregular figure___ .

Produce Language

Write how to find perimeter and area. Use your vocabulary cards to help you. Draw and label pictures to explain each idea.

Assess Understanding

Your Turn

Model Draw a simple grid on the board. Then draw a rectangle on the grid. Use the squares of the grid to determine the perimeter and area and write these measures on the board. Use the term *units* for perimeter and *square units* for area.

Talk and Write About It

On Their Own Have students work independently to complete the sentences. Then have partners share and compare their ideas.

Produce Language

On Their Own Have students use the support described to write what they have learned about the terms associated with perimeter and area.

Wrap Up

Table Talk Have students look back at the lesson's objectives. Allow time for them to reflect on what they have learned and then answer the essential question.

☑ **Learned** and applied vocabulary related to perimeter and area

☑ **Spoken** statements about perimeter and area

☑ **Written** statements about perimeter and area

Leveled Language Proficiency

Students at each proficiency level should be able to perform the following tasks.

Reading/Writing

Early Beginner Read some short, common words and easier vocabulary terms, if given visual support or help from a partner or adult. Copy terms and phrases from the board; write a few vocabulary terms independently.

Beginner Read a growing number of commonly used words and some lesson vocabulary terms. Use sentence starters and visual supports to write individual terms and phrases.

Early Intermediate/Intermediate Read most lesson vocabulary in isolation and in context; read sentences comprised of phonetically regular words and sight words. Write full sentences with support to describe ideas and explain vocabulary with some errors.

Advanced/Transitioning With minimal support, read and write complete sentences, that contain concrete and abstract ideas related to lesson vocabulary. Use sentence starters only as needed.

Lesson 20

Time

Vocabulary Digital clock, analog clock, hour hand, minute hand, minutes, hour, day, year, elapsed time, A.M., P.M., calendar, month, date, weeks, Sunday, Monday, Tuesday, Wednesday, Thursday, Friday, Saturday, January, February, March, April, May, June, July, August, September, October, November, December

Materials Analog and digital clocks, calendar

Math Background

- The abbreviations A.M. and P.M. are used to distinguish the 12 hours from midnight to noon (A.M.) from the 12 hours between noon and midnight (P.M.). By convention, noon is 12 P.M. and midnight is 12 A.M.

Essential Question How do you use vocabulary terms to tell time and talk about the calendar?

You Will
- Read and write time on digital and analog clocks.
- Determine elapsed time.
- Work with the calendar.
- Use math vocabulary to talk about time.

Talk About It

Rate these mathematical terms according to the following scale:

1 I do not know this term.
2 I have heard this term, but I do not know how to use it in math.
3 I understand this term and know how to use it in math.

_____ time	_____ hour	_____ calendar
_____ clock	_____ minute	_____ digital clock
_____ A.M.	_____ day	_____ minute hand
_____ P.M.	_____ date	_____ analog clock
_____ month	_____ week	_____ elapsed time
_____ hour hand	_____ year	

Explain what you know about these terms. Use the sentence starters.

I do not know what ... means.
I think that ... means ...
In math I know that ... means ...

Your Turn
Look at the objectives under You Will at the top of the page. Working with a partner, predict what you are going to learn. Use the sentence starter for support.

I am going to learn about ...

Time **77**

⟳ Frontload the Lesson

Essential Question

How do you use vocabulary terms to tell time and talk about the calendar?

Talk About It

Build Background Have students tell what they already know about these terms related to time and calendars.

⟳ Content and Language

You Will

Model Read the objectives aloud and explain them in your own words. Use visual examples and models for support.

Your Turn

Guide Discussion Have students read the objectives and discuss what these objectives mean to them.

Leveled Instruction

Early Beginner Early beginners may not use many English words in their responses. Encourage them to use gestures and pictures to communicate. Allow students to provide yes/no responses.

Beginner Have students partner with students of higher English language proficiency to complete activities. Expect short, simple sentences as responses.

Early Intermediate Encourage students to use sentence starters for support. Model using these sentence starters as needed.

Intermediate Encourage students to express their ideas without sentence starters, if possible. Have them use complete sentences. Expect some grammatical mistakes.

Advanced/Transitioning Expect students to form sentences of increasing complexity. Encourage them to use more advanced terms, and to try different sentence structures.

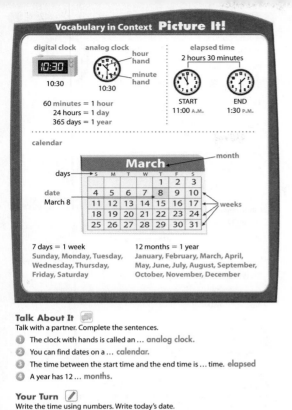

Vocabulary in Context Picture It!

digital clock

10:30

analog clock

10:30

hour hand

minute hand

elapsed time
2 hours 30 minutes

START
11:00 A.M.

END
1:30 P.M.

60 minutes = 1 hour
24 hours = 1 day
365 days = 1 year

calendar

month

March

days

date
March 8

weeks

7 days = 1 week
Sunday, Monday, Tuesday,
Wednesday, Thursday,
Friday, Saturday

12 months = 1 year
January, February, March, April,
May, June, July, August, September,
October, November, December

Talk About It
Talk with a partner. Complete the sentences.
1. The clock with hands is called an ... **analog clock.**
2. You can find dates on a ... **calendar.**
3. The time between the start time and the end time is ... time. **elapsed**
4. A year has 12 ... **months.**

Your Turn
Write the time using numbers. Write today's date.

Academic Vocabulary

- Distinguish some meanings of *date* (an agreement to meet; fruit of a palm tree) from its math meaning (the specific day of the month).

- Differentiate between the meanings of *hand:* a body part with palm and fingers, and a pointer on a clock or watch.

- Emphasize that the *h* in *hour* is silent. Clarify differences in meaning and spelling between the homophones *our* (adjective meaning having to do with us) and *hour* (unit of time equal to 60 minutes).

Additional resources for building and reinforcing vocabulary are provided on pages T37–T41.

Cultural Consideration

Students from other countries may abbreviate dates differently than we do in the United States. Here we write 5/4/11 for May 4, 2011, listing in order the month, date, and year. Some countries list that date by date, month, then year: 4/5/11. Also, calendars in some cultures begin a week on Friday or Monday, rather than Sunday. Finally, some countries do not use A.M. and P.M., but express written times using the 24-hour system. So 3:00 P.M. = 15:00.

↻ Comprehensible Input
Guide students to understanding

Vocabulary in Context Picture It!

1. **Say the Term** Have students repeat, stressing each syllable. Then combine syllables and have students repeat.

2. **Introduce Meaning** Connect the term to the visual that illustrates it.

3. **Demonstrate** Use visuals to demonstrate. Explain the use of A.M. and P.M. by presenting the terms *midnight* and *noon*. Model how to pronounce each. Then tell students that times from midnight to noon are labeled A.M., while times from noon to midnight are labeled P.M.

4. **Apply** Have students demonstrate understanding with Talk About It.

Repeat the routine for each vocabulary term.

Talk About It

Guide Discussion Have students discuss the responses with a partner. Then provide this additional sentence completion, if time permits:

There are seven days in one ... **week.**

Intervention

If students have difficulty distinguishing *day* and *date* ...

Then pronounce each word slowly and distinctly, emphasizing the final /t/ sound in *date.*

Your Turn

Guide Discussion Ask volunteers to share the current time and date for Your Turn. You might want to expand the discussion and have students tell what time the class is dismissed or goes to lunch. Then have them talk about the date of the next exam or day off from school.

↻ Language Production

Comprehension Support Use analog clocks to show different times, and model various ways to state that time. Emphasize saying the term *o'clock* for times to the hour. Contrast expressing times as so many minutes *after* one hour and *before* the next. For example, 10:50 can be said as *ten fifty* or *ten to eleven*. Explain such phrases as *quarter after, quarter to, half past,* and provide examples.

Talk about the starting and ending times of special classes in students' school day. Have students determine the elapsed times.

Discuss and practice saying the names for days of the week and the months of the year.

Model Before students work with the calendar, review ordinal numbers and the terms *first* and *last*. Then say: *A calendar is a kind of table. It has a row for each week. It has columns for the days of the week. Let's read the dates of all the Fridays in January.*

Talk About It

Guide Discussion Have students complete the Talk About It sentences with a partner. Remind them to look back at Vocabulary in Context Picture It! if they need help with the terms.

Your Turn

Guide Discussion Have partners talk about how they wrote each time, and figured out the elapsed time. You might want to ask them to figure out how long it is from now until school ends.

Do You Understand?

Look at the clock.
- The hour hand is between __2__ and __3__ .
- The minute hand is on the __8__ .
- The time is __2__ : __40__ .
- It is 20 minutes before __3:00 (or 3 o'clock)__ .

Answer the questions. Draw the clocks if it will help.
- Use numbers to write the time: 25 minutes after four __4:25__
- Use numbers to write the time: 15 minutes before 11 A.M __10:45 A.M.__
- A game starts at 2:30. It ends at 4:45. What is the elapsed time?

  __2 hours 15 minutes__

Use the calendar.
- January 19 is on a __Friday__ .
- There are __5__ Tuesdays in the month shown.
- 2 weeks before January 20 is __January 6__ .
- The date of the last day of the month is __January 31__ .

January						
S	M	T	W	T	F	S
	1	2	3	4	5	6
7	8	9	10	11	12	13
14	15	16	17	18	19	20
21	22	23	24	25	26	27
28	29	30	31			

Talk About It 🗨
Complete the sentences.
1. There are 24 hours in one … day.
2. There are 12 months in one … year.
3. There are 60 minutes in one … hour.
4. The first day of the week is … Sunday.
5. The first month of the year is … January.

Your Turn ✏️
Write the time school starts. Write the time school ends. Find the elapsed time in hours and minutes. Share your work with a partner.

Leveled Language Proficiency

Students at each proficiency level should be able to perform the following tasks.

Listening/Speaking

Early Beginner Recognize a few vocabulary terms and follow very simple conversations with support. Repeat simple phrases and use vocabulary terms to answer questions. Answer yes/no and choice questions.

Beginner Follow simple directions. Recognize and use some vocabulary terms. Say individual terms and simple phrases, and repeat longer phrases and short sentences.

Early Intermediate/Intermediate Begin to follow and take part in more abstract discussions about vocabulary terms in spoken phrases and sentences. Show an ability to express abstract ideas about target vocabulary.

Advanced/Transitioning Understand complex sentence structures; follow abstract conversations involving lesson vocabulary. Speak on abstract topics, including those that involve lesson vocabulary, with few, if any, errors.

Your Turn

Use the calendar and clocks to answer the questions.

May

S	M	T	W	T	F	S
			1	2	3	4
5	6	7	8	9	10	11
12	13	14	15	16	17	18
19	20	21	Field Day 22	23	24	25
26	27	28	29	30	31	

Field Day STARTS

Field Day ENDS

2:15

1. The date of Field Day is ___May 22___ .
2. What day of the week is Field Day? ___Wednesday___
3. What date is 2 weeks and 2 days *before* Field Day? ___May 6___
4. What date is the Monday *after* Field Day? ___May 27___
5. Field Day starts at ___9:30 A.M.___ . Field Day ends at ___2:15 P.M.___ .
   The elapsed time for Field Day is ___4 hours 45 minutes___ .
6. Lunch is 2 hours 15 minutes after Field Day starts. What time is lunch? ___11:45 A.M.___

Talk and Write About It

Complete the sentences about time.

Vocabulary	time	month	analog clock	digital clock
	year	week	date	calendar
	hour	minute	day	hour hand

7. There are 7 days in one ___week___ .
8. There are 365 days in one ___year___ .
9. Use a clock to tell ___time___ .
10. You can see days, dates, and weeks on a ___calendar___ .

Produce Language

Use vocabulary terms to write a set of instructions telling another student how to use a clock and calendar.

80   Lesson 20

↻ Assess Understanding

Your Turn

Model Invite students to talk about the calendar and the two kinds of clocks shown on the page. Explain that Field Day is a day of outdoor activities. Ask: *How can you know the date of Field Day?* As students read the times shown on both clocks, ask: *Which time is A.M.? Which is P.M.? How do you know?* Read the questions aloud with students. Encourage students to work with partners and communicate as they work.

Talk and Write About It

On Their Own Have students work on their own to complete the statements. Then have partners share and compare their ideas.

Produce Language

On Their Own Have students write what they have learned about the terms associated with time.

Wrap Up

Table Talk Have students look back at the lesson's objectives. Allow time for them to reflect on what they have learned and then answer the essential question.

☑ **Learned** and applied vocabulary related to time

☑ **Spoken** statements about time

☑ **Written** statements about time

Leveled Language Proficiency

Students at each proficiency level should be able to perform the following tasks.

Reading/Writing

Early Beginner Read some short, common words and easier vocabulary terms, if given visual support or help from a partner or adult. Copy terms and phrases from the board; write a few vocabulary terms independently.

Beginner Read a growing number of commonly used words and some lesson vocabulary terms. Use sentence starters and visual supports to write individual terms and phrases.

Early Intermediate/Intermediate Read and understand increasingly detailed text. Write full sentences with support to describe ideas and explain vocabulary with some errors.

Advanced/Transitioning With minimal support, read and write complete sentences, with few errors, that contain concrete and abstract ideas related to lesson vocabulary.

Lesson 21

Collecting and Organizing Data

Vocabulary Survey, record, data, data set, organize, tally chart, tally marks, table

Materials Index cards, small classroom objects, class name list

Math Background

- *Surveys* are a common data-collection method in which a group of people are asked the same question or set of questions.

- *Tally marks* are shown in groups of five, with the fifth mark drawn across the previous four.

For 4: |||| For 7: ⨭⨭ ||

↻ Frontload the Lesson

Essential Question What vocabulary terms will help you discuss ways to collect and organize data?

Talk About It

Build Background Have students tell what they already know about tables and tally charts.

↻ Content and Language

You Will

Model Read the objectives aloud and explain them in your own words. Discuss collecting things and then explain that *data*, or information, can also be collected.

Your Turn

Guide Discussion Have students read the objectives and discuss what these objectives mean to them.

Collecting and Organizing Data

Essential Question What vocabulary terms will help you discuss ways to collect and organize data?

You Will
- Understand how to collect data.
- Organize data into tables and tally charts.
- Use math vocabulary to describe ways to collect and organize data.

Talk About It

Copy each term from Vocabulary in Context on a card. As your teacher reads each term, create three piles of cards.

1. Place terms that you know in **Pile 1.**
2. Place terms that you have heard but are not sure what they mean in **Pile 2.**
3. Place terms that you do not know in **Pile 3.**

What do you know about each term? Explain, using the sentence starters for support.

I know … means …
I think … means …
I do not know what … means.

data

table

survey

Your Turn 💬
Look at the objectives under You Will at the top of the page. Working with a partner, predict what you are going to learn. Use the sentence starter for support.

I am going to learn about …

Leveled Instruction

Early Beginner Early beginners may not use many English words in their responses. Encourage them to use gestures and pictures to communicate.

Beginner Have students partner with students of higher English language proficiency to complete activities. Expect short and simple sentences as responses.

Early Intermediate Encourage students to use sentence starters for support. Model using these sentence starters as needed.

Intermediate Encourage students to express their ideas without sentence starters, if possible. Have them use complete sentences. Expect some grammatical mistakes.

Advanced/Transitioning Expect students to form sentences of increasing complexity. Encourage them to try different sentence structures.

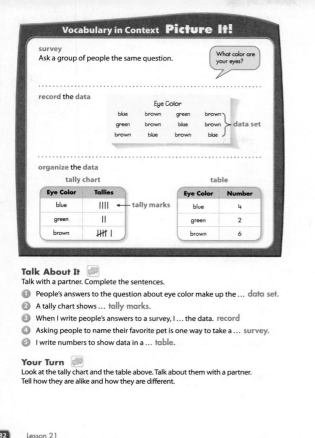

Vocabulary in Context Picture It!

survey
Ask a group of people the same question.

What color are your eyes?

record the data

Eye Color

| blue | brown | green | brown |
| green | brown | blue | brown | data set
| brown | blue | brown | blue |

organize the data

tally chart

Eye Color	Tallies
blue	IIII ← tally marks
green	II
brown	HH I

table

Eye Color	Number
blue	4
green	2
brown	6

Talk About It
Talk with a partner. Complete the sentences.
1. People's answers to the question about eye color make up the ... data set.
2. A tally chart shows ... tally marks.
3. When I write people's answers to a survey, I ... the data. record
4. Asking people to name their favorite pet is one way to take a ... survey.
5. I write numbers to show data in a ... table.

Your Turn
Look at the tally chart and the table above. Talk about them with a partner.
Tell how they are alike and how they are different.

Academic Vocabulary

- Differentiate between the meanings of *table* (furniture with flat top and legs) and *table* in math (arrangement of facts or figures, usually in row and columns).

- Help students learn the two different pronunciations of *record*. When used as a verb, the stress is on the second syllable (ri KORD). As a noun, the term is pronounced REK urd. Students may be familiar with sports records. They might think of recording in the context of music or video. Explain that you can also record by writing.

- Clarify that *data* can be pronounced dā′ tə or dat′ ə. Note that *data* is plural, so one says *the data are*, not *the data is*. However, it is not necessary to emphasize the point at this time.

- Discuss both the verb form and noun form of *survey*, and provide examples of each.

Additional resources for building and reinforcing vocabulary are provided on pages T37–T41.

Cultural Consideration

Not all cultures use sets of five "rods" to tally data. China, Korea, Japan, and some South American countries use other tally symbols.

↻ Comprehensible Input
Guide students to understanding

Vocabulary in Context Picture It!

1. **Say the Term** Have students repeat, stressing each syllable. Then combine syllables and have students repeat.

2. **Introduce Meaning** Connect the term to the visual that illustrates it.

3. **Demonstrate** Show an assortment of classroom objects (such as crayons, markers, erasers, pens) in a single set. Model sorting the set, using a tally mark to represent each kind of item counted. Highlight the fifth tally as the signal to begin a new group of marks. Show that the table uses numbers to display the same data.

4. **Apply** Have students demonstrate understanding with Talk About It.

Repeat the routine for each vocabulary term.

Talk About It

Guide Discussion Have students discuss the responses with a partner. Then provide this additional sentence completion if time permits:

A tally chart helps you ... data. **organize**

Intervention

If students confuse *data* and *date* ...

Then write both words on the board, circle the final vowels, and pronounce each term to emphasize the differences.

Your Turn

Guide Discussion Ask students to share their discussions for Your Turn.

Language Production

Comprehension Support Help students understand that the list shows the first names of boys and girls on a soccer team. Explain that the question *How long are the names?* asks not about a measure (i.e., inches or centimeters), but the number of letters used to spell each name. Students tally how many names of each letter length comprise the list. Emphasize that the table shows the same data but with numbers instead of tally marks.

Model *First I'll collect data about the name Arata. Arata has 1, 2, 3, 4, 5 letters. Arata is a 5-letter name. So I make one tally mark in the row for 5-letter names. Now I do Dakarai. I can see that this is a longer name. I'll count all the letters to know where to make the next tally mark.*

Talk About It

Guide Discussion Have students complete the Talk About It sentences with a partner. Remind them that if they need help with the terms, they can look back at Vocabulary in Context Picture It!

Your Turn

Guide Discussion Have partners talk about how and where the tally chart and data table change as other names are added to the data set. Ask them to share their responses with other students.

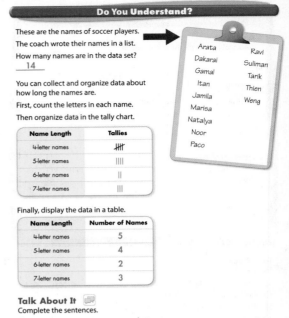

These are the names of soccer players. The coach wrote their names in a list. How many names are in the data set?

____14____

You can collect and organize data about how long the names are.
First, count the letters in each name.
Then organize data in the tally chart.

Name Length	Tallies
4-letter names	卌
5-letter names	IIII
6-letter names	II
7-letter names	III

Finally, display the data in a table.

Name Length	Number of Names
4-letter names	5
5-letter names	4
6-letter names	2
7-letter names	3

Talk About It 💬
Complete the sentences.
1. The list of soccer players is a … data set.
2. First I organize the data in a … tally chart.
3. Then I show the data in a … table.

Your Turn 💬 ✏️
What if you join the soccer team? Write your name on the list. Change the tally chart. Change the table. Share your work with a partner.

Leveled Language Proficiency

Students at each proficiency level should be able to perform the following tasks.

Listening/Speaking

Early Beginner Recognize a few vocabulary terms and follow very simple conversations with support. Repeat simple phrases, and use vocabulary terms to answer questions.

Beginner Follow simple directions. Recognize and use some vocabulary terms. Say individual terms and simple phrases, and repeat longer phrases and short sentences.

Early Intermediate/Intermediate Begin to follow and take part in more abstract discussion about vocabulary terms in spoken phrases and sentences. Show an ability to express abstract ideas about target vocabulary.

Advanced/Transitioning Understand complex sentence structures; follow abstract conversations involving lesson vocabulary. Speak on abstract topics, including those that involve lesson vocabulary, with few if any grammatical and syntactical errors.

Your Turn

Survey your class to get a list of first names.
How many names are in the data set? _____

1. How long are the names?
Count the letters in each name.
Then organize the data in the
tally chart. Check students' work.

2. Make a table in the space below
to display the data.

Name Length	Tallies
2-letter names	
3-letter names	
4-letter names	
5-letter names	
6-letter names	
7-letter names	
8-letter names	
More than 8 letters	

Talk and Write About It

Complete the sentences about collecting and organizing data.

Vocabulary

organize	table	tally chart	data set
survey	data	tally marks	record

3. I can collect data by taking a ___survey___ .

4. The answers I record are the ___data or (data set)___ .

5. I write tally marks in a ___tally chart___ .

6. I count the tally marks and put the numbers in a ___table___ .

Produce Language

Write about collecting data. Tell how you organize data. Use your vocabulary cards for support.

84 Lesson 21

Leveled Language Proficiency

Students at each proficiency level should be able to perform the following tasks.

Reading/Writing

Early Beginner Read some short, common words and easier vocabulary terms, if given visual support or help from a partner or adult. Copy terms and phrases from the board; write a few vocabulary terms independently.

Beginner Read a growing number of commonly used words and some lesson vocabulary terms. Use sentence starters and visual supports to write individual terms and phrases.

Early Intermediate/Intermediate Read most lesson vocabulary in isolation and in context; read sentences composed of phonetically regular words and sight words, including directions. Write full sentences with support to describe ideas and explain vocabulary, with some spelling and grammatical errors.

Advanced/Transitioning With minimal support, read and write complete sentences, with few errors, that contain concrete and abstract ideas related to lesson vocabulary. Use sentence starters only as needed.

⟳ Assess Understanding

Your Turn

Model Have students individually collect and record at least 10 names from their classmates, or provide a class list with the first names of students. (Alternatively, provide names of countries, states, school subjects, math terms, etc.) Compare and contrast the tally charts on pages 83 and 84. Then allow students to work in pairs to organize and display the data. Encourage them to communicate and verify their work as they go.

Talk and Write About It

On Their Own Have students work independently to complete the sentences. Then have them share their responses with a partner.

Produce Language

On Their Own Have students write what they have learned about the terms associated with collecting and organizing data. Ask volunteers to share their ideas with the class.

Wrap Up

Table Talk Have students look back at the lesson's objectives. Allow time for them to reflect on what they have learned and then answer the essential question.

☑ **Learned** and applied vocabulary related to collecting and organizing data

☑ **Spoken** statements about collecting and organizing data

☑ **Written** statements about collecting and organizing data

Representing Data

Vocabulary Bar graph, title, scale, line graph, labels, circle graph, line plot, symbol, stem-and-leaf plot, stem, leaf, data, key

Materials Clippings or printouts of graphs in the media

Math Background

- *Line plots* display the frequency of numeric data.

- In a stem-and-leaf plot, the stem represents the tens digit of a piece of data, and the leaf represents the corresponding ones digits.

 ## Frontload the Lesson

How can you talk about different types of graphs?

Essential Question

Talk About It

Build Background Read the terms aloud and have students complete the first two columns of the Know-Want-Learned chart. (See page T43 for additional copies.) Have students tell what they already know about different types of graphs.

Content and Language

You Will

Model Read the objectives aloud and explain them in your own words. Use graphs from printed media to support your explanations.

Your Turn

Guide Discussion Have students read the objectives and discuss what these objectives mean to them.

Essential Question How can you talk about different types of graphs?

You Will
- Understand what graphs are and how they are used.
- Learn to tell one kind of graph from another.
- Use math vocabulary to describe different kinds of graphs.

Talk About It

Look at the list of terms below. In the first two columns of the chart, write terms you **know** or **want** to know more about.

bar graph	labels	symbol	leaf
title	circle graph	stem-and-leaf plot	data
scale	line plot	stem	key
line graph			

Know	Want	Learned

What do you know about each term? Explain, using the sentence starters for support.

I know … means …
I want to know more about …

Your Turn
Look at the objectives under You Will at the top of the page. Working with a partner, predict what you are going to learn. Use the sentence starter for support.

I am going to learn about …

Leveled Instruction

Early Beginner Early beginners may not use many English words in their responses. Encourage them to use gestures and pictures to communicate.

Beginner Have students partner with students of higher English language proficiency to complete activities. Expect short, simple sentences as responses.

Early Intermediate Expect phrases and simple sentences from these students as answers to questions.

Intermediate Encourage students to express their ideas without sentence starters, if possible. Have them use complete sentences. Expect some grammatical mistakes.

Advanced/Transitioning Expect students to form sentences of increasing complexity. Encourage them to use more advanced terms and to try different sentence structures.

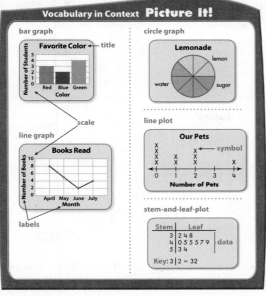

Talk About It 💬
Talk with a partner. Complete the sentences.

1. A graph with bars that show data is a … bar graph.
2. A graph made out of a circle is a … circle graph.
3. A graph with symbols above a number line is a … line plot.
4. A graph with connected line segments is a … line graph.

Your Turn 💬 ✏️
Choose three of the graphs above. Write a sentence about how each graph looks. Talk about your ideas in a small group.

 Lesson 22

Academic Vocabulary

- Clarify that *line segments*, not *lines*, link the points of data on a *line graph*.

- Distinguish the common meanings of these words from the mathematical meanings: *scale* (device for weighing; series of musical notes); *bar* (counter; piece of rigid material; solid piece of soap); *key* (device for opening a lock; system of related notes in music; a button to press on a keyboard); *plot* (secret plan; events that form the main story in fiction; small piece of land).

Additional resources for building and reinforcing vocabulary are provided on pages T37–T41.

♻ Comprehensible Input
Guide students to understanding

Vocabulary in Context Picture It!

1. **Say the Term** Have students repeat, stressing each syllable. Then combine syllables and have students repeat.

2. **Introduce Meaning** Connect the term to the visual that illustrates it.

3. **Demonstrate** Help students to see how the name of each graph describes it. For example, draw a plant with a stem and leaves, and compare it to stem-and-leaf plots.

4. **Apply** Have students demonstrate understanding with Talk About It.

Repeat the routine for each vocabulary term.

Talk About It

Guide Discussion Have students discuss the responses with a partner. Then provide this additional sentence completion, if time permits:

The main idea of a graph is told by its … title.

Intervention

If students confuse line graph and line plot …

Then point out that a line graph is often drawn on what is commonly known as *graph* paper. If you have samples of line graphs and line plots, take turns holding them up, and have students repeat *graph* and *plot*.

Your Turn

Guide Discussion Have students work in a small group for Your Turn. Then ask students to share their discussions. Touch upon each type of graph.

Language Production

Comprehension Support Help students understand the context of each graph. Read the titles and labels, and discuss the nature of the data being displayed. *The first graph shows heights of students. Each height is in inches. So the data are numbers of inches.*

Model Have students identify the first graph and explain how they figured it out. Then discuss the data. *The stem represents the tens digit and the leaf represents the ones digit. The first height listed is shown with a 4 for the stem and a 7 for the leaf. That number is 4 tens 7 ones, or 47. So, the first height listed is 47 inches.*

Talk About It

Guide Discussion Have students complete the Talk About It sentences with a partner. Remind them to look back at Vocabulary in Context Picture It! if they need help with the terms.

Your Turn

Guide Discussion Have partners share their descriptions of one of the graphs with other students.

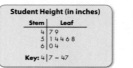

Do You Understand?

Write which type of graph is shown. Then answer the question.

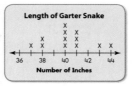

Student Height (in inches)	
Stem	Leaf
4	7 9
5	1 4 4 6 8
6	0 4

Key: 4 | 7 = 47

stem-and-leaf plot

What is the greatest height?

64 inches

Fruits at School

circle graph

What fraction of the fruits are pears?

$\frac{1}{4}$

Length of Garter Snake

line plot

How many snakes are 38 inches?

2 snakes

Tickets Sold

line graph

How many tickets were sold in 3 hours?

6 tickets

Talk About It 💬
Complete the sentences about the graphs.
1. Graphs are used to display ... data.
2. In the first graph, the tens digits are in the ... stem.
3. In the circle graph, "Fruits at School" is the ... title.
4. In the last graph, the numbers 0, 2, 4, 6, 8, 10 are the ... scale.

Your Turn 💬
Describe the parts of one of the graphs to a partner.

Leveled Language Proficiency

Students at each proficiency level should be able to perform the following tasks.

Listening/Speaking

Early Beginner Recognize a few vocabulary terms and follow very simple conversations with support. Repeat simple phrases, and use vocabulary terms to answer questions.

Beginner Follow simple directions. Recognize and use some vocabulary terms. Say individual terms and simple phrases, and repeat longer phrases and short sentences.

Early Intermediate/Intermediate Begin to follow and take part in more abstract discussions about vocabulary terms in spoken phrases and sentences. Show an ability to express abstract ideas about target vocabulary.

Advanced/Transitioning Understand complex sentence structures; follow abstract conversations involving lesson vocabulary. Speak on abstract topics, including those that involve lesson vocabulary, with few if any grammatical and syntactical errors.

Your Turn Check students' facts.
For each graph, write the type of graph. Then tell your partner a fact about the data.

1 **Favorite Drink**

Type of Drink: Juice, Milk, Cola, Water
Number of People: 0 4 8 12 16 20 24

Graph: ___bar graph___

2 **Length of Bullfrog**

x x
x x x   x x
6   8   10   12   14
Number of Centimeters

Graph: ___line plot___

3 **Age of Club Members (in years)**

Stem	Leaf
1	8 8 9
2	2 3 3 6 7 8 9 9
3	0 1 1 5 8 8
4	1 3

Key: 1 | 8 = 18

Graph: ___stem-and-leaf plot___

Talk and Write About It 💬 ✏️
Complete the sentences about different kinds of graphs.

Vocabulary

| line plot | title | scale | stem-and-leaf plot |
| key | symbols | line graph | labels |

4 A graph that lists data by tens and ones is a ___stem-and-leaf plot___ .

5 The number labels on the bar graph are the ___scale___ .

6 In a line plot, data is graphed using ___symbols___ .

Produce Language ✏️
Write the terms you learned about in this lesson in the third column of the chart on page 85. Then write what you have learned about different kinds of graphs.

88   Lesson 22

Leveled Language Proficiency

Students at each proficiency level should be able to perform the following tasks.

Reading/Writing

Early Beginner Read some short, common words and easier vocabulary terms, if given visual support or help from a partner or adult. Copy terms and phrases from the board; write a few vocabulary terms independently.

Beginner Read a growing number of commonly used words and some lesson vocabulary terms. Use sentence starters and visual supports to write individual terms and phrases.

Early Intermediate/Intermediate Read most lesson vocabulary in isolation and in context; read sentences composed of phonetically regular words and sight words, including directions. Write full sentences with support to describe ideas and explain vocabulary, with some spelling and grammatical errors. Read and understand some abstract ideas.

Advanced/Transitioning With minimal support, read and write complete sentences, with few errors, that contain concrete and abstract ideas related to lesson vocabulary. Use sentence starters only as needed.

↻ Assess Understanding

Your Turn

Model Provide an example of a fact about the bar graph. Show students that the bar for Water goes to 16, and then say: *16 people chose water as their favorite drink.* Ask students to state a different fact about the graph.

Talk and Write About It

On Their Own Have students work with a partner to identify the graphs and talk about the data shown.

Produce Language

On Their Own Have students complete the Know-Want-Learned chart from the beginning of the lesson. Have students write what they have learned about these terms and share their ideas with others. Then have them write about what they have learned about different kinds of graphs.

Wrap Up

Table Talk Have students look back at the lesson's objectives. Allow time for them to reflect on what they have learned and then answer the essential question.

☑ **Learned** and applied vocabulary related to representing data

☑ **Spoken** statements about representing data

☑ **Written** statements about representing data

STUDENT BOOK RESOURCES

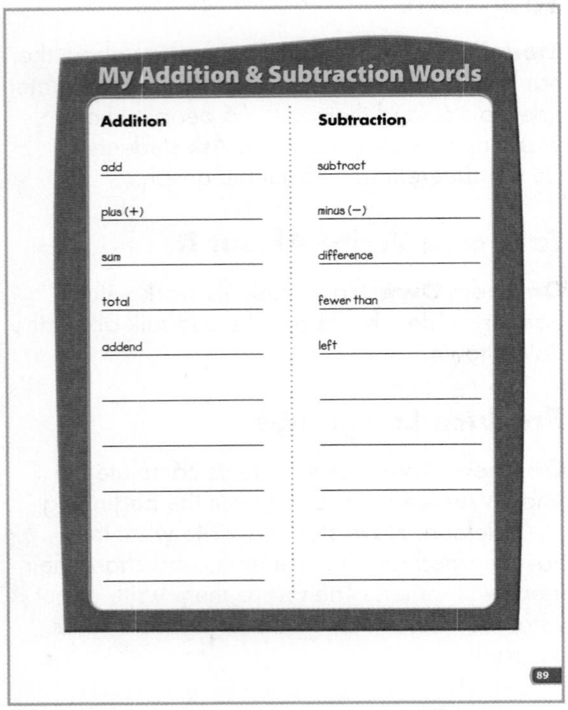

My Addition & Subtraction Words

Addition	Subtraction
add	subtract
plus (+)	minus (−)
sum	difference
total	fewer than
addend	left

page 89

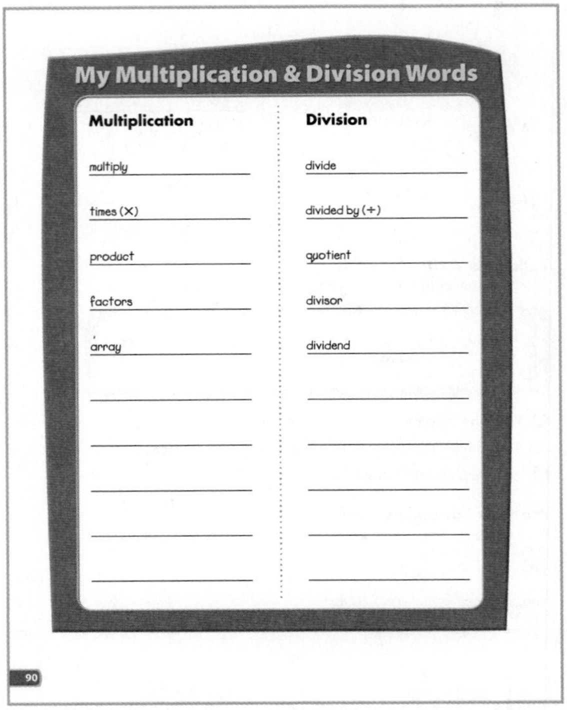

My Multiplication & Division Words

Multiplication	Division
multiply	divide
times (×)	divided by (÷)
product	quotient
factors	divisor
array	dividend

page 90

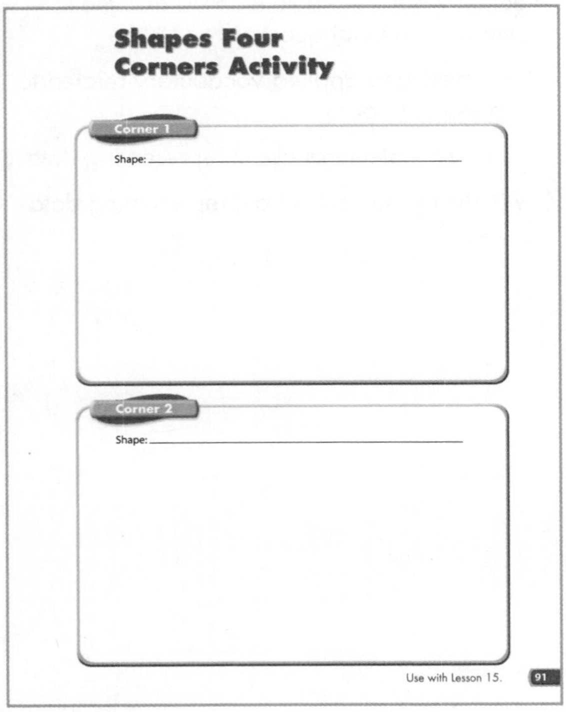

Shapes Four Corners Activity

Corner 1
Shape: _____

Corner 2
Shape: _____

Use with Lesson 15. 91

page 91

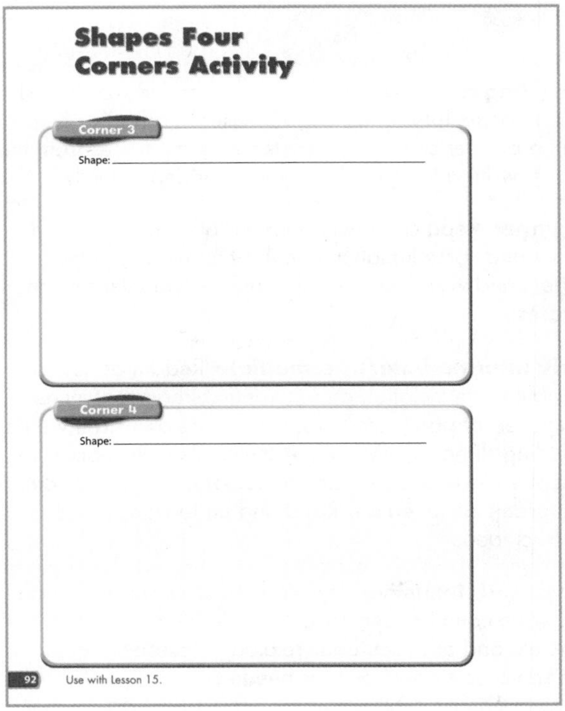

Shapes Four Corners Activity

Corner 3
Shape: _____

Corner 4
Shape: _____

92 Use with Lesson 15.

page 92

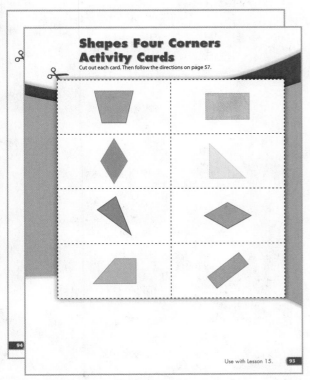

pages 93–94

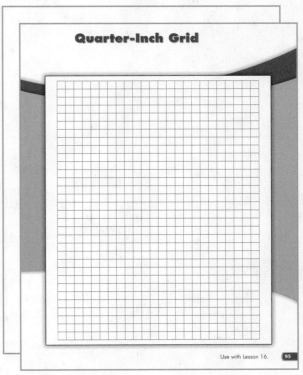

pages 95–96

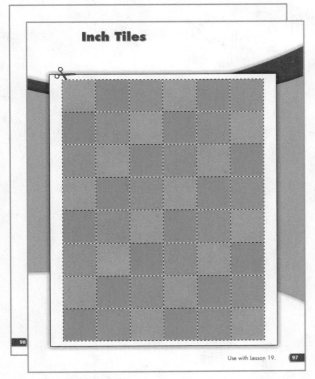

pages 97–98

CONTENTS
Grade 5

Place Value

Vocabulary Digits, decimal, decimal point, place value, millions, hundred thousands, ten thousands, thousands, hundreds, tens, ones, tenths, hundredths, thousandths, value, standard form, expanded form, word form, compare, is greater than, is less than, is equal to

Math Background

- In the number 24.35, the *place value* of the 2 is tens; the *value* of the 2 is 20.

- 24.35 is written in *standard form*. The *expanded form* is 20 + 4 + 0.3 + 0.05. The *word form* is twenty-four and thirty-five hundredths.

Frontload the Lesson

Essential Question

What vocabulary terms will help you discuss place value and compare numbers?

Talk About It

Build Background Have students tell what they already know about these terms related to place value.

Content and Language

You Will

Model Read the objectives aloud and explain them in your own words. Use visual examples to support your explanations.

Your Turn

Guide Discussion Have students read the objectives. Discuss what the objectives mean to them.

Place Value

Essential Question What vocabulary terms will help you discuss place value and compare numbers?

You Will
- Represent and compare numbers from thousandths to millions.
- Use standard form, word form, and expanded form to write numbers.
- Use math vocabulary to express place-value ideas.

Talk About It

Rate these mathematical terms according to the following scale:

1. I have never heard of this term.
2. I have heard this term, but I do not know how to use it in math.
3. I understand this term and I know how to use it in math.

_____ millions	_____ thousandths
_____ hundred thousands	_____ place value
_____ ten thousands	_____ decimal
_____ thousands	_____ standard form
_____ hundreds	_____ expanded form
_____ tens	_____ word form
_____ ones	_____ digits
_____ tenths	_____ is greater than
_____ hundredths	_____ is less than

Explain what you know about each term, using the sentence starters.

I do not know what … means.
I think … means …
I know … means … in math.

Your Turn
Look at the objectives under You Will at the top of the page. Working with a partner, predict what you are going to learn. Use the sentence starter for support.

I am going to learn about …

Place Value 1

Leveled Instruction

Early Beginner Early beginners should partner with students at higher language proficiency to complete the activities. Single words and gestures should be expected as answers.

Beginner Encourage students to use sentence starters to help them construct answers.

Early Intermediate Expect phrases and simple sentences from these students as answers to the activities.

Intermediate Encourage students to express their ideas without sentence starters if possible. They should use complete sentences. Anticipate some grammatical errors.

Advanced/Transitioning Expect students to form sentences of increasing complexity. Have them use more advanced terms, and encourage them to try new sentence structures.

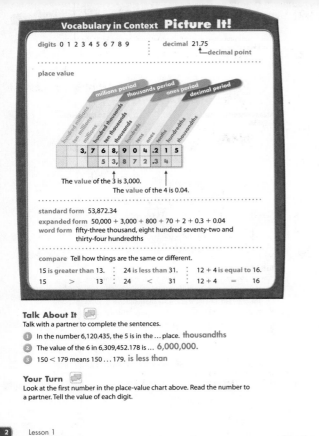

digits 0 1 2 3 4 5 6 7 8 9   decimal 21.75
                                    └decimal point

place value

millions period			thousands period			ones period			decimal period		
hundred millions	ten millions	millions	hundred thousands	ten thousands	thousands	hundreds	tens	ones	tenths	hundredths	thousandths
	3,	7	6	8,	9	0	4	.2	1	5	
				5	3,	8	7	2 .3	4		

The value of the 3 is 3,000.
The value of the 4 is 0.04.

standard form 53,872.34
expanded form 50,000 + 3,000 + 800 + 70 + 2 + 0.3 + 0.04
word form fifty-three thousand, eight hundred seventy-two and
thirty-four hundredths

compare Tell how things are the same or different.

15 is greater than 13.	24 is less than 31.	12 + 4 is equal to 16.
15 > 13	24 < 31	12 + 4 = 16

Talk About It 💬
Talk with a partner to complete the sentences.
1. In the number 6,120.435, the 5 is in the ... place. thousandths
2. The value of the 6 in 6,309,452.178 is ... 6,000,000.
3. 150 < 179 means 150 ... 179. is less than

Your Turn 💬
Look at the first number in the place-value chart above. Read the number to a partner. Tell the value of each digit.

2   Lesson 1

Academic Vocabulary

- *Point* (noun vs. verb) may be confusing. Model with gestures and by drawing. Point and say "I point." Compare a decimal point and a period.

- Help students understand that the location of a digit in a number means the same thing as place. Point to your desk and say, *This is my place.* Point to a digit in a number and say, *This is the (tens) place. So this is the (tens) digit.*

- State *tens, tenths, hundreds, hundredths, thousands,* and *thousandths* in random order. Enunciate the word endings slowly and clearly. Have students write 10; 0.1; 100; 0.01; 1,000; or 0.001 as they distinguish the word endings.

- Point out that one may say *is equal to* or *equals* for the symbol =.

Additional resources for building and reinforcing vocabulary are provided on pages T37–T41.

Cultural Consideration

In some countries, decimal points are used the way we use commas in the United States. One hundred thousand would be written 100.000 rather than 100,000. Clarify this for students as needed.

↻ Comprehensible Input
Guide students to understanding

Vocabulary in Context Picture It!

1. **Say the Term** Have students repeat, stressing each syllable. Then combine syllables and have students repeat.

2. **Introduce Meaning** Connect the term to the visual that illustrates it.

3. **Demonstrate** Use gestures and visuals to demonstrate. For example, when teaching the term *digit*, write a 3-digit number and point to each digit, one at a time.

4. **Apply** Have students demonstrate understanding with Talk About It.

Repeat the routine for each vocabulary term.

Talk About It

Guide Discussion Have students discuss their responses with a partner. Then provide this additional sentence starter if time permits:

The word form of 6.075 is ... six and seventy-five thousandths

Intervention

If students have difficulty distinguishing *tens/tenths, hundred/hundredths,* and *thousands/thousandths* ...

Then write the word pairs on the board and have students practice listening by pointing to the correct word in each pair as you say it aloud.

Your Turn

Guide Discussion Remind students to use the names of the places in the place-value chart to help them read the number and give the value of each digit.

↻ Language Production

Comprehension Support Discuss the data for each animal pictured at the top of the page. Talk about the place-value chart. Read the headings in each column. Explain that each place value describes a digit in a number.

Model Point to the height of the elephant and say: *This number is a decimal. The word form of this number is three and six tenths. The digit 3 is in the ones place. A decimal point goes after the ones place. The digit 6 is in the tenths place.* Guide students as they complete the place-value chart.

Talk About It

Guide Discussion Have students complete the Talk About It sentences with a partner. Remind them that if they need help with the terms, they can check the place-value chart or Vocabulary in Context Picture It!

Your Turn

Guide Discussion Pair students who are at different language proficiency levels. As needed, encourage the higher level student to model how to say a number and to listen to the partner repeat the number. Partners can record their work on copies of T44.

Do You Understand?

Here is some information about elephants and giraffes. Write the green numbers in the place-value chart.

3.6 meters   4.85 meters

About 660,000 elephants in the world   About 150,000 giraffes in the world

hundred millions	ten millions	millions	hundred thousands	ten thousands	thousands	hundreds	tens	ones	.	tenths	hundredths	thousandths
								3	.	6		
								4	.	8	5	
			6	6	0,	0	0	0				
			1	5	0,	0	0	0				

Talk About It 💬
How can you describe these numbers? Complete the sentences.

① The value of the 6 in 3.6 is … 0.6 (or 6 tenths).
② The ones and the tenths places are separated by a … decimal point.
③ The number 150,000 has a 5 in the … place. ten thousands
④ The word form for the number of elephants is … six hundred sixty thousand.
⑤ The number of elephants … the number of giraffes. is greater than

Your Turn ✏️
Use at least 4 digits to write a number without a decimal point. Write another number that has at least 4 digits *and* a decimal point. Say the word form of each number to a partner. Then tell the value of each digit.

Leveled Language Proficiency

Students at each proficiency level should be able to perform the following tasks.

Listening/Speaking

Early Beginner Understand vocabulary terms and follow simple conversations and activities, when supported by visual cues. Respond to questions with single words and gestures.

Beginner Respond to questions with gestures, words, or short phrases. Repeat longer phrases and short sentences, and complete sentences with support.

Early Intermediate Use simple sentences when responding orally; complete written sentences with lesson vocabulary; show an increasing ability to use lesson vocabulary.

Intermediate Participate in limited discussions and write complete sentences with little support.

Advanced/Transitioning Provide details and explanations in oral and written responses, with few grammatical and syntactical errors.

Your Turn

1. Write 1,583,018 in standard form, word form, and expanded form.

Standard Form: 1,583,018

Word Form: one million, five hundred eighty-three thousand, eighteen

Expanded Form: 1,000,000 + 500,000 + 80,000 + 3,000 + 10 + 8

2. Write 852.76 in standard form, word form, and expanded form.

Standard Form: 852.76

Word Form: eight hundred fifty-two and seventy-six hundredths

Expanded Form: 800 + 50 + 2 + 0.7 + 0.06

3. Compare these numbers. Write >, <, or =.

27,609 ___<___ 29,540

Talk and Write About It

Complete the sentences about place value and comparing numbers.

Vocabulary			
millions	is greater than	ones	is less than
value	ten thousands	tenths	hundredths
digit	hundred thousands	hundreds	thousandths

4. In 1,583,018, the 5 is in the ___hundred thousands___ place.

5. In the number 852.76, the 6 is in the ___hundredths___ place.

6. In Problem 3, the symbol I wrote means ___is less than___ .

Produce Language

Write about how place value helps you read and write numbers. Use as many vocabulary terms as you can. Share with a partner.

4   Lesson 1

Leveled Language Proficiency

Students at each proficiency level should be able to perform the following tasks.

Reading/Writing

Early Beginner Demonstrate motivation to read for meaning when given visual support or assistance from others. Copy lists of words; write 1–2 vocabulary terms independently.

Beginner Read a growing number of everyday words and some lesson vocabulary terms. Use sentence starters and visual supports to write individual terms and phrases.

Early Intermediate Read a variety of vocabulary terms in isolation or in context; read sentences made up of simple phonetically regular words and sight words. Write simple sentences, with some errors.

Intermediate Read lesson vocabulary both in and out of context, and read and follow simple directions. Read and understand some abstract ideas. Write complete sentences and make ideas clear and logical. Use sentence starters when necessary.

Advanced/Transitioning Read with minimal support and obtain information from print and nonprint sources. Express written ideas with increasing detail and precision of language.

↻ Assess Understanding

Your Turn

Model Read aloud the directions for Problem 1. Write 1,583,018 on the board. Say: *one million, five hundred eighty-three thousand, eighteen. Repeat with me.* Repeat the number and point to each digit as you say its name. Have students complete the activity.

Talk and Write About It

On Their Own Have students work on their own and with a partner.

Produce Language

On Their Own Have students review how they rated the terms on page 1. Have students use the terms they have learned in this lesson to write about place value.

Wrap Up

Table Talk Have students look back at the lesson's objectives. Allow time for them to reflect on what they have learned and then answer the essential question.

☑ **Learned** and applied vocabulary related to place value and comparing numbers

☑ **Spoken** statements about place value and comparing numbers

☑ **Written** statements about place value and comparing numbers

Lesson 2

Whole-Number Operations

Vocabulary Whole numbers, add, addition, plus, equals, addends, sum, subtract, subtraction, minus, difference, algorithm, multiply, multiplication, factors, times, product, divide, division, dividend, divided by, divisor, quotient, operations, regroup

Materials Index cards

 Math Background

- Whole numbers are the integers greater than or equal to zero. Whole numbers do not include fractions, decimals, or negative numbers.

- An algorithm is a set of rules or procedures that can be followed to solve a problem.

↻ Frontload the Lesson

 Essential Question **What words and symbols should you understand and use when you talk about operations?**

Talk About It

Build Background Ask students to say what they might already know about these terms.

↻ Content and Language

You Will

Model Read the objectives aloud and explain them in your own words. Use diagrams and whole numbers to support your explanations.

Your Turn

Guide Discussion Have students read the objectives. Discuss what these objectives mean. Invite partners to take turns discussing what the objectives mean to them.

Whole-Number Operations

Essential Question What words and symbols should you understand and use when you talk about operations?

You Will
- Add and subtract whole numbers using an algorithm.
- Multiply and divide whole numbers using an algorithm.
- Use math vocabulary to describe addition, subtraction, multiplication, and division.

Talk About It

Copy each term from Vocabulary in Context on a card. As your teacher reads each term, create three piles of cards.

Pile 1 I know what this term means.
Pile 2 I have heard of this term, but I am not sure how it is used in math.
Pile 3 I have not heard of this term.

What do you know about each term? Explain, using the sentence starters for support.

I know … means …
I think … means …
I do not know what … means.

Your Turn
Look at the objectives listed under You Will at the top of the page. Working with a partner, predict what you will learn. Use the sentence starter below.

I am going to learn about …

product

divide

subtraction

Leveled Instruction

Early Beginner Early beginners may need longer response times to formulate their thoughts and words. Encourage these students to use words, gestures, and pictures to complete activities. If necessary, pair students with partners of higher language proficiency.

Beginner Remind beginning students to speak slowly and confer with each other for needed support. Students at this level will use phrases and short sentences to complete activities.

Early Intermediate Encourage early intermediate students to use sentence starters for support. Provide immediate feedback so students can self-correct.

Intermediate Encourage students to speak in simple, complete sentences. Have them repeat their sentences to build fluency.

Advanced/Transitioning You can expect these students to synthesize information and use elaborate sentences to complete activities. Encourage students to model speaking for those students of low level language proficiency.

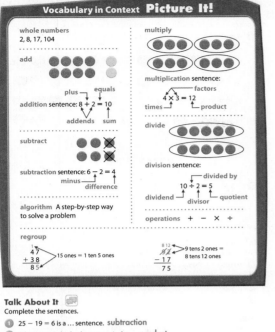

whole numbers
2, 8, 17, 104

add

plus — equals

addition sentence: 8 + 2 = 10

addends   sum

subtract

subtraction sentence: 6 − 2 = 4
minus   difference

algorithm A step-by-step way to solve a problem

regroup

$$47 + 38 = 85$$ 15 ones = 1 ten 5 ones

9 tens 2 ones = 8 tens 12 ones

multiply

multiplication sentence:
factors
4 × 3 = 12
times   product

divide

division sentence:
divided by
10 ÷ 2 = 5
dividend   divisor   quotient

operations + − × ÷

Talk About It
Complete the sentences.
1. 25 − 19 = 6 is a … sentence. **subtraction**
2. When you multiply, the answer is the … **product.**
3. 7, 38, and 210 are all … **whole numbers.**
4. When you divide, the answer is called the … **quotient.**

Your Turn
Choose an operation on this page. Think about what it means to you. Tell a partner.

6   Lesson 2

Academic Vocabulary

- Point out the roots and suffixes in the words *add, addition, subtract, subtraction, multiply, multiplication,* and *divide, division.*

- Provide examples to distinguish the more common medical meaning of *operation* from the mathematical meaning as an arithmetic process.

- Provide examples to distinguish the homophones *sum* and *some,* as well as *whole* and *hole.*

- Point out that while *difference* or *different* in everyday language means *not the same,* in math *difference* means the answer to a subtraction problem.

- Explain the difference between time on a clock and *times* in multiplication.

Additional resources for building and reinforcing vocabulary are provided on pages T37–T41.

Cultural Consideration

Some countries outside the United States use different algorithms for long division. The quotient is always the same, but the calculations are often written in a different form.

↻ Comprehensible Input
Guide students to understanding

Vocabulary in Context Picture It!

1. **Say the Term** Have students repeat, stressing each syllable. Then combine syllables and have students repeat.

2. **Introduce Meaning** Connect the term to the visual that illustrates it.

3. **Demonstrate** Use gestures and visuals to demonstrate. When you discuss *division,* act out cutting a desk in two halves and pushing the two halves apart.

4. **Apply** Have students demonstrate understanding with Talk About It.

Repeat the routine for each vocabulary term.

Remind students that they can review vocabulary terms for the operations on pages 89–90 and record more terms as they learn them.

Talk About It

Guide Discussion Have students discuss the sentences with a partner. Remind students that there are special terms that are used with each operation. Then provide this additional sentence completion, if time permits:

Numbers that are added are called … **addends.**

Intervention

If students confuse words with similar prefixes, like *divide* and *division* …

Then write examples of division problems on the board. Say, *We* divide *when we do* division. Have students say the sentence with you.

Your Turn

Guide Discussion Ask volunteers to use their operation in a sentence. Have others repeat the sentences.

Language Production

Comprehension Support Direct students' attention to the directions at the top of the page. Explain that they will show the steps of the algorithms they use to solve the problems.

Model Read aloud Problem 1 for students. Talk about the numbers and the steps of the algorithm. *The numbers 4 and 13 are* factors. *Each row has 13 plants, so we will multiply 13 times 4. The answer will be the* product. *The product will tell us how many plants in all.* Help students complete the problem, describing the steps aloud. *4 times 3 equals 12. Regroup 12 ones as 1 ten and 2 ones.* Show students how to record the 2 in the ones place and a small 1 at the top of the tens column. *4 times 1 equals 4, plus 1 equals 5. So, the product is 52.*

Talk through Problems 2–4, offering assistance as needed.

Talk About It

Guide Discussion Have students complete the Talk About It sentences with a partner. Remind students that if they need help with the terms, they can check the Vocabulary in Context Picture It!

Your Turn

Guide Discussion Some students may wish to write out what they are going to say. Then have them share with a partner.

Do You Understand?

Complete each problem. Show the steps of each algorithm you use.

1. A garden has 4 rows of plants with 13 plants in each row. How many plants are there in all?

$$\begin{array}{r} 13 \\ \times\ 4 \\ \hline 52 \end{array}$$

There are __52__ plants in all.

2. $\begin{array}{r} 548 \\ +171 \\ \hline 719 \end{array}$ 3. $\begin{array}{r} 632 \\ -315 \\ \hline 317 \end{array}$ 4. $3\overline{)42}$ with 14 on top

Talk About It
Complete the sentences.

5. In Problem 1, the numbers 13 and 4 are called … factors (or whole numbers).
6. The answer to Problem 2 is called the … sum.
7. To subtract the ones in Problem 3, first I had to … regroup.
8. To solve Problem 4, I had to … divide.

Your Turn
Talk with a partner. Tell what you know about the parts of a division problem. Use the sentence starter below if you need help.

In a division problem, …

Leveled Language Proficiency

Students at each proficiency level should be able to perform the following tasks.

Listening/Speaking

Early Beginner Follow oral directions that are supported by visual clues. Repeat words or simple phrases to answer questions.

Beginner Recognize some vocabulary terms. Answer using vocabulary terms, simple phrases, or short sentences.

Early Intermediate Begin to follow more abstract discussion about vocabulary. Speak in phrases and simple sentences, showing an increasing understanding of vocabulary terms and their relationships to one another.

Intermediate Understand abstract concepts; recognize vocabulary as individual terms and in the context of spoken sentences. Show an ability to express abstract ideas about vocabulary terms.

Advanced/Transitioning Understand complex sentence structures; follow abstract conversations involving lesson vocabulary. Speak on abstract topics, including those that involve lesson vocabulary, with few if any grammatical and syntactical errors.

Think, Talk, and Write

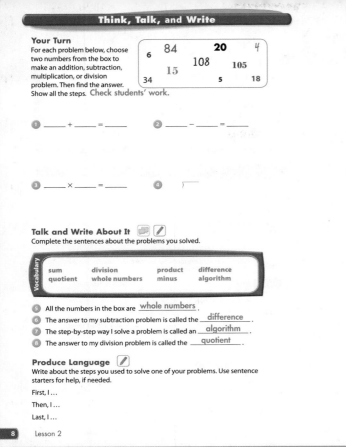

Your Turn

For each problem below, choose two numbers from the box to make an addition, subtraction, multiplication, or division problem. Then find the answer. Show all the steps. Check students' work.

6	84		20	4
	15	108		105
34			5	18

1. ____ + ____ = ____
2. ____ − ____ = ____
3. ____ × ____ = ____
4. $\overline{)\quad}$

Talk and Write About It

Complete the sentences about the problems you solved.

Vocabulary

sum	division	product	difference
quotient	whole numbers	minus	algorithm

5. All the numbers in the box are whole numbers.
6. The answer to my subtraction problem is called the difference.
7. The step-by-step way I solve a problem is called an algorithm.
8. The answer to my division problem is called the quotient.

Produce Language

Write about the steps you used to solve one of your problems. Use sentence starters for help, if needed.

First, I . . .

Then, I . . .

Last, I . . .

8 Lesson 2

Leveled Language Proficiency

Students at each proficiency level should be able to perform the following tasks.

Reading/Writing

Early Beginner Read a few short, common words and some vocabulary terms, with help from a partner. Copy words and phrases from the board; write a few vocabulary terms independently.

Beginner/Early Intermediate Read some vocabulary terms independently. Use sentence starters that use vocabulary terms.

Intermediate Read and comprehend lesson vocabulary in context and read simple directions independently. Write complete sentences with some grammar, usage, mechanics, and spelling errors.

Advanced/Transitioning Read and carry out simple and complex written instructions; read sentences about lesson concepts and rephrase ideas and thoughts to express meaning. Write complete sentences with very few errors, using words and phrases to make ideas clearer and more logical.

Assess Understanding

Your Turn

Model Point to the numbers in the box and explain that there are different possibilities for problems. For the division problem, point out that some combinations will result in a remainder. *Sometimes when you are done dividing, there is an amount left over. This is called the* remainder. *If your problem has a remainder, don't forget that extra step in your algorithm.*

Talk and Write About It

On Their Own Have students work independently to complete the sentences.

Produce Language

On Their Own Have students write about the steps of the algorithm they used to solve one of their problems. Have them share their ideas with the class.

Wrap Up

Table Talk Have students look back at the lesson's objectives. Allow time for them to reflect on what they have learned and then answer the essential question.

☑ **Learned** and applied vocabulary about whole-number operations and algorithms

☑ **Spoken** statements about whole-number operations and algorithms

☑ **Written** statements about whole-number operations and algorithms

Decimal Operations

Vocabulary Digits, decimal, decimal point, place value, ones, tenths, hundredths, thousandths, add, sum, subtract, difference, multiply, product, divide, quotient

Materials School Shopping Four Corners Activity (pages 91—93), scissors, glue, place-value blocks (optional)

Math Background

- When a decimal is less than one, a zero is typically written in the ones place as a placeholder (e.g., 0.23).

↻ Frontload the Lesson

What vocabulary terms do you need in order to learn about decimals?

Talk About It

Build Background Read aloud the steps in the School Shopping Four Corners Activity. Post the following directions in each corner of the room: (1) Choose 1 card. (2) Choose 2 cards. (3) Choose 1 card. (4) Choose 2 cards. Ask for volunteers to say what they might know about the terms shown in red in the Four Corner boxes (*multiply, sum, divide, difference*).

↻ Content and Language

You Will

Model Read the objectives aloud and restate them in your own words. Use diagrams and symbols to support your explanations.

Your Turn

Guide Discussion Have students read the objectives. Invite partners to give examples of what the objectives mean to them.

Decimal Operations

Essential Question What vocabulary terms do you need in order to learn about decimals?

You Will
- Add, subtract, multiply, and divide decimals.
- Solve word problems involving decimals.
- Use math vocabulary to talk and write about decimals.

Talk About It

Tear out the School Shopping Four Corners Activity sheet on pages 91–92. Then cut out the activity cards on page 93.

Work with a partner.

You will use the activity cards to solve problems. Each corner of the room tells you how many cards to choose.

Step 1 Place the cards facedown in a pile.

Step 2 Go to a corner of the room. Follow the directions. Choose the correct number of activity cards.

Step 3 Find the box on your activity sheet that matches the corner. Paste the activity card(s) in the box. Then solve the problem written in the box.

Repeat Steps 1, 2, and 3 for each corner of the room.

Look at the red terms in each box. What do you know about these terms? Use the sentence starters for support.

I know … means …
I think … means …
I do not know what … means.

Your Turn
Look at the objectives listed under You Will at the top of the page. Working with a partner, predict what you will learn. Use the sentence starter below.

I am going to learn about …

Decimal Operations 9

Leveled Instruction

Early Beginner Early beginners may need longer response times to formulate their answers. Encourage these students to use both pictures and gestures to complete activities. If necessary, pair students with partners of higher language proficiency.

Beginner Encourage students to use sentence starters for support. Provide immediate feedback so students can self-correct.

Early Intermediate/Intermediate Encourage students to use sentence starters as support, and to use them as models to build fluency.

Advanced/Transitioning You can expect these students to classify previously learned vocabulary terms and phrases into concept-based categories. Encourage advanced students to work with those students of low level language proficiency.

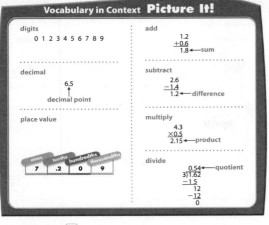

Vocabulary in Context **Picture It!**

digits

0 1 2 3 4 5 6 7 8 9

decimal

6.5
↑
decimal point

place value

ones	tenths	hundredths	thousandths
7	.2	0	9

add

```
  1.2
+ 0.6
  1.8 ←—— sum
```

subtract

```
  2.6
- 1.4
  1.2 ←—— difference
```

multiply

```
  4.3
× 0.5
 2.15 ←—— product
```

divide

```
        0.54 ←—— quotient
    3) 1.62
      - 1 5
         12
       -  12
          0
```

Talk About It

Complete the sentences.

1. The answer to 4.4 ÷ 1.1 is called a … **quotient.**
2. The answer to a multiplication problem is called the … **product.**
3. The number 5.63 is called a … **decimal.**
4. In the decimal 8.435, the 5 is in the … place. **thousandths**
5. The decimal 4.385 has four … **digits.**
6. The answer to a subtraction problem is called the … **difference.**

Your Turn

Talk with a partner about the terms on this page. Tell your partner what you know about them.

Academic Vocabulary

- Model the correct pronunciation of the soft *g* in *digit*. Explain that in English, when a *g* is followed by *e* or *i*, it usually has a /j/ sound.

- *Point* (noun vs. verb) may be confusing. Model with gestures and by drawing. Point and say *I point*. Compare a decimal point and a period.

Additional resources for building and reinforcing vocabulary are provided on pages T37–T41.

Cultural Consideration

In some countries, decimal points are used the way we use commas in the United States. One hundred thousand would be written 100.000 rather than 100,000. Clarify this for students as needed.

↻ Comprehensible Input

Guide students to understanding

Vocabulary in Context Picture It!

1. **Say the Term** Have students repeat, stressing each syllable. Then combine syllables and have students repeat.

2. **Introduce Meaning** Connect the term to the visual that illustrates it.

3. **Demonstrate** Use gestures and visuals to demonstrate. As you discuss the digits in the ones, tenths, hundredths, and thousandths places, you might want to use place-value blocks to reinforce the value of each digit.

4. **Apply** Have students demonstrate understanding with Talk About It.

Repeat the routine for each vocabulary term.

Remind students that they can review vocabulary terms for the operations on pages 89–90 and record more terms as they learn them.

Talk About It

Guide Discussion Have students discuss the sentences with a partner. Then provide this additional sentence completion, if time permits:

The ones place is separated from the tenths place by a … **decimal point.**

Intervention

If students confuse the place value of decimals …

Then compare ones, tenths, and hundredths to dollar bills, dimes, and pennies.

Your Turn

Guide Discussion Have partners share their discussions from Your Turn. Encourage pairs to provide numerical examples to help explain what the terms mean to them.

↻ Language Production

Comprehension Support Direct students' attention to the weights shown in the four pictures. Say the names of the fruits and their weights. Explain that pounds measure how heavy something is.

Model Introduce the first problem. *The problem asks you to find the total weight of the watermelon and the grapes. You need to add 9.6 and 0.44.* Work through the computation with students. *When you add decimals, you need to line up the decimal points. 9.6 is the same as 9.60. You can write the 0 in the hundredths place if you wish. Add the hundredths first. 0 hundredths plus 4 hundredths is 4 hundredths. Next, add the tenths. 6 tenths plus 4 tenths is 10 tenths. Regroup that as 1 one and 0 tenths.* Show students how to record the 0 in the tenths place and a small 1 at the top of the ones column. Have students complete the problem, reminding them to place the decimal point directly below the points in the problem. *What is the sum? So, what is the total weight of the watermelon and grapes?*

Talk through Problems 2–4, discussing the steps of the computations as needed.

Talk About It

Guide Discussion Have students complete the Talk About It sentences with a partner. Remind students that if they need help with the terms, they can check Vocabulary in Context Picture It!

Your Turn

Guide Discussion Partners can record their work on copies of T44. Ask volunteers to share their decimals and write sample problems on the board to refer to during the discussion.

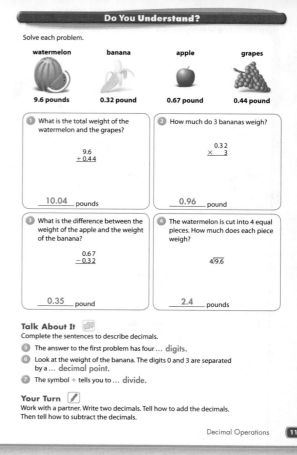

Do You Understand?

Solve each problem.

watermelon — 9.6 pounds
banana — 0.32 pound
apple — 0.67 pound
grapes — 0.44 pound

1. What is the total weight of the watermelon and the grapes?

$$\begin{array}{r} 9.6 \\ + 0.44 \\ \hline \underline{10.04} \text{ pounds} \end{array}$$

2. How much do 3 bananas weigh?

$$\begin{array}{r} 0.32 \\ \times \quad 3 \\ \hline \underline{0.96} \text{ pound} \end{array}$$

3. What is the difference between the weight of the apple and the weight of the banana?

$$\begin{array}{r} 0.67 \\ - 0.32 \\ \hline \underline{0.35} \text{ pound} \end{array}$$

4. The watermelon is cut into 4 equal pieces. How much does each piece weigh?

$$4\overline{)9.6} \qquad \underline{2.4} \text{ pounds}$$

Talk About It
Complete the sentences to describe decimals.

5. The answer to the first problem has four ... digits.

6. Look at the weight of the banana. The digits 0 and 3 are separated by a ... decimal point.

7. The symbol ÷ tells you to ... divide.

Your Turn
Work with a partner. Write two decimals. Tell how to add the decimals. Then tell how to subtract the decimals.

Decimal Operations   11

Leveled Language Proficiency

Students at each proficiency level should be able to perform the following tasks.

Listening/Speaking

Early Beginner Follow one-step directions and recognize a few vocabulary terms. Repeat simple phrases and use 1–2 vocabulary terms in context.

Beginner Identify verbal and nonverbal cues to determine when to focus attention. Answer simple questions about vocabulary terms. Answer using vocabulary terms, simple phrases, or short sentences.

Early Intermediate Begin to follow more abstract discussions. Speak in phrases and simple sentences, showing an increasing understanding of vocabulary terms and their relationships to one another.

Intermediate Recognize vocabulary as individual terms and in the context of spoken sentences. Participate in limited discussion using words and phrases.

Advanced/Transitioning Distinguish between irrelevant information and important information. Speak on abstract topics, including those that involve lesson vocabulary, with few if any grammatical and syntactical errors.

Your Turn

Begin with the purple box. Follow the arrows to solve the problems. Write the answers in the orange boxes. The last answer will be the one in the purple box.

3.1	→	+ 2.3	→	**A.** 5.4	→	÷ 2
						↓
+ 1.68	←	**E.** 3	←	÷ 1.1	←	**B.** 2.7
↓						
G. 1.42	→	− 0.16	→	**D.** 3.3	→	× 1.6
						↓
× 0.5	←	**F.** 2.84	←	− 1.02	←	**C.** 4.32

Talk and Write About It 💬 ✏️

Complete the sentences about the problem you solved.

Vocabulary

| product | sum | digits | decimals |
| tenths | thousandths | difference | hundredths |

1. To get to Box A, I added two ___decimals___ .
2. The answer in Box C is called a ___product___ .
3. The answer in Box F has an 8 in the ___tenths___ place.
4. The answer in Box G has a 2 in the ___hundredths___ place.

Produce Language ✏️

Write about the steps you use to multiply decimals. Use sentence starters for help if needed.

First, I…

Then, I…

12   Lesson 3

Leveled Language Proficiency

Students at each proficiency level should be able to perform the following tasks.

Reading/Writing

Early Beginner Read and understand previously learned sight words and some vocabulary terms with help from a partner. Copy words and phrases from the board. Write a few vocabulary terms independently.

Beginner/Early Intermediate Read simple sentences with the help of a partner or an adult and visual support; read some vocabulary terms independently. Use sentence starters and other organizers to write individual words and phrases that use vocabulary terms.

Intermediate Read lesson vocabulary both in and out of context, and read and follow simple directions. Read and understand some abstract ideas. Write in full sentences with some spelling and grammatical errors, using sentence starters as needed and including vocabulary as appropriate.

Advanced/Transitioning Read and carry out simple and complex written instructions; read sentences about lesson concepts that use lesson vocabulary. Write complete sentences with very few errors.

↻ Assess Understanding

Your Turn

Model Work through the first step of the chart. Say *The first step asks us to add* 3.1 *and* 2.3. *We will write the sum in the orange box labeled* A. Ask students which digits they should add first. tenths Make sure students understand that they should use their answer as the first decimal for the next step in the chart.

Talk and Write About It

On Their Own Have students work with a partner to complete the sentences.

Produce Language

On Their Own Have students write about multiplying decimals. Refer them to boxes C and G on the chart they completed as well as the multiplication problems on pages 10 and 11. Encourage students to share their ideas.

Wrap Up

Table Talk Have students look back at the lesson's objectives. Allow time for them to reflect on what they have learned and then answer the essential question.

☑ **Learned** and applied vocabulary about decimal operations

☑ **Spoken** statements about decimal operations

☑ **Written** statements about decimal operations

Estimation

Vocabulary Exactly, about, reasonable, unreasonable, round, nearest ten, nearest hundred, estimate

 Math Background

- An estimate is a logical guess based on the information that is given.

- Rounding to the nearest ten, hundred, or other number is one step in estimating results to computations.

 Frontload the Lesson

Essential Question What do you need to know to understand and discuss estimation?

Talk About It

Build Background Have students tell what they already know about these terms related to estimation. (See page T43 for additional copies of the Know-Want-Learn chart.)

Content and Language

You Will

Model Read the objectives aloud and explain them in your own words. Use visual examples to support your explanations.

Your Turn

Guide Discussion Have students read the objectives. Discuss what these objectives mean. Encourage students to use their own words.

Estimation

Essential Question What do you need to know to understand and discuss estimation?

You Will
- Understand rounding numbers.
- Estimate when computing with numbers.
- Use math vocabulary for estimating.

Talk About It

Look at the list of terms below. In the first two columns of the chart, write terms you **know** or **want** to know more about.

nearest	exactly	estimate
reasonable	about	unreasonable
round		

Know	Want	Learned

Tell what you know about each term you wrote in the chart. Use the sentence starters for help.

I know the term …
I think … means …

Your Turn
Look at the objectives listed under You Will at the top of the page. Working with a partner, predict what you are going to learn. Use the sentence starter below to help you.

I am going to learn about …

Leveled Instruction

Early Beginner Encourage students to use single words and gestures, as well as pictures. Allow ample time so students can organize their thoughts.

Beginner/Early Intermediate Expect phrases and simple sentences from these students as answers to the activities. Encourage students to use sentence starters to help them construct answers.

Intermediate Intermediate students are able to speak about some abstract ideas. They often recognize vocabulary as individual terms and in the context of spoken sentences.

Advanced/Transitioning These students can form sentences of increasing complexity. Encourage them to try new sentence structures.

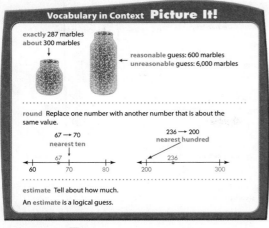

Vocabulary in Context Picture It!

exactly 287 marbles
about 300 marbles

reasonable guess: 600 marbles
unreasonable guess: 6,000 marbles

round Replace one number with another number that is about the same value.

67 → 70
nearest ten

236 → 200
nearest hundred

67

60   70   80

236

200   300

estimate Tell about how much.

An **estimate** is a logical guess.

Talk About It
Talk with a partner. Complete the sentences.
1. There are … 7 days in one week. exactly
2. There are … 500 trees in the park. about
3. A logical guess is an … estimate.
4. An estimate of 1,000 pages for my math book is … unreasonable.

Your Turn
Think of how you would describe the vocabulary terms. Write and/or draw to show what those terms mean to you.

14   Lesson 4

Academic Vocabulary

- Distinguish between *round* as a verb, as in "round the number," and as an adjective, as in "a circle is round."

- Students may confuse the verb and noun pronunciations and meanings of *estimate*. Discuss these in context.

- Point out that the word *about* has multiple meanings. Students might read a story and tell what it is about. In math, *about* means "close to."

Additional resources for building and reinforcing vocabulary are provided on pages T37–T41.

↻ Comprehensible Input
Guide students to understanding

Vocabulary in Context Picture It!

1. **Say the Term** Have students repeat, stressing each syllable. Then combine syllables and have students repeat.

2. **Introduce Meaning** Connect the term to the visual that illustrates it.

3. **Demonstrate** Use gestures and visuals to demonstrate. For example, when teaching the term *nearest,* stand by and point to the nearest student.

4. **Apply** Have students demonstrate understanding with Talk About It.

Repeat the routine for each vocabulary term.

Talk About It

Guide Discussion Have students discuss their responses with a partner. Then provide this additional sentence starter, if time permits:

When you round 82 to 80, you have rounded to the … **nearest ten.**

Intervention

If students have difficulty distinguishing between *reasonable* and *unreasonable* …

Then point out the prefix *un-* and give other examples, such as *tie/untie; wind/unwind;* and *curl/uncurl.*

Your Turn

Guide Discussion Have volunteers offer their ideas and drawings for Your Turn.

↻ Language Production

Comprehension Support Talk about the table with students. Read the headings in each column. Clarify the meaning of the word *route* in the first column, and point out that the numbers in the second column are the exact number of miles, not estimates.

Model Use lesson vocabulary terms to explain the activity. Work though the sample problem. Say: *We need to round and then add to estimate the total miles in Route W and Route Z. Route W is exactly 33 miles. The number 33 is between 30 and 40. If we round to the nearest ten, then 33 is nearest to 30. For Route Z, 41 is nearest to 40. 30 plus 40 is 70.* Guide students through each item.

If students ask how to round a "halfway" number, such as 65, tell them to round it up to 70. They will practice rounding "halfway" numbers in math class.

Talk About It

Guide Discussion Have students complete the Talk About It sentences with a partner. Remind them that if they need help with the terms, they can check the chart or the Vocabulary in Context Picture It!

Your Turn

Guide Discussion Encourage students to use steps to describe their work: *First, I … Then, I … Next, I … Finally, I …*

Do You Understand?

A truck driver travels Route W and Route Z. About how many miles is that?

You can round to the nearest ten to estimate the answer.

Route	Number of Miles
Route W	33
Route X	26
Route Y	18
Route Z	41

33 + 41
↓   ↓
30 + 40 = 70

The distance is about 70 miles.

1. The driver travels Route X and Route Y. About how many miles is that? about __50__ miles

2. For 12 days, the driver travels Route Y each day. About how many miles is that? about __240__ miles

3. The driver uses 2 gallons of gas to travel Route Z. About how many miles does the driver travel on 1 gallon of gas? about __20__ miles

Talk About It
What terms can you use to estimate? Complete the sentences to explain.

4. My answer to Problem 1 is a … estimate. **reasonable**

5. The number of miles for Route X is … 26. **exactly**

6. Route Z is … 40 miles long. **about**

Your Turn
Round the miles for Route Y and Route Z to the nearest ten. Subtract to estimate the difference between the two routes. Explain to your partner how you found your answer.

Leveled Language Proficiency

Students at each proficiency level should be able to perform the following tasks.

Listening/Speaking

Early Beginner Demonstrate comprehension of simple sentences. Follow conversations when spoken slowly. Use a few vocabulary terms and participate in simple conversations, supported by visual cues.

Beginner Listen and respond to simple questions, using some vocabulary terms. Say individual terms and simple phrases, and repeat longer phrases and short sentences.

Early Intermediate Show understanding of vocabulary terms that require a short answer. Respond briefly to questions, showing an increasing understanding of lesson vocabulary.

Intermediate Recognize vocabulary as individual terms and in spoken sentences. Participate in limited discussion using words and phrases.

Advanced/Transitioning Clarify meanings of words as needed by asking questions or using resources. Support responses with additional details.

Your Turn

Sam's family takes car trips to visit relatives. They come home between visits. Round the number of miles to the nearest hundred to find each estimate.

Person	Number of Miles (round trip)
Grandma	312
Aunt Pat	124
Uncle Bob	188

1. Sam's family visited Grandma and Uncle Bob. About how many miles did they drive?

about ___500___ miles

2. About how many more miles is a visit to Grandma's than a visit to Aunt Pat's?

about ___200___ more miles

Talk and Write About It

Complete the sentences about estimation.

Vocabulary: nearest ten · round · exactly · estimate · reasonable · nearest hundred · about · unreasonable

3. A visit to Grandma is ___about___ 300 miles.

4. A visit to Aunt Pat is ___exactly___ 124 miles.

5. An estimate of 800 miles for two visits to Uncle Bob is ___unreasonable___ .

Produce Language

Write the terms you learned about in this lesson in the third column of the chart on page 13. Write what you know about these terms. Use sentence starters from throughout the lesson for support.

↻ Assess Understanding

Your Turn

Model Read aloud the directions to students. Read the chart with them and explain that it shows how many miles it is from Sam's house to each person's house and back. Discuss how to round the numbers to the nearest hundred. Say, *312 is between 300 and 400.* Draw a number line to illustrate this. *312 is closer to 300 than 400. So, 312 rounded to the nearest hundred is 300.* Have students complete the activity.

Talk and Write About It

On Their Own Have students work on their own for ten minutes to complete the sentences. Then have partners share their responses.

Produce Language

On Their Own Have students review the chart on page 13. Have them complete the third column and write what they have learned about these terms. If students have no new terms to add to the third column, ask them to write about several of the other terms in the lesson.

Wrap Up

Table Talk Have students look back at the lesson's objectives. Allow time for them to reflect on what they have learned and then answer the essential question.

☑ **Learned** and applied vocabulary related to estimation

☑ **Spoken** statements about estimation

☑ **Written** statements about estimation

Leveled Language Proficiency

Students at each proficiency level should be able to perform the following tasks.

Reading/Writing

Early Beginner Read and understand previously learned sight words and phrases. Copy short lists of words independently.

Beginner Read a growing number of everyday words and some lesson vocabulary terms. Use sentence starters and visual supports to write individual terms and phrases.

Early Intermediate Read simple sentences and some vocabulary terms with assistance when needed. Use sentence starters to write words and phrases that use vocabulary terms.

Intermediate Apply knowledge of context clues to determine the meaning of unfamiliar words. Write in full sentences with some errors. Use sentence starters when needed.

Advanced/Transitioning Read with minimal support, obtaining information from print and non-print sources. Select words that address the audience and purpose for writing.

Simplifying Fractions

Vocabulary Fraction, numerator, denominator, whole, half, halves, third, fourth, fifth, sixth, eighth, equivalent, simplify, greatest common factor

Materials Index cards

Math Background

- Equivalent fractions are found by multiplying (or dividing) the numerator and denominator of a fraction by the same nonzero number.

- A fraction is simplified when the numerator and denominator have no common factor other than one.

↻ Frontload the Lesson

Essential Question **What vocabulary terms will help you understand fractions and how to simplify them?**

Talk About It

Build Background Have students create word cards as described. Read each word aloud as students sort them into piles. Ask students to say what they might already know about these terms.

↻ Content and Language

You Will

Model Read the objectives aloud and explain them in your own words. Use visual examples to support your explanations.

Your Turn

Guide Discussion Have students read the objectives and tell what the objectives mean to them.

Simplifying Fractions

Essential Question What vocabulary terms will help you understand fractions and how to simplify them?

You Will
- Understand equivalent fractions.
- Simplify fractions.
- Use math vocabulary to discuss simplifying fractions.

Talk About It

Copy each term from Vocabulary in Context on a card. As your teacher reads each term, make three piles of cards.

Pile 1 I know what this term means.

Pile 2 I have heard of this term, but I am not sure how it is used in math.

Pile 3 I have not heard of this term.

What do you know about each term? Explain, using the sentence starters for support.

I know ... means ...
I think ... means ...
I do not know what ... means.

Your Turn
Look at the objectives listed under You Will at the top of the page. Working with a partner, predict what you are going to learn. Use the sentence starter below to help you.

I am going to learn about ...

Leveled Instruction

Early Beginner Early beginners should partner with students at higher language proficiency to complete the activities. Expect single words and gestures.

Beginner These students benefit from gestures, drawings, and simple phrases to help them understand and discuss concepts.

Early Intermediate Expect phrases and simple sentences from these students as they participate in the activities.

Intermediate These students need minimal assistance to complete activities. Help students include details in their written and oral responses.

Advanced/Transitioning Expect students to form sentences of increasing difficulty. Have them use more sophisticated vocabulary, and encourage them to express themselves using more complex sentence structures.

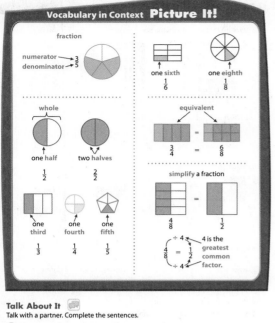

Academic Vocabulary

- Check that students understand that a *fraction* is a part of a whole. Then clear up potential confusion with the homophones *whole* and *hole*.

- Fraction words are not formed consistently in English. While *eight* becomes *eighth,* English uses *half* and *third* rather than *twoth* or *threeth*. Note, too, that while *fourth* follows standard rules, its synonym *quarter* does not.

- Connect the word *simplify* to the word *simple* (easy). Point out that when you *simplify* a fraction, you make the numerator and denominator smaller, which makes the fraction easier to work with.

- Help students connect the terms *equals* and *equivalent:* when one fraction *equals* another fraction, the two fractions are *equivalent*.

Additional resources for building and reinforcing vocabulary are provided on pages T37–T41.

Cultural Consideration

Fractions may be unfamiliar to some students. Many students may come from schools outside the United States where the metric system emphasizes decimals more than fractions.

↻ Comprehensible Input
Guide students to understanding

Vocabulary in Context Picture It!

1. **Say the Term** Have students repeat, stressing each syllable. Then combine syllables and have students repeat.

2. **Introduce Meaning** Connect the term to the visual that illustrates it.

3. **Demonstrate** Use gestures and visuals to demonstrate. For example, when teaching the terms *numerator* and *denominator,* have students stand up as you say *numerator* and sit down as you say *denominator*. This reinforces the location of these numbers in a fraction.

4. **Apply** Have students demonstrate understanding with Talk About It.

Repeat the routine for each vocabulary term.

Talk About It

Guide Discussion Ask students which terms they put in Pile 1 and their meanings. Model the sentence starters. Provide time for students to plan their answers. Compile information in a class list. Then provide this additional sentence starter, if time permits:

A whole with six equal parts is divided into … sixths.

Intervention

If students have difficulty distinguishing *half/halves, third/thirds,* and so forth …

Then write the word pairs on the board. Say one word in a pair and have students point to it. Repeat with the other words, in random order. Then say one word in the word pair and have students say the other word.

Your Turn

Guide Discussion Have volunteers offer their ideas for Your Turn.

↻ Language Production

Comprehension Support Direct students' attention to the pictures and fractions on the page. Explain that the pizzas and shapes are divided into equal parts.

Model Work through the first problem with students. Say: *The pizza is divided into six equal parts. We call them sixths. Four pieces remain, so we say this is four sixths of a pizza. The second pizza is divided into three equal parts. We call them thirds. Two pieces remain, so we say this is two thirds of a pizza. The same amount of pizza is shown in each pan, so these are equivalent amounts. The second fraction is simplified.* Guide students as they record the words and numbers for each fraction.

Have students complete the page.

Talk About It

Guide Discussion Have students complete the Talk About It sentences with a partner. Remind them that if they need help with the terms, they can check Vocabulary in Context Picture It!

Your Turn

Guide Discussion Have students pair up to explain their strategy and share their drawing if they used one. Remind them to use as many vocabulary terms as they can.

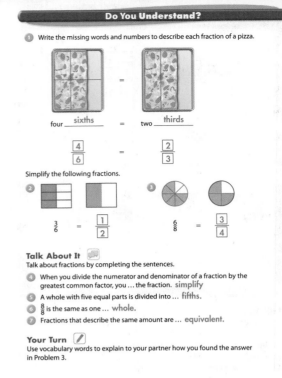

Do You Understand?

1 Write the missing words and numbers to describe each fraction of a pizza.

four __sixths__ = two __thirds__

$\frac{4}{6}$ = $\frac{2}{3}$

Simplify the following fractions.

2 $\frac{3}{6}$ = $\frac{1}{2}$

3 $\frac{6}{8}$ = $\frac{3}{4}$

Talk About It
Talk about fractions by completing the sentences.

4 When you divide the numerator and denominator of a fraction by the greatest common factor, you ... the fraction. __simplify__

5 A whole with five equal parts is divided into ... __fifths__.

6 $\frac{8}{8}$ is the same as one ... __whole__.

7 Fractions that describe the same amount are ... __equivalent__.

Your Turn ✏
Use vocabulary words to explain to your partner how you found the answer in Problem 3.

Leveled Language Proficiency

Students at each proficiency level should be able to perform the following tasks.

Listening/Speaking

Early Beginner Listen to and follow simple directions. Recognize a few vocabulary terms supported by visual cues. Repeat simple phrases, and use vocabulary terms to answer questions.

Beginner Follow basic directions. Listen and respond to simple questions, using some vocabulary terms. Say individual terms and simple phrases, and repeat longer phrases and short sentences.

Early Intermediate Demonstrate comprehension of oral questions that are based on academic content. Respond briefly to questions about content.

Intermediate Clarify meanings of unknown words, using context and examples. Participate in limited discussions using words and phrases.

Advanced/Transitioning Clarify meanings of words both in and out of context. Give examples. Summarize information that is heard during the lesson.

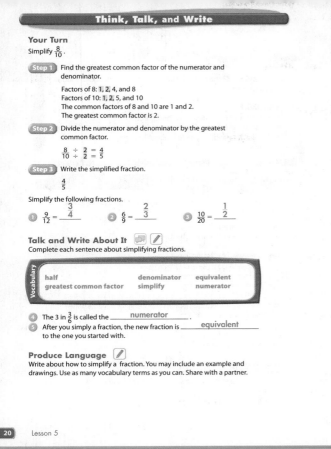

Your Turn

Simplify $\frac{8}{10}$.

Step 1 Find the greatest common factor of the numerator and denominator.

Factors of 8: **1**, **2**, 4, and 8
Factors of 10: **1**, **2**, 5, and 10
The common factors of 8 and 10 are 1 and 2.
The greatest common factor is 2.

Step 2 Divide the numerator and denominator by the greatest common factor.

$$\frac{8}{10} \div \frac{2}{2} = \frac{4}{5}$$

Step 3 Write the simplified fraction.

$$\frac{4}{5}$$

Simplify the following fractions.

① $\frac{9}{12} = \frac{3}{4}$ ② $\frac{6}{9} = \frac{2}{3}$ ③ $\frac{10}{20} = \frac{1}{2}$

Talk and Write About It

Complete each sentence about simplifying fractions.

Vocabulary

| half | denominator | equivalent |
| greatest common factor | simplify | numerator |

④ The 3 in $\frac{3}{6}$ is called the ___numerator___ .
⑤ After you simply a fraction, the new fraction is ___equivalent___ to the one you started with.

Produce Language

Write about how to simplify a fraction. You may include an example and drawings. Use as many vocabulary terms as you can. Share with a partner.

20   Lesson 5

Leveled Language Proficiency

Students at each proficiency level should be able to perform the following tasks.

Reading/Writing

Early Beginner Read for meaning when visual support or the assistance of others is provided. Copy lesson vocabulary words and read them aloud.

Beginner Read a growing number of sight words and phonetically regular words, as well as lesson vocabulary terms. Use sentence starters and visual supports to write lesson vocabulary.

Early Intermediate Read sentences made up of simple phonetically regular words and sight words. Write brief sentences using lesson vocabulary.

Intermediate Read lesson vocabulary both in and out of context. Write full sentences using lesson vocabulary.

Advanced/Transitioning Read the lesson with minimal support. Write full sentences using lesson vocabulary and including examples to clarify meaning.

↻ Assess Understanding

Your Turn

Model Explain to students that there are several ways to simplify a fraction. On this page, they will see a method that they likely used in their math class. It involves finding the *greatest common factor* of the numerator and denominator. The greatest common factor of two numbers is the largest number that divides evenly into both numbers. An example is shown in Vocabulary in Context Picture It!

Read the steps aloud and discuss each one carefully. Summarize the procedure and say: *To simplify a fraction, first find the greatest common factor. Then divide the numerator and denominator by this factor.* Have students work in pairs to complete the activity.

Talk and Write About It

On Their Own Have students work on their own for five minutes to complete the sentences. Then have partners share and compare their responses.

Produce Language

On Their Own Have students write about what they have learned about simplifying fractions and then discuss their responses with a partner.

Wrap Up

Table Talk Have students look back at the lesson's objectives. Allow time for them to reflect on what they have learned and then answer the essential question.

☑ **Learned** and applied vocabulary related to simplifying fractions

☑ **Spoken** statements about simplifying fractions

☑ **Written** statements about simplifying fractions

Lesson 6

Fractions, Decimals, and Percents

Vocabulary Whole, part, fraction, numerator, denominator, equivalent, decimal, decimal point, percent, convert

Materials Index cards, colored pencils or markers

Math Background

- To convert a fraction to a decimal, write the fraction with a denominator of 100 and use decimal place value. Or divide the numerator by the denominator.

- To convert a decimal to a percent, move the decimal point to the right two places and write a percent symbol.

Frontload the Lesson

Essential Question How can you use vocabulary terms to talk about fractions, decimals, and percents?

Talk About It

Build Background Ask students to say what they might already know about these terms.

Content and Language

You Will

Model Read the objectives aloud and explain them in your own words. Use diagrams and examples to support your explanations.

Your Turn

Guide Discussion Have students read the objectives. Invite partners to take turns discussing what the objectives mean to them.

Fractions, Decimals, and Percents

Essential Question How can you use vocabulary terms to talk about fractions, decimals, and percents?

You Will
- Identify fractions, decimals, and percents.
- Understand how fractions, decimals, and percents are related.
- Use math vocabulary to talk about fractions, decimals, and percents.

Talk About It

Work with a partner. Make an index card for each vocabulary term below. Place each card in one of three piles.

Pile 1 I know what this term means.
Pile 2 I have heard of this term, but I am not sure how it is used in math.
Pile 3 I have not heard of this term.

percent	convert	part
fraction	equivalent	whole
numerator	denominator	decimal point
decimal		

What do you know about each term? Explain, using the sentence starters for support.

I know ... means ...
I think ... means ...
I do not know what ... means.

Your Turn
Look at the objectives listed under You Will at the top of the page. Working with a partner, predict what you are going to learn. Use the sentence starter below.

I am going to learn about ...

Leveled Instruction

Early Beginner Early beginners may not use many English words in their responses. Encourage them to use gestures and drawings to communicate.

Beginner Have students partner with students of higher English language proficiency to complete activities. Use gestures, drawings, and simple phrases to help beginners understand vocabulary terms and concepts.

Early Intermediate Students benefit from scaffolding of language. Model using sentence starters and sentence frames for support.

Intermediate Students should produce complete sentences in tackling the activities with little assistance.

Advanced/Transitioning Expect students to form sentences of increasing difficulty with minimal assistance. Have advanced students partner with students at lower language proficiency levels to offer them assistance.

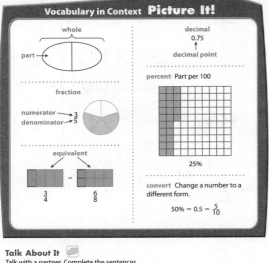

Vocabulary in Context **Picture It!**

whole

part →

decimal
0.75
↑
decimal point

fraction

numerator → $\frac{3}{5}$
denominator →

percent Part per 100

25%

equivalent

$\frac{3}{4}$ = $\frac{6}{8}$

convert Change a number to a different form.
$50\% = 0.5 = \frac{5}{10}$

Talk About It
Talk with a partner. Complete the sentences.
1. 60% is a … **percent**.
2. The top number in a fraction is the … **numerator**.
3. 50% and $\frac{1}{2}$ are … **equivalent**.

Your Turn
Write these numbers: $\frac{4}{10}$, 40%, 0.4. Describe these numbers to a partner. Use as many vocabulary terms as possible.

22 Lesson 6

Academic Vocabulary

- Students may confuse *whole* and *hole*. Point out that a *hole* is an opening, like a hole in the ground. Explain that *whole* describes something that is complete, such as a whole pizza.

- Point out to students that the term *percent* refers to both a type of number and the percent symbol itself. For example, the number 50% is a *percent*; it is said *fifty percent*.

- *Point* (noun vs. verb) may be confusing. Model with gestures and by drawing. Point and say *I point*. Compare a decimal point and a period.

Additional resources for building and reinforcing vocabulary are provided on pages T37–T41.

Cultural Consideration

When numbers are written outside of the United States, decimal points are often used as commas, and vice versa. One million would be written as 1.000.000 and one hundredth would be written 0,01. Clarify this for students.

↻ Comprehensible Input

Guide students to understanding

Vocabulary in Context Picture It!

1. **Say the Term** Have students repeat, stressing each syllable. Then combine syllables and have students repeat.

2. **Introduce Meaning** Connect the term to the visual that illustrates it.

3. **Demonstrate** Use gestures and visuals to reinforce meaning. For example, when teaching the term *equivalent*, stretch out your arms to resemble the two sides of a balance scale. Point out that the scale will only balance when both sides are equivalent in weight.

4. **Apply** Have students demonstrate understanding with Talk About It.

Repeat the routine for each vocabulary term.

Talk About It

Guide Discussion Model the sentence starters. Allow time for students to plan their answers. If time permits, have students complete the following sentence:

The bottom number in a fraction is the … **denominator**.

Intervention

If students have difficulty saying final consonant blends of vocabulary terms …

Then practice the following word pairs aloud: *par/part, Len/lent, her/hurt*.

Your Turn

Guide Discussion Have pairs of students share their discussions from Your Turn.

↻ Language Production

Comprehension Support Tell students that this is a drawing of a quilt. Talk about the dimensions of the quilt.

Model Describe the number of orange squares. Say: *The quilt is made up of 10 rows of 10 squares. This means that the quilt has 100 squares. There are 16 orange squares. So, the quilt is $\frac{16}{100}$ orange squares. That fraction can be simplified to $\frac{4}{25}$. The decimal for $\frac{16}{100}$ is 0.16. And 0.16 is equivalent to 16%. So, I can also say that 16% of the quilt is orange squares.*

Have partners figure out the number of pink squares in the quilt. Then have them write the fraction, decimal, and percent that describe the portion of pink squares in the quilt. Have pairs share their answers in small groups.

Students should be able to do the conversions easily because the denominator of the fraction is 100. Some students might know, or they will learn in math class, that any fraction can be converted to a decimal by dividing the numerator by the denominator. To convert a decimal to a percent, move the decimal point two places to the right and write the percent symbol.

Talk About It

Guide Discussion Have students discuss the sentences with a partner. Remind them that if they need help with the terms, they can check Vocabulary in Context Picture It! on page 22.

Your Turn

Guide Discussion As students plan their responses, you might want to suggest that they use examples in their explanations.

Do You Understand?

Look at the quilt pictured below. Write about the pink squares. Write the fraction, decimal, and percent for the pink squares. Use the numbers for the orange squares as a model.

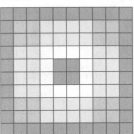

Orange

16 of the 100 squares are orange.

$\frac{16}{100}$, or $\frac{4}{25}$, of the quilt is orange.

0.16 of the quilt is orange.

16% of the quilt is orange.

Pink

40 of the 100 squares are pink.

$\frac{40}{100}$, or $\frac{2}{5}$

0.40, or 0.4

40%

Talk About It 💬

Complete the sentences to tell about fractions, decimals, and percents.

1. Fractions, decimals, and percents show parts of a … whole.
2. $\frac{12}{100}$ is the … of the quilt that is white. fraction
3. 64% equals a fraction with numerator 64 and … 100. denominator
4. $\frac{16}{100}$, 0.16, and 16% are all … equivalent.

Your Turn ✏️

Write a few sentences that describe fractions, decimals, and percents. Use the definitions on page 22 for support.

Leveled Language Proficiency

Students at each proficiency level should be able to perform the following tasks.

Listening/Speaking

Early Beginner Listen to and follow simple directions. Recognize a few vocabulary terms supported by visual cues. Use simple phrases to ask questions.

Beginner Follow basic directions. Listen and respond to simple questions, using some vocabulary terms. Ask questions using longer phrases and short sentences.

Early Intermediate/Intermediate Demonstrate comprehension of oral questions that are based on academic content. Connect new information to background knowledge. Participate in limited discussions using adequate words and phrases.

Advanced/Transitioning Clarify meanings of words both in and out of context. Elaborate on and extend other people's ideas using extended discourse.

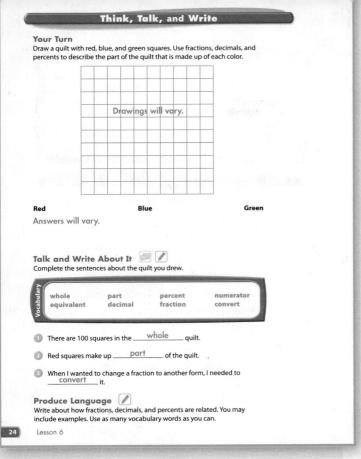

Think, Talk, and Write

Your Turn

Draw a quilt with red, blue, and green squares. Use fractions, decimals, and percents to describe the part of the quilt that is made up of each color.

Drawings will vary.

Red   **Blue**   **Green**

Answers will vary.

Talk and Write About It

Complete the sentences about the quilt you drew.

Vocabulary			
whole	part	percent	numerator
equivalent	decimal	fraction	convert

1. There are 100 squares in the ___whole___ quilt.

2. Red squares make up ___part___ of the quilt.

3. When I wanted to change a fraction to another form, I needed to ___convert___ it.

Produce Language

Write about how fractions, decimals, and percents are related. You may include examples. Use as many vocabulary words as you can.

24   Lesson 6

Leveled Language Proficiency

Students at each proficiency level should be able to perform the following tasks.

Reading/Writing

Early Beginner Understand materials read to them with visual support or the assistance of others. Copy lists of words and read them aloud.

Beginner Identify cognates in printed vocabulary terms. Write lists of words and phrases needed to accomplish an assigned task.

Early Intermediate Apply knowledge of word context to gain meaning from text. Identify the purpose and audience for writing. Organize information for writing.

Intermediate Read lesson vocabulary both in and out of context. Read and comprehend multi-step directions. Read and understand some abstract ideas. Write in full sentences to make ideas clearer and more logical.

Advanced/Transitioning Read content area material with minimal support, including abstract concepts. Enhance precision of language to improve writing.

↻ Assess Understanding

Your Turn

Model Read aloud the directions to students and then say: *This quilt will have a different design. If there are 10 red squares, then $\frac{10}{100}$, or $\frac{1}{10}$, of the quilt is red squares. We could also say 0.10, or 10%, of the quilt is red squares.* Encourage small groups to share their quilt designs. Have them write the fractions, decimals, and percents for each color.

Talk and Write About It

On Their Own Have students work on their own to complete the sentences. Then have pairs of students share and compare their responses.

Produce Language

On Their Own Have students look over the work they did in the lesson to write about what they have learned.

Wrap Up

Table Talk Have students look back at the lesson's objectives. Allow time for them to reflect on what they learned and then answer the essential question.

☑ **Learned** and applied vocabulary related to fractions, decimals, and percents

☑ **Spoken** statements about fractions, decimals, and percents

☑ **Written** statements about fractions, decimals, and percents

Fractions, Decimals, and Percents   **24**

Comparing and Ordering Fractions and Decimals

Vocabulary Point, number line, is less than, is equal to (equals), is greater than, mixed number, order, least to greatest, greatest to least, symbols

Materials Counters, place-value blocks, or number line (optional)

Math Background

- Any two numbers can be compared using the words (and symbols) *is equal to* (=), *is greater than* (>), or *is less than* (<).

- If the order of the numbers in an inequality is reversed, the symbol is also reversed. For example, when comparing 2.7 and 4.5, it is correct to write 4.5 > 2.7 or 2.7 < 4.5.

Frontload the Lesson

Essential Question **How do you use words and symbols (<, >, =) to compare and order fractions and decimals?**

Talk About It

Build Background Have students tell what they know about these terms related to comparing and ordering fractions and decimals.

Content and Language

You Will

Model Read the objectives aloud and explain them in your own words. Use diagrams or a number line to support your explanations.

Your Turn

Guide Discussion Have students read the objectives. Discuss what these objectives mean to them. Invite students to share terms they know or want to learn from their rated list of terms.

Comparing and Ordering Fractions and Decimals

Essential Question How do you use words and symbols (<, >, =) to compare and order fractions and decimals?

You Will
- Use the symbols >, <, and = to compare and order fractions and decimals.
- Use math vocabulary to compare and order fractions and decimals.

Talk About It

Rate these mathematical terms according to the following scale.

1 I do not know this term.

2 I have heard this term, but I do not know how to use it in math.

3 I understand this term and I know how to use it in math.

_____ point	_____ is greater than (>)
_____ number line	_____ mixed number
_____ is less than (<)	_____ is equal to (=)
_____ least to greatest	_____ greatest to least
_____ symbols	_____ order

Explain what you know about each term, using the sentence starters.

I do not know what ... means.
I think ... means ...
I know ... means ... in math.

Your Turn
Look at the objectives under You Will at the top of the page. Working with a partner, predict what you are going to learn. Use the sentence starter for support.

I am going to learn about ...

Comparing and Ordering Fractions and Decimals   25

Leveled Instruction

Early Beginner These students benefit from working with partners of higher language proficiency. Early beginners need more time to organize their thoughts. Encourage these students to use words and gestures to complete activities.

Beginner/Early Intermediate. Students at this level will use phrases and short sentences to complete activities. These students benefit from scaffolded instruction, such as sentence starters. Provide immediate feedback so students can self-correct.

Intermediate Encourage students to speak in simple, complete sentences. You can expect these students to demonstrate comprehension of many words and phrases. Have them repeat their sentences to build fluency.

Advanced/Transitioning Advanced students can successfully synthesize information and use elaborate sentences to complete activities. Encourage students to participate in classroom discussions using basic and complex sentence structures and addressing abstract topics.

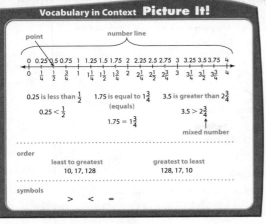

Inside the "Picture It!" panel:

Vocabulary in Context **Picture It!**

point   number line

0 0.25 0.5 0.75 1 1.25 1.5 1.75 2 2.25 2.5 2.75 3 3.25 3.5 3.75 4

0 $\frac{1}{4}$ $\frac{1}{2}$ $\frac{3}{4}$ 1 $1\frac{1}{4}$ $1\frac{1}{2}$ $1\frac{3}{4}$ 2 $2\frac{1}{4}$ $2\frac{1}{2}$ $2\frac{3}{4}$ 3 $3\frac{1}{4}$ $3\frac{1}{2}$ $3\frac{3}{4}$ 4

0.25 is less than $\frac{1}{2}$ 1.75 is equal to $1\frac{3}{4}$ 3.5 is greater than $2\frac{3}{4}$

$0.25 < \frac{1}{2}$ (equals) $3.5 > 2\frac{3}{4}$

$1.75 = 1\frac{3}{4}$

mixed number

order

least to greatest	greatest to least
10, 17, 128	128, 17, 10

symbols   >   <   =

Talk About It

Talk with a partner to complete these sentences.

1. 2.5 > 0.75 means two and five tenths ... seventy-five hundredths. **is greater than**
2. $2\frac{1}{4}$ ... 2.25. **is equal to (or equals, =)**
3. $3\frac{1}{4}$ is a ... **mixed number.**
4. $\frac{1}{4}$ ... 0.75. **is less than (or <)**
5. 2.25 ... $1\frac{1}{2}$. **is greater (or >)**

Your Turn

Tell a partner what you know about the terms and symbols on this page.

Academic Vocabulary

- Discuss words similar in meaning to *greater,* such as *bigger, more,* or *larger.* Also, discuss words similar in meaning to *less,* such as *smaller, fewer,* or *littler.*

- Discuss both the noun and verb interpretations of *order.* Compare and contrast the mathematical meaning of the word *order* with everyday meanings.

Additional resources for building and reinforcing vocabulary are provided on pages T37–T41.

Cultural Consideration

Fractions may be unfamiliar to some students. They may have come from an environment where decimals receive more emphasis than fractions.

↻ Comprehensible Input

Guide students to understanding

Vocabulary in Context Picture It!

1. **Say the Term** Have students repeat, stressing each syllable. Then combine syllables and have students repeat.

2. **Introduce Meaning** Connect the term to the visual that illustrates it.

3. **Demonstrate** Use gestures and visuals to demonstrate. As *is greater than* and *is less than* are discussed, you might want to verify the relative sizes of the two numbers by using counters, place-value blocks, or a number line.

4. **Apply** Have students demonstrate understanding with Talk About It.

Repeat the routine for each vocabulary term.

Talk About It

Guide Discussion Ask students to discuss the sentences with a partner. Encourage them to refer to the number line for help. If time permits, provide the following sentence completion:

$\frac{1}{2}$, 2.5, and 7.2 are listed in order from ... **least to greatest.**

Intervention

If students have trouble remembering the symbols of inequality, > and < ...

Then show them that the smaller part of the "arrow" points to the smaller number.

Your Turn

Guide Discussion Encourage students to provide examples to help explain their understanding of the vocabulary. Some students may wish to draw a number line.

↻ Language Production

Comprehension Support Review *feet*, the unit of measure for this number line.

Model Help students locate the points marked on the number line and determine the value of each one. Then say: *The number lines are marked in fourths of a foot. Look at the point where Grasshopper A landed. It is 2.75, or $2\frac{3}{4}$, feet. Look at the point where Grasshopper B landed. It is 1.5, or $1\frac{1}{2}$, feet. Look at the point where Grasshopper C landed. It is 3.25, or $3\frac{1}{4}$, feet.*

Talk About It

Guide Discussion Have students share the words and symbols they used with a partner. Encourage them to use their own examples to reinforce vocabulary terms.

Your Turn

Guide Discussion Partners can record their work on copies of T44. Have them share their answers and explain how they determined the correct order of the numbers.

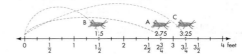

Do You Understand?

The distances three grasshoppers jumped are shown below.

Grasshopper A jumped 2.75 feet. Grasshopper B jumped 1.5 feet. To compare these distances, you can write:

2.75 > 1.5 or 1.5 < 2.75

1. Write Grasshopper C's distance as a decimal. ___3.25___

   Write Grasshopper B's distance as a decimal. ___1.5___

   Compare the distances. ___3.25 > 1.5 (or 1.5 < 3.25)___

2. Write Grasshopper A's distance as a mixed number ___$2\frac{3}{4}$___

   Write the Grasshopper C's distance as a mixed number. ___$3\frac{1}{4}$___

   Compare the distances. ___$2\frac{3}{4} < 3\frac{1}{4}$ (or $3\frac{1}{4} > 2\frac{3}{4}$)___

3. Write one grasshopper's distance as a decimal. ___Answers will vary.___

   Write another grasshopper's distance as a fraction. _____

   Compare the distances. _____

Talk About It
What words and symbols can you use to compare and order numbers? Complete the sentences to explain.

4. The symbol > means … is greater than.
5. The symbol < means … is less than.
6. The symbol = means … equals (or is equal to).

Your Turn
Choose the distance one grasshopper jumped. Compare this number to $2\frac{1}{2}$ and 0.75. Write the three numbers in order from least to greatest.

Leveled Language Proficiency

Students at each proficiency level should be able to perform the following tasks.

Listening/Speaking

Early Beginner Recognize some vocabulary terms. Use pictures, actions, and/or objects to talk about vocabulary terms.

Beginner Identify and follow classroom expectations. Make and respond to oral requests.

Early Intermediate Begin to follow more abstract discussion. Participate orally in activities, using appropriate words, phrases, and expressions.

Intermediate Demonstrate comprehension of subject area content. Participate in reaching consensus in groups. Express abstract ideas about vocabulary terms.

Advanced/Transitioning Understand complex sentence structures; follow abstract conversation involving lesson vocabulary. Speak on abstract topics, including those that involve lesson vocabulary.

Your Turn

Samira ran $4\frac{1}{4}$ miles. John ran 3.75 miles. Estelle ran $5\frac{1}{2}$ miles. Draw a point at each of these numbers. Write the number and the runner's name near each point.

1. The distance Samira ran is greater than (or >) the distance John ran.

2. The distance Estelle ran is greater than (or >) the distance Samira ran.

3. The distance Samira ran is less than (or <) the distance Estelle ran.

4. Write the distances in order from greatest to least. $5\frac{1}{2}$, $4\frac{1}{4}$, 3.75

Talk and Write About It

Complete each sentence about comparing and ordering numbers.

Vocabulary
is greater than (>)   is equal to (=)   is less than (<)   point least to greatest   greatest to least   order   symbols

5. If two numbers are the same, use the symbol ___=___ .

6. If the first number is greater than the second number, use the symbol ___>___ .

7. If you write numbers in order with the biggest one first, they are listed from ___greatest to least___ .

Produce Language

Write what you have learned about comparing and ordering numbers. You may use examples. Include as many vocabulary terms and symbols as you can.

Leveled Language Proficiency

Students at each proficiency level should be able to perform the following tasks.

Reading/Writing

Early Beginner Read and understand previously learned sight words, with help from a partner. Copy words and phrases from the board; write a few vocabulary terms independently.

Beginner/Early Intermediate Read a list of everyday words and most of the vocabulary terms. Use simple sentences with the help of a partner or an adult. Read vocabulary terms independently. Use sentence starters and frames for support.

Intermediate Identify words, phrases, and sentences that determine meaning in extended context. Write complete sentences with some grammar, usage, mechanics, and spelling errors.

Advanced/Transitioning Read and carry out simple and complex written instructions. Write complete sentences with very few errors, using words and phrases to make ideas clearer and more logical.

↻ Assess Understanding

Your Turn

Model Read aloud the directions to students. Discuss the unit of measure, *mile*. Then discuss how to mark the point for Samira. *The number line is divided into fourths. Where should I mark $4\frac{1}{4}$? Remember, you need to write the number and the name near the point.* Have pairs complete the activity.

Talk and Write About It

On Their Own Have students work independently or with a partner to complete the sentences.

Produce Language

On Their Own Have students write what they have learned about comparing and ordering fractions and decimals. Remind them to refer to Vocabulary in Context Picture It! for help. Encourage students to share their responses.

Wrap Up

Table Talk Have students look back at the lesson's objectives. Allow time for them to reflect on what they have learned and then answer the essential question.

- ☑ **Learned** and applied vocabulary related to comparing and ordering fractions and decimals

- ☑ **Spoken** statements about comparing and ordering fractions and decimals

- ☑ **Written** statements about comparing and ordering fractions and decimals

Prime and Composite Numbers

Vocabulary Multiples, divisible, factors, factor pair, prime number, composite number, factor tree, prime factors

 Math Background

- A whole number greater than 1 is either *prime* or *composite*. A prime number has only 1 and itself as *factors*. A composite number has factors other than 1 and itself.

- There is often more than one *factor tree* for a composite number. However, each of these factor trees will display the same prime factors.

⟳ Frontload the Lesson

Essential Question **What vocabulary terms will help you explain prime and composite numbers?**

Talk About It

Build Background Have students complete the first two columns of the Know-Want-Learned chart. (See page T43 for additional copies.) Encourage them to say what they know about familiar terms.

⟳ Content and Language

You Will

Model Read the objectives aloud and explain them in your own words. Use diagrams to support your explanations. Display a composite number so you can write and say its factor pairs.

Your Turn

Guide Discussion Have students read the objectives. Discuss what the objectives mean to them.

Prime and Composite Numbers

Essential Question What vocabulary terms will help you explain prime and composite numbers?

You Will
- Identify prime and composite numbers.
- Use factor trees to break down composite numbers into prime factors.
- Use math vocabulary to explain prime and composite numbers.

Talk About It

Look at the list of terms below. In the first two columns of the chart, write terms you **know** or **want** to know more about.

multiple	factor tree	prime number
factor	composite number	divisible
factor pair	prime factor	

Know	Want	Learned

Tell what you know about each term.

I know the term …
I want to learn …

Your Turn
Look at the objectives under You Will at the top of the page. Working with a partner, predict what you are going to learn. Use the sentence starter for support.

I am going to learn about …

Prime and Composite Numbers `29`

Leveled Instruction

Early Beginner Encourage students to partner with students at higher language proficiency to complete the activities.

Beginner/Early Intermediate It is common for students at this level to use phrases and short sentences to complete activities. These students benefit from repetition such as sentence starters. Self-correction is important at this stage of instruction.

Intermediate Students can demonstrate comprehension of many words and phrases. They are able to speak about some abstract ideas. Have them repeat their sentences to build fluency.

Advanced/Transitioning Students can form sentences of increasing complexity. Therefore, they should be encouraged to model language for students at lower language proficiency. They should be encouraged to use more sophisticated language when they speak and write.

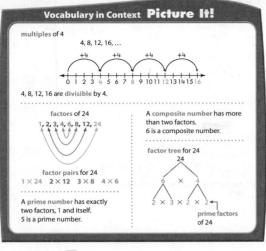

multiples of 4

4, 8, 12, 16, ...

+4   +4   +4   +4

0 1 2 3 4 5 6 7 8 9 10 11 12 13 14 15 16

4, 8, 12, 16 are **divisible** by 4.

factors of 24

1, 2, 3, 4, 6, 8, 12, 24

factor pairs for 24

1 × 24   **2 × 12**   3 × 8   4 × 6

A **prime number** has exactly
two factors, 1 and itself.
5 is a prime number.

A **composite number** has more
than two factors.
6 is a composite number.

factor tree for 24

24

6   ×   4

2 × 3 × 2 × 2

prime factors
of 24

Talk About It

Talk with a partner. Complete the sentences.

① The numbers 5, 10, and 15 are ... by 5. divisible
② The number 8 is a ... of 32. factor
③ The numbers 2, 3, 5, 7, and 11 are ... prime numbers.
④ I can use a factor tree to find a number's ... prime factors.
⑤ There is only one ... for a prime number. factor pair
⑥ The number 12 is a ... composite number.

Your Turn

Write a 2-digit number smaller than 40. Use as many vocabulary terms as
you can to describe your number to a partner.

Academic Vocabulary

- Point out that *factor trees* are not real trees. They
  got their name because they are shaped like the
  tops of trees.

- Tell students there is more than one meaning for
  the term *prime*. Remind them that they learned
  that a *prime* number is divisible only by 1 and
  itself. Explain that prime can also mean valuable,
  first, or important, as in *prime location*, *prime
  meridian,* or *prime time.*

Additional resources for building and reinforcing
vocabulary are provided on pages T37–T41.

↻ Comprehensible Input

Guide students to understanding

Vocabulary in Context Picture It!

1. **Say the Term** Have students repeat,
   stressing each syllable. Then combine
   syllables and have students repeat.

2. **Introduce Meaning** Connect the term to
   the visual that illustrates it.

3. **Demonstrate** Use visuals to demonstrate.
   As you discuss *multiples*, write a multiple
   pattern on the board, such as skip-counting
   by 10s. Skip-count aloud with students and
   touch each number on the board as you say
   the number aloud.

4. **Apply** Have students demonstrate
   understanding with Talk About It.

Repeat the routine for each vocabulary term.

Remind students that they can review
vocabulary terms for multiplication and division
on page 90 and record more terms as they
learn them.

Talk About It

Guide Discussion Have students discuss the
sentences with a partner. Encourage them to use
examples of prime and composite numbers to
reinforce meaning. Then provide this additional
sentence completion, if time permits:

8, 16, 24, and 32 are all ... of 8. multiples

Intervention

If students have trouble remembering the
concept of prime and composite numbers ...

Then have them use a hundred chart to color
in all the multiples of 2, 3, 5, and 7 except 2,
3, 5, and 7. The numbers greater than 1 that
are not colored are prime while the colored
numbers are composite.

Your Turn

Guide Discussion Have students share their
number with a partner. Encourage students to
describe it using vocabulary terms.

Prime and Composite Numbers

↻ Language Production

Comprehension Support Point out the arrangement of 30 chairs. Have students number the six rows.

Model Remind students that the arrangement of chairs is an array. Point out that the number of rows and the number in each row yield a factor pair. *There are 6 rows with 5 in each row. So 6 × 5 is a factor pair for 30.* If students have difficulty coming up with another factor pair, suggest that they draw a different array for 30.

Guide students as they complete the rest of the activity.

Talk About It

Guide Discussion Have students share what they wrote with a partner. Encourage them to come up with other examples to reinforce vocabulary terms.

Your Turn

Guide Discussion Ask students to identify whether the number they chose is prime or composite and to explain why. Partners can record their work on copies of T44.

Do You Understand?

There are 30 chairs in a classroom. They are placed in 6 rows. There are 5 chairs in each row.

1. 6 × 5 is one factor pair for 30. Write another factor pair.

   1 × 30, 2 × 15, or 3 × 10

2. Does 30 have more than 2 factors? <u>yes</u>
   Is 30 a prime number or a composite number? <u>composite number</u>

3. Use the number of chairs in each row to skip count by 5s. Write down the multiples of 5.

   <u>5</u>, <u>10</u>, <u>15</u>, <u>20</u>, <u>25</u>, <u>30</u>

4. Use the factor tree below. Find the prime factors of 30.

   30
   5 × 6
   5 × 2 × 3

5. What are the prime factors of 30?

   5, 2, and 3

Talk About It 💬
What words can you use to talk about prime and composite numbers? Complete the sentences to explain.

6. The numbers 10 and 3 are a ... for 30. factor pair
7. A number that has only two factors is a ... prime number.
8. The numbers 7, 14, 21, and 28 are ... of 7. multiples

Your Turn ✏️
Choose a number from the box. Make a factor tree. Tell your partner whether the number is prime or composite. Explain how you know.

13	20	17
19	22	31

Prime and Composite Numbers   31

Leveled Language Proficiency

Students at each proficiency level should be able to perform the following tasks.

Listening/Speaking

Early Beginner Follow one-step directions and recognize a few vocabulary terms. Use pictures, actions, and/or objects to talk about terms.

Beginner Demonstrate comprehension of one-step oral directions. Ask and respond to questions to clarify information.

Early Intermediate Identify important information about academic content, using visual cues as needed. Employ vocabulary essential for grade-level content learning.

Intermediate Demonstrate comprehension of classroom discussions and interactions when clarification is given. Compare and contrast information orally.

Advanced/Transitioning Understand classroom discussions. Participate in classroom discussions and academic interactions, using basic and complex sentence structures and addressing abstract topics.

Your Turn

In the space below, draw a plan for planting 28 trees. Place trees in more than one row. Put the same number of trees in each row. Then draw a factor tree for 28. **Check students' drawings and factor trees.**

1. How many rows of trees are in your plan? _Answers will vary for 1–3._
2. How many trees are in each row? _____
3. What factor pair is represented by your plan? _____
   What is another factor pair for 28? _____
4. Is 28 a prime or a composite number? __composite__ .
5. What are the prime factors of 28? __2, 2, and 7__ .
6. Is 29 prime or composite? __prime__ .

Talk and Write About It

Complete each sentence about prime and composite numbers.

Vocabulary			
multiples	factor pair	composite numbers	prime numbers
factors	factor tree	prime factors	divisible

7. 35 is __divisible__ by 5.
8. The numbers 1, 2, 4, 8, 16, and 32 are __factors__ of 32.
9. The numbers 2, 3, 5, 7, and 11 are __prime numbers__ .
10. A diagram that helps you find the prime factors of a number is a __factor tree__ .
11. The numbers 2 and 5 are the only __prime factors__ of 10.

Produce Language

Write the terms you learned about in this lesson in the third column of the chart on page 29. Write what you have learned about these terms.

32   Lesson 8

Leveled Language Proficiency

Students at each proficiency level should be able to perform the following tasks.

Reading/Writing

Early Beginner Read and understand previously learned sight words and decodable words with help. Copy words and phrases from the board; write a few vocabulary terms independently.

Beginner Read and understand previously learned sight words and phrases. Write lists of words and phrases needed to accomplish a task.

Early Intermediate Identify, compare, and provide examples of some linguistic features of English in print. Organize information for writing in a way that makes sense for the purpose and the audience.

Intermediate Read and understand some abstract ideas. Identify and use words and phrases to make ideas clearer or more logical. Write complete sentences with some errors.

Advanced/Transitioning Read and write complete sentences that contain concrete and abstract ideas related to lesson vocabulary.

↻ Assess Understanding

Your Turn

Model Read aloud the directions to students. Demonstrate how an arrangement of trees can be drawn. *Suppose I have only 10 trees. I could arrange them like this.* Draw two rows of triangles with 5 triangles in a row. Have student pairs complete the activity.

Talk and Write About It

On Their Own Have students work independently or with a partner to complete the sentences.

Produce Language

On Their Own Have students complete the Know-Want-Learn chart from the beginning of the lesson. Have students write what they have learned about the terms in the third column of the chart and share their ideas with others. If some students did not need to add any terms to the third column, have them write about three or four vocabulary terms.

Wrap Up

Table Talk Have students look back at the lesson's objectives. Allow time for them to reflect on what they have learned and then answer the essential question.

☑ **Learned** and applied vocabulary related to prime and composite numbers

☑ **Spoken** statements about prime and composite numbers

☑ **Written** statements about prime and composite numbers

Greatest Common Factor and Least Common Multiple

Vocabulary Composite number, prime number, common multiples, least common multiple (LCM), common factors, greatest common factor (GCF)

Materials Index cards, colored pencils (red, blue, yellow)

Math Background

- The least common multiple (LCM) of two numbers is the smallest multiple these two numbers have in common.

- The greatest common factor (GCF) of two numbers is the largest factor these two numbers have in common.

Greatest Common Factor and Least Common Multiple

Essential Question How can you use vocabulary terms to discuss greatest common factor and least common multiple?

You Will
- Find the greatest common factor and least common multiple of two or more numbers.
- Use math vocabulary to discuss greatest common factor and least common multiple.

Talk About It

Make an index card for each vocabulary term below. Place each card in one of three piles.

Pile 1 I know what this term means.
Pile 2 I have heard of this term, but I am not sure how it is used in math.
Pile 3 I have not heard of this term.

common factor

prime number	greatest common factor (GCF)
composite number	common multiple
common factor	least common multiple (LCM)

What do you know about each term? Explain, using the sentence starters for support.

I know … means …
I think … means …
I do not know what … means.

Your Turn
Look at the objectives under You Will at the top of the page. Working with a partner, predict what you are going to learn. Use the sentence starter for support.

I am going to learn about …

Frontload the Lesson

Essential Question

How can you use vocabulary terms to discuss greatest common factor and least common multiple?

Talk About It

Build Background Read each word aloud as students sort them. Ask students to tell what they know about the terms they placed in the first two piles.

Content and Language

You Will

Model Read and explain the objectives. Use examples to support your explanations.

Your Turn

Guide Discussion Have students read the objectives. Discuss what these objectives mean to them.

Leveled Instruction

Early Beginner Encourage these students to respond with single words and gestures. It is beneficial for early beginners to partner with students at higher language proficiency to complete the activities.

Beginner Encourage beginning students to speak slowly and consult each other for needed support. Students at this level will use phrases and short sentences to complete activities.

Early Intermediate Encourage students to use sentence starters for support. Provide immediate feedback so students can self-correct.

Intermediate These students are able to speak about some abstract ideas. Encourage them to speak in simple, complete sentences.

Advanced/Transitioning Expect students to form sentences of increasing difficulty. Have them use more sophisticated terms, and encourage them to express themselves using more complex sentence structures.

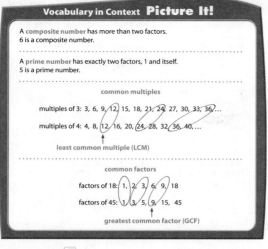

Vocabulary in Context **Picture It!**

A **composite number** has more than two factors.
6 is a composite number.

A **prime number** has exactly two factors, 1 and itself.
5 is a prime number.

common multiples

multiples of 3: 3, 6, 9, 12, 15, 18, 21, 24, 27, 30, 33, 36, …

multiples of 4: 4, 8, 12, 16, 20, 24, 28, 32, 36, 40, …

least common multiple (LCM)

common factors

factors of 18: 1, 2, 3, 6, 9, 18

factors of 45: 1, 3, 5, 9, 15, 45

greatest common factor (GCF)

Talk About It

Talk with a partner. Complete the sentences.

1. The smallest multiple that two numbers share is the … of those numbers. **least common multiple**
2. The numbers 5 and 13 are … **prime numbers.**
3. The largest factor that two numbers share is the … of those numbers. **greatest common factor**
4. A number with more than two factors is a … **composite number**

Your Turn

Choose two different numbers from 1–9. Use vocabulary terms to describe the numbers to a partner. Then find the least common multiple. Explain your work to a partner.

Academic Vocabulary

- Point out the root in the words *multiply* and *multiple*.

- The phrase *least common multiple* may be confusing. "Least common" generally means "most uncommon." Here the term *least* means "smallest" and *common* means "shared." Say: *The least common multiple of two numbers is the smallest multiple these numbers share.*

- As you discuss *least common multiple* and *greatest common factor*, be aware that it may be difficult for students to learn these new terms as well as the abbreviations, LCM and GCF. However, students will need to understand both forms of these new terms because both forms will be used in their math class.

Additional resources for building and reinforcing vocabulary are provided on pages T37–T41.

Comprehensible Input

Guide students to understanding

Vocabulary in Context Picture It!

1. **Say the Term** Have students repeat, stressing each syllable. Then combine syllables and have students repeat.

2. **Introduce Meaning** Connect the term to the visual that illustrates it.

3. **Demonstrate** Use visuals to demonstrate. As you discuss *least common multiple*, draw diagrams to illustrate different examples.

4. **Apply** Have students demonstrate understanding with Talk About It.

Repeat the routine for each vocabulary term.

Remind students that they can review vocabulary terms for multiplication and division on page 90 and record more terms as they learn them.

Talk About It

Guide Discussion Have students discuss the sentences in pairs. If time permits, provide this additional sentence completion:

8 and 12 are … of 2 and 4. **common multiples**

Intervention

If students have trouble identifying the greatest common factor of two numbers …

Then point out that the greatest common factor of two numbers will always be less than or equal to the lesser number.

Your Turn

Guide Discussion Have volunteers offer their numbers and least common multiples. Encourage students to use vocabulary terms as they discuss the numbers with their partner.

↻ Language Production

Comprehension Support Read the directions to Problem 1 and point out the different lengths of the boards. For this problem, tell students that the cut pieces must be a whole number of feet.

Model Starting with 1 × 12, find all of the factor pairs of 12. Do the same with 16. Say: *Numbers that are factors of both 12 and 16 are the factors 12 and 16 have in common, meaning the factors 12 and 16 share.* Guide students through the activity. When students are done, point out that the boards could be cut into equal size pieces using any of the common factors as the length. The *greatest* common factor determines the *longest* piece possible.

Discuss Problem 2. Help students find some of the multiples of 4 and 5. Guide students through the activity. Discuss the results. The common multiples determine where the two rows of bricks will meet evenly, for example, 20, 40, 60, 80 inches, and so on. The *least* common multiple determines the *first* time the bricks line up.

Talk About It

Guide Discussion Have students share their responses with a partner. Encourage them to check each other that they are not confusing least common multiple and greatest common factor.

Your Turn

Guide Discussion Partners can record their work on copies of T44. Have them share how they found the greatest common factor and least common multiple of the two numbers they chose. Then ask pairs to share their work in small groups.

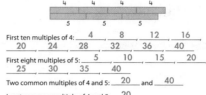

Do You Understand?

1. Find the greatest common factor (GCF) to solve this problem:

Jasmine has a 12-foot board and a 16-foot board. She wants to cut the boards into pieces that are all the same length. What is the longest she can cut those pieces?

| 12 feet | 16 feet |

Factors of 12: 1 2 3 4 6 12
Factors of 16: 1 2 4 8 16
Common factors of 12 and 16: 1 2 4
Greatest common factor of 12 and 16: 4
The longest the pieces can be is __4__ feet.

2. Find the least common multiple (LCM) to solve this problem:

Look at the brick pattern. The top row is made of 4-inch bricks. The bottom row is made of 5-inch bricks. At how many inches will both rows line up?

First ten multiples of 4: 4 8 12 16 20 24 28 32 36 40
First eight multiples of 5: 5 10 15 20 25 30 35 40
Two common multiples of 4 and 5: 20 and 40
Least common multiple of 4 and 5: 20
The bricks will line up at __20__ inches.

Talk About It
Complete the sentences.

3. The largest factor that two numbers share is the ... greatest common factor.

4. The smallest multiple that two numbers share is the ... least common multiple.

Your Turn ✎
Choose two numbers from the box. Write the factors and some multiples of each number. Tell your partner about the greatest common factor and least common multiple of both numbers.

4	5	8
6	9	10

Greatest Common Factor and Least Common Multiple   **35**

Leveled Language Proficiency

Students at each proficiency level should be able to perform the following tasks.

Listening/Speaking

Early Beginner Listen to and follow simple directions. Use words and gestures to communicate ideas.

Beginner Show understanding when simple information is given. Ask and respond to questions to clarify information.

Early Intermediate Clarify meanings of words using beginning and bilingual dictionaries. Participate orally in class activities using appropriate words, phrases, and expressions.

Intermediate Apply knowledge of terms to understand spoken directions and discussions. Participate in classroom discussions and activities when frequent clarification is given.

Advanced/Transitioning Identify characteristics of English words, phrases, and expressions, and compare and contrast them with these features in the students' first language. Support a conclusion or finding by stating facts or logical reasons.

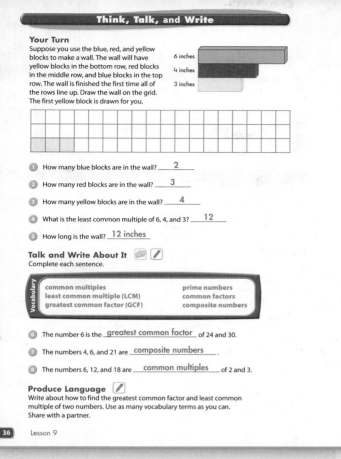

Your Turn

Suppose you use the blue, red, and yellow blocks to make a wall. The wall will have yellow blocks in the bottom row, red blocks in the middle row, and blue blocks in the top row. The wall is finished the first time all of the rows line up. Draw the wall on the grid. The first yellow block is drawn for you.

6 inches
4 inches
3 inches

1. How many blue blocks are in the wall? __2__
2. How many red blocks are in the wall? __3__
3. How many yellow blocks are in the wall? __4__
4. What is the least common multiple of 6, 4, and 3? __12__
5. How long is the wall? _12 inches_

Talk and Write About It
Complete each sentence.

Vocabulary

common multiples	prime numbers
least common multiple (LCM)	common factors
greatest common factor (GCF)	composite numbers

6. The number 6 is the _greatest common factor_ of 24 and 30.
7. The numbers 4, 6, and 21 are _composite numbers_ .
8. The numbers 6, 12, and 18 are _common multiples_ of 2 and 3.

Produce Language
Write about how to find the greatest common factor and least common multiple of two numbers. Use as many vocabulary terms as you can. Share with a partner.

36   Lesson 9

Leveled Language Proficiency

Students at each proficiency level should be able to perform the following tasks.

Reading/Writing

Early Beginner Read for meaning when visual support or the assistance of others is provided. Copy lists of words and read them aloud.

Beginner Understand English words already taught in class. Write lists of words and phrases in English that are needed to accomplish an assigned writing task.

Early Intermediate Identify, compare, and provide examples of the linguistic features of English in print. Write directions, instructions, or explanations with multiple sentences and provide information in logical order.

Intermediate Use word analysis to understand text. Use words and phrases to make ideas clearer or more logical.

Advanced/Transitioning Read and carry out simple and complex written instructions; read sentences about lesson ideas and rephrase ideas and thoughts to express meaning. Revise writing to improve organization of ideas.

↻ Assess Understanding

Your Turn

Model Read aloud the directions to students. Then say: *Draw the wall across the grid. Stop when the edges of the blocks match up evenly.*

Talk and Write About It

On Their Own Have students work in small groups to complete the statements.

Produce Language

On Their Own Have students write about how to find the least common multiple and greatest common factor. Remind them to refer to Vocabulary in Context Picture It! for help. Encourage students to share their responses.

Wrap Up

Table Talk Have students look back at the lesson's objectives. Allow time for them to reflect on what they have learned and then answer the essential question.

☑ **Learned** and applied vocabulary related to greatest common factor and least common multiple

☑ **Spoken** statements about greatest common factor and least common multiple

☑ **Written** statements about greatest common factor and least common multiple

Fraction Operations

Vocabulary Improper fraction, mixed number, reciprocals, equivalent, least common multiple (LCM), common denominator (like denominator), unlike denominators, least common denominator (LCD)

Materials Index cards

Math Background

- An improper fraction can be written as a mixed number or whole number and vice versa.

- Dividing by a fraction is the same as multiplying by its reciprocal.

Frontload the Lesson

Essential Question

What words and symbols should you use when you talk about fraction operations?

Talk About It

Build Background Read each term aloud. Ask students to say what they might already know about these terms.

Content and Language

You Will

Model Read the objectives aloud and explain them in your own words. Use diagrams and fractions to support your explanations.

Your Turn

Guide Discussion Have students read the objectives. Discuss what these objectives mean. Invite partners to take turns discussing what the objectives mean to them.

Essential Question What words and symbols should you use when you talk about fraction operations?

You Will
- Add, subtract, multiply, and divide fractions.
- Use math vocabulary to describe addition, subtraction, multiplication, and division of fractions.

Talk About It

Copy each term from Vocabulary in Context on a card. As your teacher reads each term, create three piles of cards.

1. Place terms that you know in **Pile 1.**
2. Place terms you have heard but are not sure what they mean in **Pile 2.**
3. Place terms you do not know in **Pile 3.**

What do you know about each term? Explain, using the sentence starters for support.

I know … means …
I think … means …
I do not know what … means.

common denominator

mixed number

reciprocal

Your Turn
Look at the objectives listed under You Will at the top of the page. Working with a partner, predict what you are going to learn. Use the sentence starter for support.

I am going to learn about …

Leveled Instruction

Early Beginner May need longer response times to formulate their thoughts and words. Use words, pictures, and gestures to complete activities. Benefit from working with partners of higher language proficiency.

Beginner Speak slowly and confer with each other for needed support. Use phrases and short sentences to complete activities.

Early Intermediate Rely on sentence starters to express ideas. Need immediate feedback to self-correct.

Intermediate Speak in simple, complete sentences. Repeat sentences to build fluency.

Advanced/Transitioning Synthesize information and use elaborate sentences to complete activities. Model speaking for those students of low level language proficiency.

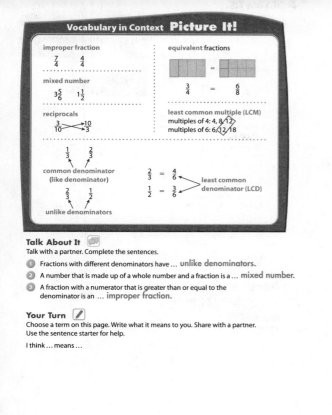

improper fraction

$\frac{7}{4}$ $\frac{4}{4}$

mixed number

$3\frac{5}{6}$ $1\frac{1}{2}$

reciprocals

$\frac{3}{10}$ → $\frac{10}{3}$

equivalent fractions

$\frac{3}{4}$ = $\frac{6}{8}$

least common multiple (LCM)
multiples of 4: 4, 8, 12
multiples of 6: 6, 12, 18

$\frac{1}{3}$ $\frac{2}{3}$
common denominator
(like denominator)

$\frac{2}{3}$ $\frac{1}{2}$
unlike denominators

$\frac{2}{3}$ = $\frac{4}{6}$
$\frac{1}{2}$ = $\frac{3}{6}$ least common denominator (LCD)

Talk About It

Talk with a partner. Complete the sentences.

1. Fractions with different denominators have … **unlike denominators.**
2. A number that is made up of a whole number and a fraction is a … **mixed number.**
3. A fraction with a numerator that is greater than or equal to the denominator is an … **improper fraction.**

Your Turn

Choose a term on this page. Write what it means to you. Share with a partner. Use the sentence starter for help.

I think … means …

Academic Vocabulary

- Be careful with the word *common* as in *common denominator.* A *common denominator* is a denominator that two or more fractions have *in common,* or share. Students who know that *common* can mean *widespread* or *frequent* (e.g., *Sparrows are very common this time of year.*) may be confused by the *common denominator* phrase.

- Even native English speakers can sometimes argue that an improper fraction isn't a "real" fraction because a fraction has to be less than 1. That can be tricky for ELL students, who may have the same notion without necessarily having sufficient English to express it. Make it clear that improper fractions like $\frac{13}{8}$ are acceptable fractions.

- Students with schooling outside the United States may have less experience with fractions because the metric system relies more heavily on decimals for amounts less than one whole.

Additional resources for building and reinforcing vocabulary are provided on pages T37–T41.

↻ Comprehensible Input

Guide students to understanding

Vocabulary in Context Picture It!

1. **Say the Term** Have students repeat, stressing each syllable. Then combine syllables and have students repeat.

2. **Introduce Meaning** Connect the term to the visual that illustrates it.

3. **Demonstrate** Use gestures and visuals to demonstrate. When you discuss *reciprocals,* hold up two flashcards with numbers, one above the other to represent the numerator and denominator of a fraction, and exchange them.

4. **Apply** Have students demonstrate understanding with Talk About It.

Repeat the routine for each vocabulary term.

Remind students that they can review vocabulary terms for the operations on pages 89 and 90 and record more terms as they learn them.

Talk About It

Guide Discussion Have students discuss the sentences with a partner. Then provide this additional sentence completion, if time permits:

10 is the … of 2 and 5. **least common multiple**

Intervention

If students have difficulty with the concept of mixed numbers …

Then write examples of mixed numbers on the board. Say, *We are mixing whole numbers and fractions.* Have students say the sentence with you.

Your Turn

Guide Discussion Have partners practice using the term they have chosen in a sentence. After everyone has the chance to practice, call for volunteers to share their sentences. Have others repeat each shared sentence.

↻ Language Production

Comprehension Support Direct students' attention to the first problem. Read aloud the problem to students. Use vocabulary terms to discuss the problem and the rest of the problems on the page.

Model Talk about the first problem. Be sure students understand that they need to add. Write the addition problem on the board. Students can use the fraction strips to find the sum. Then discuss the computational steps for finding the sum. *These fractions have unlike denominators. Unlike means "not the same, or different." First, we find a common denominator. We list the multiples of 3 and the multiples of 4.* Do this on the board. *12 is the least common multiple. 12 is also the least common denominator. We have to rewrite the fractions with the common denominator.* Discuss the equivalent fractions, referring to the fraction strips if necessary. Rewrite the fractions. *Then, we add the fractions together. Add the numerators and keep the same denominator.* Complete the problem on the board. Then have students work together to complete the other examples on the page.

Talk About It

Guide Discussion Have students complete the Talk About It sentences with a partner. Remind students that if they need help with the terms, they can check the Vocabulary in Context Picture It!

Your Turn

Guide Discussion Have students explain how to divide fractions. Suggest that they use an example in their explanation.

Do You Understand?

1. Mr. Bennett bought two pieces of cloth. One piece is $\frac{1}{3}$ yard and the other is $\frac{1}{4}$ yard. How much cloth did he buy?

$\frac{7}{12}$ yard

2. Complete these examples of fraction operations.

Fraction Addition and Subtraction

- Find the least common denominator.
- Rewrite the fractions.
- Add or subtract the numerators.
- Keep the same denominator.

$\frac{3}{4} - \frac{1}{3} = \frac{9}{12} - \frac{4}{12} = \boxed{\frac{5}{12}}$

Fraction Multiplication

- Multiply the numerators.
- Multiply the denominators.

$\frac{4}{5} \times \frac{2}{3} = \frac{\boxed{8}}{\boxed{15}}$

Fraction Division

- Change the second fraction to its reciprocal.
- Change ÷ to × and multiply.

$2 \div \frac{1}{4} = \frac{2}{1} \times \frac{4}{1} = \boxed{\frac{8}{1}} = \boxed{8}$

Talk About It
Complete the sentences.

3. The fractions $\frac{1}{3}$ and $\frac{4}{12}$ are … equivalent.

4. To add or subtract fractions, first find the … least common denominator.

Your Turn
Talk with a partner. Share what you know about dividing fractions.

Leveled Language Proficiency

Students at each proficiency level should be able to perform the following tasks.

Listening/Speaking

Early Beginner Follow oral directions that are supported by visual cues. Repeat words or simple phrases to answer questions.

Beginner Recognize some vocabulary terms. Answer using pictures, vocabulary terms, simple phrases, or short sentences.

Early Intermediate Begin to follow more abstract discussion about math concepts. Speak in phrases and simple sentences, showing an increasing understanding of vocabulary terms and their relationship to one another.

Intermediate Understand abstract concepts; recognize vocabulary as individual terms and in the context of spoken sentences. Show an ability to express abstract ideas about vocabulary terms.

Advanced/Transitioning Understand complex sentence structures; follow abstract conversation involving lesson vocabulary. Speak on abstract topics, including those that involve lesson vocabulary, with few if any grammatical and syntactical errors.

Your Turn

Choose numbers from the box. Use the numbers to write your own problems using addition, subtraction, multiplication, and division. Solve your problems. Be sure to show your work.

$\frac{1}{2}$ $1\frac{1}{2}$
$\frac{7}{2}$ $\frac{1}{3}$
$\frac{1}{4}$ $2\frac{1}{8}$

addition sentence:

_____ + _____ = _____

subtraction sentence:

_____ − _____ = _____

multiplication sentence:

_____ × _____ = _____

division sentence:

5 ÷ _____ = _____

Talk and Write About It

Complete the sentences about the fractions in the box.

Vocabulary
reciprocals	like denominators
mixed number	least common multiple
improper fraction	unlike denominators

① The denominators of $\frac{7}{2}$ and $\frac{1}{2}$ are <u>like denominators (or common denominators)</u>

② $2\frac{1}{8}$ is a <u>mixed number</u> .

③ The denominators of $\frac{1}{4}$ and $\frac{1}{3}$ are <u>unlike denominators</u> .

Produce Language

Write about the steps you used to solve one of your problems. Use sentence starters for help if needed.

I know how to solve …
First, I …
Then, I …
Last, I …

↻ Assess Understanding

Your Turn

Model Point to the numbers in the box and explain that there are different choices students can make for creating problems. For the subtraction problem tell students to subtract a smaller number from a larger number. For the division problem, tell students to divide 5 by $\frac{1}{2}$, $\frac{1}{3}$, or $\frac{1}{4}$ and remind students of reciprocals. *When you are dividing fractions, you must flip the fraction that follows the division symbol so that the numerator and denominator are switched. Remember, the flipped fraction is called the* reciprocal. *Then switch the divided by symbol to a multiplication symbol and multiply the first fraction by the reciprocal.*

Talk and Write About It

On Their Own Have students work independently to complete the sentences.

Produce Language

On Their Own Have students write about the steps they used to add, subtract, multiply, or divide fractions.

Wrap Up

Table Talk Have students look back at the lesson's objectives. Allow time for them to reflect on what they have learned and then answer the essential question.

☑ **Learned** and applied vocabulary related to fraction operations

☑ **Spoken** statements about fraction operations

☑ **Written** statements about fraction operations

Leveled Language Proficiency

Students at each proficiency level should be able to perform the following tasks.

Reading/Writing

Early Beginner Read a few short, common words and some vocabulary terms, with help from a partner. Copy words and phrases from the board; write a few vocabulary terms independently.

Beginner/Early Intermediate Read some vocabulary terms independently. Use sentence starters to write about vocabulary terms. These students benefit from a partner who is at a higher level of English language acquisition when writing about the vocabulary terms.

Intermediate Read and comprehend lesson vocabulary in context and read simple directions independently. Write complete sentences with some grammar, usage, mechanics, and spelling errors.

Advanced/Transitioning Read and carry out simple and complex written instructions; read sentences about lesson ideas and rephrase ideas and thoughts to express meaning. Write complete sentences with very few errors, using words and phrases to make ideas clearer and more logical.

Lesson 11

Ratios

Vocabulary Ratio, equal ratios, table, data, data set, simplify

Math Background

- A ratio is a comparison of two quantities.

- The colon in a ratio replaces the word *to* (3 : 1 and 3 to 1). The colon notation is often used on maps or scale drawings to show the scale.

- An equal ratio is formed when both terms of a ratio are multiplied or divided by the same nonzero number.

Frontload the Lesson

Essential Question

How can you use vocabulary terms to talk about ratios?

Talk About It

Build Background Have students rate the terms as described. Encourage them to say what they know about familiar terms.

Content and Language

You Will

Model Read the objectives aloud and explain them in your own words. Use diagrams and symbols to support your explanations.

Your Turn

Guide Discussion Have students read the objectives. Discuss what they mean. Ask students to tell what the objectives mean to them.

Ratios

Essential Question How can you use vocabulary terms to talk about ratios?

You Will
- Use data and models to find ratios.
- Multiply and divide to make equal ratios.
- Use math vocabulary to talk and write about ratios.

Talk About It

Rate these mathematical terms according to the following scale.

1. I do not know this term.
2. I have heard this term, but I do not know how to use it in math.
3. I understand this term and I know how to use it in math.

_____ ratio   _____ table
_____ equal ratios   _____ data
_____ simplify   _____ data set

Explain what you know about each term, using the sentence starters.

I do not know what … means.
I think … means …
I know … means … in math.

Your Turn
Look at the objectives under You Will at the top of the page. Working with a partner, predict what you are going to learn. Use the sentence starter for support.

I am going to learn about …

Leveled Instruction

Early Beginner Early beginners can benefit the most from partnering with students at higher language proficiency to complete activities.

Beginner/Early Intermediate These students most often use phrases and short sentences to communicate their ideas. They benefit from scaffolded instruction, such as sentence starters.

Intermediate Encourage students to use sentence starters as support, and to repeat them to build fluency. These students are able to speak in simple, complete sentences.

Advanced/Transitioning Expect these students to classify previously learned vocabulary terms and phrases into concept-based categories. Encourage advanced students to work with students of low level language proficiency.

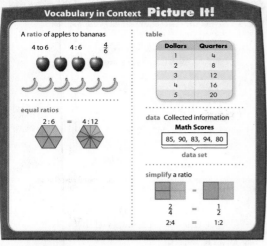

Vocabulary in Context **Picture It!**

A **ratio** of apples to bananas

4 to 6   4 : 6 $\frac{4}{6}$

equal ratios

2 : 6 = 4 : 12

table

Dollars	Quarters
1	4
2	8
3	12
4	16
5	20

data Collected information
Math Scores

85, 90, 83, 94, 80

data set

simplify a ratio

$\frac{2}{4}$ = $\frac{1}{2}$

2:4 = 1:2

Talk About It
Talk with a partner. Complete the sentences.

① A group of information is called a … data set.

② 9 : 5, $\frac{9}{5}$, and 9 to 5 are three different ways to write a … ratio.

③ 2 : 4 and 3 : 6 are … equal ratios.

Your Turn
Write and/or draw what you know about the terms on this page. Tell your partner what you know about them.

Academic Vocabulary

- Point out that the word *simplify* is made up of the word *simple* and the suffix *-ify,* which means "to make." Explain that *simplify* means "to make simple."

- Tell students that a table is not always a piece of furniture. In math, a table is a chart used to show facts in an easy-to-read way.

Additional resources for building and reinforcing vocabulary are provided on pages T37–T41.

♻ Comprehensible Input
Guide students to understanding

Vocabulary in Context Picture It!

1. **Say the Term** Have students repeat, stressing each syllable. Then combine syllables and have students repeat.

2. **Introduce Meaning** Connect the term to the visual that illustrates it.

3. **Demonstrate** Use gestures and visuals to demonstrate. As you discuss equal ratios, you might want to use equivalent fractions to reinforce that equal quantities can be represented in different ways.

4. **Apply** Have students demonstrate understanding with Talk About It.

Repeat the routine for each vocabulary term.

Talk About It

Guide Discussion Have students discuss their responses with a partner. Then provide this additional sentence completion, if time permits:

You can show information in a graph, chart, or … table.

Intervention

If students have trouble pronouncing the word *ratio* …

Then show students the *tio* combination in other words, such as *station, fraction,* and *motion.* Help students spell and pronounce each word. Point out that the long *o* is pronounced in ratio, but it is not pronounced in the other words.

Your Turn

Guide Discussion Encourage students to use their own words or examples to explain the vocabulary terms. Have partners share their ideas.

↻ Language Production

Comprehension Support Read the problem at the top of the page. Then read the title and column heads in the table.

Model Stress that every time Tabby eats one bowl of food, Wags eats twice as much. Be sure students understand *twice*. Then say: *Look at the data in the first row of numbers in the table. It shows that when Tabby eats 1 bowl of food, Wags eats 2 bowls. The next row shows that when Tabby eats 2 bowls, Wags eats 4. Continue this pattern to fill in the missing numbers in the table.*

Talk About It

Guide Discussion Have students complete the Talk About It sentences in pairs. Remind students that if they need help with the terms, they can check the Vocabulary in Context Picture It!

Your Turn

Guide Discussion Have partners share their ideas. Some students might draw pictures or use the table to justify that the ratios are equal. Since ratios can be written as fractions, some students might draw on their knowledge of fractions. They might explain that if they simplify each one, they get the original ratio of $\frac{1}{2}$.

Do You Understand?

Each time Dan's cat, Tabby, eats 1 bowl of cat food, his dog, Wags, eats 2 bowls of dog food. Complete the table.

Bowls of Food Dan's Pets Eat

Tabby	Wags
1	2
2	4
3	6
4	8
5	10
6	12
7	14

Use the table to write three equal ratios that compare the number of bowls of cat food to the number of bowls of dog food. **Sample answer is given.**

$$\frac{1}{2} = \frac{2}{4} = \frac{7}{14}$$

Talk About It 💬
What terms can you use to talk about ratios? Complete the sentences to explain.

1. Collected information is called … data.
2. 2 : 3 is the same as 4 : 6 because they are … equal ratios.
3. You change 6 : 12 to 1 : 2 when you … simplify.

Your Turn ✏️
Look back at the three ratios you wrote about bowls of pet food. Write to explain how you know the three ratios are equal. Use vocabulary terms. Share your answer with a partner.

Leveled Language Proficiency

Students at each proficiency level should be able to perform the following tasks.

Listening/Speaking

Early Beginner Use pictures, actions, and/or objects to demonstrate comprehension. Ask and respond to questions to clarify information.

Beginner/Early Intermediate Identify important information about academic content, using prior knowledge and/or visual cues as needed. Retell steps of a process in logical order.

Intermediate Demonstrate comprehension of oral, multiple-step directions. Participate in classroom discussions and activities when frequent clarification is given.

Advanced/Transitioning Understand words and phrases of grade-level academic content, including technical and abstract terms. Communicate academic language orally, using specific, technical, and abstract vocabulary of grade-level academic content.

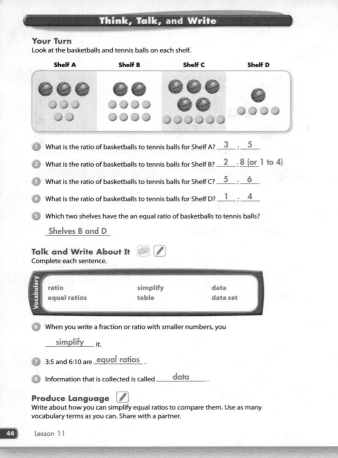

Think, Talk, and Write

Your Turn

Look at the basketballs and tennis balls on each shelf.

Shelf A   Shelf B   Shelf C   Shelf D

1. What is the ratio of basketballs to tennis balls for Shelf A? _3_ : _5_

2. What is the ratio of basketballs to tennis balls for Shelf B? _2_ : _8_ (or 1 to 4)

3. What is the ratio of basketballs to tennis balls for Shelf C? _5_ : _6_

4. What is the ratio of basketballs to tennis balls for Shelf D? _1_ : _4_

5. Which two shelves have the an equal ratio of basketballs to tennis balls?

   Shelves B and D

Talk and Write About It

Complete each sentence.

Vocabulary		
ratio	simplify	data
equal ratios	table	data set

6. When you write a fraction or ratio with smaller numbers, you

   simplify it.

7. 3:5 and 6:10 are _equal ratios_ .

8. Information that is collected is called _data_ .

Produce Language

Write about how you can simplify equal ratios to compare them. Use as many vocabulary terms as you can. Share with a partner.

44   Lesson 11

↻ Assess Understanding

Your Turn

Model Discuss the pictures and then read Problem 1 aloud to students. Say: *There are 3 basketballs and 5 tennis balls. The ratio is 3: 5.* Have students complete Problems 2–5.

Talk and Write About It

On Their Own Have students work with a partner to complete the sentences.

Produce Language

On Their Own Have students write about how they can simplify equal ratios to compare them. Suggest that they look back to the equal ratios in Problem 5 on this page and the problem under the table on page 43.

Wrap Up

Table Talk Have students look back at the lesson's objectives. Allow time for them to reflect on what they have learned and then answer the essential question.

☑ **Learned** and applied vocabulary related to ratios

☑ **Spoken** statements about ratios

☑ **Written** statements about ratios

Leveled Language Proficiency

Students at each proficiency level should be able to perform the following tasks.

Reading/Writing

Early Beginner Read and understand learned sight words and some vocabulary terms with help. Copy words and phrases from the board. Write a few vocabulary terms independently.

Beginner Identify cognates in printed, grade-level, academic content vocabulary terms. Write lists of words and phrases needed to accomplish a task.

Early Intermediate Apply knowledge of word context to gain meaning from text. Organize information to be expressed in writing.

Intermediate Identify words, phrases, and sentences that determine meaning in extended text. Use words and phrases to make ideas clearer or more logical.

Advanced/Transitioning Read and carry out simple and complex instructions; read sentences about lesson ideas that use lesson vocabulary. Increase detail and precision of language to improve writing skills.

Variables

Vocabulary Expression, equation, equals, variable, missing number, represent, algebraic expression, algebraic equation, inverse operations, solve, value, solution

Math Background

- A variable is a shape, letter, or symbol that stands for a number. Its value can vary.

- Two operations are inverses if they "undo" each other. For example, addition and subtraction are *inverse operations*: subtracting 6 is the inverse of adding 6.

↻ Frontload the Lesson

Essential Question

What words do you need to know to discuss variables?

Talk About It

Build Background Read the terms aloud and have students complete the first two columns of the Know-Want-Learn chart. Ask volunteers to tell what they already know about the terms they wrote in these columns. (See page T43 for additional copies of the chart.)

↻ Content and Language

You Will

Model Read the objectives aloud and explain them in your own words. Use diagrams and symbols to support your explanations.

Your Turn

Guide Discussion Have students read the objectives. Discuss what these objectives mean. Invite partners to take turns discussing what the objectives mean to them.

Variables

Essential Question What words do you need to know to discuss variables?

You Will
- Identify variables.
- Write algebraic expressions.
- Use math vocabulary to discuss variables.

Talk About It

Look at the list of terms below. In the first two columns of the chart, write terms you **know** or **want** to know more about.

variable	algebraic equation	missing number	inverse operations
expression	equals	solve	represents
equation	algebraic expression	solution	value

Know	Want	Learned

Tell what you know about each term.

I know the term …
I want to learn …

Your Turn
Look at the objectives under You Will at the top of the page. Working with a partner, predict what you are going to learn. Use the sentence starter for support.

I am going to learn about …

Variables 45

Leveled Instruction

Early Beginner Students may not use many English words in their responses. Encourage them to use gestures and pictures to communicate. Partner these students with students of higher English language proficiency.

Beginner Have students partner with students of higher English language proficiency to complete activities. Expect short and simple sentences as responses.

Early Intermediate Encourage students to use sentence starters for support. Model using these sentence starters if necessary.

Intermediate Encourage students to express their ideas without sentence starters if possible. They should use complete sentences. Anticipate some grammatical errors.

Advanced/Transitioning Expect students to form sentences of increasing complexity. Have them use more advanced terms, and encourage them to try new sentence structures.

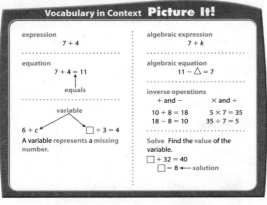

Vocabulary in Context **Picture It!**

expression	algebraic expression
7 + 4	7 + k

equation	algebraic equation
7 + 4 = 11	11 − △ = 7

equals

variable

inverse operations

+ and −	× and ÷
10 + 8 = 18	5 × 7 = 35
18 − 8 = 10	35 ÷ 7 = 5

$6 + c$ $\square ÷ 3 = 4$

A variable represents a missing number.

Solve Find the value of the variable.

$\square + 32 = 40$
$\square = 8 \leftarrow$ solution

Talk About It
Talk with a partner. Complete the sentences.

① The △ in 5 + △ is a … variable or missing number.
② 8 − 3 is an … expression.
③ = means … equals.
④ 8 × b is an … algebraic expression.
⑤ 15 ÷ 3 = 5 is an … equation.
⑥ Multiplication and division are … inverse operations.

Your Turn
Think about the new vocabulary terms.

- Write an algebraic equation. Use *a* as the variable.
- Have your partner solve your equation.
- Use vocabulary terms to discuss your partner's work.

Academic Vocabulary

- Point out and discuss the shared word parts in *vary, variable* and *equal, equation*.

- Explain the difference between an expression (a saying) and a math expression (a phrase with numbers and variables). Be sure students understand that an *expression* has no equal sign, whereas an *equation* does.

- Explain the relationship between *solve* and *solution*. Show students that when you solve a problem, the answer is the solution. Highlight the common letters *sol*. Clarify that in the words *solve* and *solution* there is no relation to the Spanish word *sol*, which means *sun*.

- Explain that variables are often lower-case letters. Caution students not to confuse the commonly used variable *x* and the multiplication symbol ×.

- Explain that *algebra* is the branch of mathematics that studies expressions and equations that contain variables. That is why expressions and equations with variables are called *algebraic expressions* and *algebraic equations*, respectively.

Additional resources for building and reinforcing vocabulary are provided on pages T37–T41.

↻ Comprehensible Input
Guide students to understanding

Vocabulary in Context Picture It!

1. **Say the Term** Have students repeat, stressing each syllable. Then combine syllables and have students repeat.

2. **Introduce Meaning** Connect the term to the visual that illustrates it.

3. **Demonstrate** Use gestures and visuals to demonstrate. When you discuss *equations*, write an equal sign on a note card and hold it up.

4. **Apply** Have students demonstrate understanding with Talk About It.

Repeat the routine for each vocabulary word.

Talk About It

Guide Discussion Have pairs discuss the sentences with a partner. Encourage them to use examples of expressions and equations to reinforce meaning. If time permits, provide this additional sentence completion:

8 + *g* is an expression (or algebraic expression), but 8 + *g* = 13 is an … **equation (or algebraic equation).**

Intervention

If students have difficulty differentiating between *expression* and *equation* …

Then show students the equal sign in the equation, and have students hold up a card showing *expression* or *equation* as you say the words aloud.

Your Turn

Guide Discussion Ask students to use vocabulary terms to describe their equation. Then have them use vocabulary terms to explain their partner's solution.

Variables

⟳ Language Production

Comprehension Support Point out the first problem at the top of the page. Read aloud the problem for students. Use vocabulary terms to discuss both problems on the page.

Model Point out the difference between an expression and an equation. Say: *"6 × △" by itself is an expression. We are not able to solve it because we only know that there are six boxes with an equal number of golf balls inside. When we write "= 72," it becomes an equation and tells us we have a total of 72 golf balls.* Work through each step of the problem together with students, describing the steps aloud. Ask students how they figured out the solution, 12. If they mention that they divided, point out that that is a good strategy for solving multiplication equations because multiplication and division are *inverse operations*.

Talk About It

Guide Discussion Have students complete the Talk About It sentences with a partner. Remind students that if they need help with the terms, they can check the Vocabulary in Context Picture It!

Your Turn

Guide Discussion Have students use the sentence starters to help them plan what they are going to say. Then have them share with a partner.

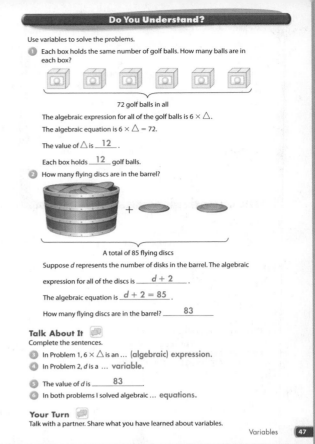

Do You Understand?

Use variables to solve the problems.

1. Each box holds the same number of golf balls. How many balls are in each box?

72 golf balls in all

The algebraic expression for all of the golf balls is $6 \times \triangle$.

The algebraic equation is $6 \times \triangle = 72$.

The value of $\triangle$ is __12__.

Each box holds __12__ golf balls.

2. How many flying discs are in the barrel?

A total of 85 flying discs

Suppose *d* represents the number of disks in the barrel. The algebraic expression for all of the discs is __$d + 2$__.

The algebraic equation is __$d + 2 = 85$__.

How many flying discs are in the barrel? __83__

Talk About It 💬
Complete the sentences.

3. In Problem 1, $6 \times \triangle$ is an … (algebraic) expression.

4. In Problem 2, *d* is a … variable.

5. The value of *d* is __83__

6. In both problems I solved algebraic … equations.

Your Turn 💬
Talk with a partner. Share what you have learned about variables.

Variables **47**

Leveled Language Proficiency

Students at each proficiency level should be able to perform the following tasks.

Listening/Speaking

Early Beginner Recognize a few vocabulary terms and follow very simple conversations with support. Repeat simple phrases, and use vocabulary terms to answer questions. Need continuous repetition to be able to internalize what answers are appropriate for the questions being asked.

Beginner Follow simple directions. Recognize and use some vocabulary terms. Say individual terms and simple phrases, and repeat longer phrases and short sentences.

Early Intermediate Begin to follow more abstract discussion about vocabulary terms. Speak in phrases and simple sentences, showing an increasing understanding of lesson vocabulary.

Intermediate Understand abstract ideas. Show an ability to express abstract ideas about vocabulary.

Advanced/Transitioning Understand complex sentence structures. Speak on abstract topics, including those that involve lesson vocabulary, with few errors.

Your Turn

Each bag holds the same number of jump ropes. How many jump ropes are in each bag?

4 of the same bags

28 jump ropes in all

Use the variable *j* to represent the number of jump ropes in each bag.

An algebraic expression for all of the jump ropes is ___ $4 \times j$ ___.

An algebraic equation is ___ $4 \times j = 28$ ___.

The value of *j* is ___ 7 ___.

There are ___ 7 ___ jump ropes in each bag.

Talk and Write About It

Complete the sentences about the problems you solved.

Vocabulary		
variable	equal	algebraic equation
expression	equation	algebraic expression
missing number	solve	inverse operations

1 In the problem, *j* is a ___ variable ___.

2 The equation has an ___ equal ___ sign.

3 $5 \times r$ is an ___ algebraic expression ___.

4 When you find the value of the variable, you ___ solve ___ the equation.

Produce Language

Write the terms you learned about in this lesson in the third column of the chart on page 45. Write what you have learned about these terms. Use sentence starters from throughout the lesson for support.

48   Lesson 12

Leveled Language Proficiency

Students at each proficiency level should be able to perform the following tasks.

Reading/Writing

Early Beginner Read and understand learned sight words and some vocabulary terms with help. Copy words and phrases from the board. Write a few vocabulary terms independently.

Beginner Identify cognates in printed, grade-level, academic content vocabulary terms. Write lists of words and phrases needed to accomplish a task.

Early Intermediate Apply knowledge of word context to gain meaning from text. Organize information to be expressed in writing.

Intermediate Identify words, phrases, and sentences that determine meaning in extended text. Use words and phrases to make ideas clearer or more logical.

Advanced/Transitioning Read and carry out simple and complex instructions; read sentences about lesson ideas that use lesson vocabulary. Increase detail and precision of language to improve writing skills.

↻ Assess Understanding

Your Turn

Model Read the directions and the problem with students. Remind students of the difference between an expression and an equation. Then say: *Use the variable* j *in your expression and equation for this problem.* Have students solve the problem, offering support as needed.

Talk and Write About It

On Their Own Have pairs work together to complete the sentences.

Produce Language

On Their Own Have students complete the Know-Want-Learn chart from the beginning of the lesson. Have students write what they have learned about these terms and share their ideas with others. If students did not need to write any terms in the third column, have them write about three or four terms from this lesson.

Wrap Up

Table Talk Have students look back at the lesson's objectives. Allow time for them to reflect on what they have learned and then answer the essential question.

☑ **Learned** and applied vocabulary related to variables

☑ **Spoken** statements about variables

☑ **Written** statements about variables

Lesson 13

The Coordinate Plane

Vocabulary Coordinate plane, ordered pair, point, *y*-axis, origin, *x*-axis, quadrant, integers, negative integers, positive integers, coordinates, *x*-coordinate, *y*-coordinate

Materials Index cards, meter stick or yardstick

Math Background

- Integers cannot have fractional or decimal parts. 0 is an integer, but it is neither positive nor negative.

- A *coordinate plane* is divided into 4 *quadrants* by the *x-axis* and *y-axis*.

- The *x*-coordinate in an ordered pair gives the horizontal distance and direction from the *origin*, (0, 0). The *y*-coordinate gives the vertical distance and direction from the origin.

Frontload the Lesson

Essential Question What terms do you need to use and understand when you discuss the coordinate plane?

Talk About It

Build Background Have students create cards as described. Read each word aloud as students sort them into piles. Model responses.

Content and Language

You Will

Model Read the objectives aloud and explain them in your own words. Use diagrams and grids to support your explanations.

Your Turn

Guide Discussion Have students tell what the objectives mean to them.

The Coordinate Plane

Essential Question What terms do you need to use and understand when you discuss the coordinate plane?

You Will
- Find points on the coordinate plane.
- Name points on the coordinate plane.
- Use math vocabulary to discuss the coordinate plane.

Talk About It

Make an index card for each vocabulary term below. Place each card in one of three piles.

Pile 1 I know what this term means.
Pile 2 I have heard of this term, but I am not sure how it is used in math.
Pile 3 I have not heard of this term.

integers	negative integer	positive integer
coordinate plane	point	ordered pair
y-axis	*y*-coordinate	*x*-axis
x-coordinate	origin	quadrant
coordinates		

What do you know about each term? Explain, using the sentence starters for support.

I know … means …
I think … means …
I do not know what … means.

Your Turn
Look at the objectives under You Will at the top of the page. Working with a partner, predict what you are going to learn. Use the sentence starter for support.

I am going to learn about …

Leveled Instruction

Early Beginner Encourage students to use single words, gestures, and pictures. Allow for more wait time so students can organize their thoughts.

Beginner Encourage beginning students to speak slowly and consult each other for needed support. Students at this level will use phrases and short sentences.

Early Intermediate Encourage early intermediate students to use sentence starters for support. Provide immediate feedback so students can self-correct.

Intermediate These students are able to speak about some abstract ideas. They often recognize vocabulary as individual terms and in the context of spoken sentences.

Advanced/Transitioning Advanced students can form sentences of increasing complexity. Have them use more advanced terms, and encourage them to try new sentence structures.

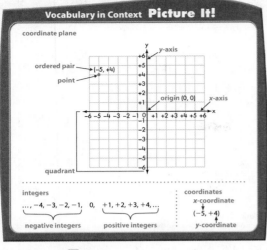

Vocabulary in Context Picture It!

coordinate plane

ordered pair → (−5, +4)
point

origin (0, 0)
y-axis
x-axis

quadrant

integers
..., −4, −3, −2, −1,   0,   +1, +2, +3, +4, ...

negative integers   positive integers

coordinates
x-coordinate
(−5, +4)
y-coordinate

Talk About It

Talk with a partner. Complete the sentences.

1. The numbers −1, −3, and −6 are all ... **negative integers (or integers).**
2. A coordinate plane has four ... **quadrants.**
3. The x-axis and y-axis cross at the ... **origin.**
4. In the ordered pair (−6, +3), the integer +3 is the ... **y-coordinate.**
5. In the ordered pair (−4, +1), the integer −4 is the ... **x-coordinate.**

Your Turn

Draw a point on the coordinate plane. Tell a partner as much as you can about the point. Use the sentence starters for help.

The ordered pair is ...

The y-coordinate is ...

Academic Vocabulary

- Differentiate between a plane (airplane) and a *coordinate plane* as used in math (flat or level surface for graphing points and lines).

- Stress that the *order* of the numbers is important in an *ordered pair*.

- Explain the difference between the meanings and pronunciations of *coordinate* ("arranging things in order" and "working together") and *coordinates* (numbers that show where a point is).

- Point out that *quad-* implies four, as in four *quadrants* and four sides of a *quadrilateral*.

Additional resources for building and reinforcing vocabulary are provided on pages T37–T41.

↻ Comprehensible Input

Guide students to understanding

Vocabulary in Context Picture It!

1. **Say the Term** Have students repeat, stressing each syllable. Then combine syllables and have students repeat.

2. **Introduce Meaning** Connect the term to the visual that illustrates it.

3. **Demonstrate** Use gestures and visuals to demonstrate. Hold a meterstick or yardstick *horizontally* to demonstrate *x-axis*. Hold it vertically to demonstrate *y-axis*. Then draw the axes on the board to create a *coordinate plane* and an *origin*.

4. **Apply** Have students demonstrate understanding with Talk About It.

Repeat the routine for each vocabulary term.

Talk About It

Guide Discussion Have students discuss the sentences with a partner. Encourage students to look at the coordinates, and whether they are positive or negative. Then provide this additional sentence completion if time permits:

A plus sign in front of an integer means that the number is a ... **positive integer.**

Intervention

If students have trouble distinguishing the x and y in the vocabulary terms, ...

Then point out that x comes before y in the alphabet, so the x-coordinate comes before the y-coordinate in an ordered pair.

Your Turn

Guide Discussion Model plotting a point and locating the coordinates. Then have students work with partners to talk about the point.

↻ Language Production

Comprehension Support Turn students' attention to the city map. Point out the locations and corresponding points on the map.

Model Have students locate the point that represents Jeff's house. Then say: *The ordered pair (+5, +4) tells us the location of Jeff's house. The x-coordinate is shown in green. The green arrow tells us to move to the right +5 along the x-axis. The y-coordinate is shown in blue. The blue arrow tells us to move up +4.* Guide students through the remainder of the activity. In Problem 3, explain that a unit is the distance on the grid from one integer to the next.

Point out to students that sometimes the little plus sign is not shown in front of a positive integer. Stress that whenever an integer has no sign, it is a positive integer.

Talk About It

Guide Discussion Have students complete the Talk About It sentences on their own. Then have them work in pairs or small groups to discuss their answers. Encourage students to check one another by referring to the definitions in Vocabulary in Context Picture It!

Your Turn

Guide Discussion Have students work in pairs. For extra practice, have one partner mark a point and ask the other partner, "What are the coordinates for my point?" The other student should respond, "The x-coordinate is …. The y-coordinate is …."

Do You Understand?

Look at the city map. Fill in the missing coordinates.

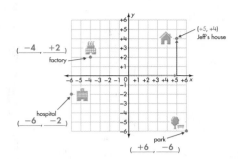

Talk About It 💬
Complete the sentences about the city map.

1. Each location on the map is described by an … ordered pair.
2. Both coordinates for Jeff's House are … positive integers.
3. The park is 6 units below the … x-axis.
4. The point at (0, 0) is called the … origin.
5. The x-coordinate for the hospital is a … negative integer.
6. The map is drawn on the … coordinate plane.

Your Turn 💬
Choose an x-coordinate and a y-coordinate from the lists below. Tell a partner how to use the two coordinates to draw a point on the coordinate plane.

x-coordinate	**y-coordinate**
−5 −3 −1 +2 +3	−6 −4 −2 +4 +5

Leveled Language Proficiency

Students at each proficiency level should be able to perform the following tasks.

Listening/Speaking

Early Beginner Use pictures, objects, and actions to demonstrate comprehension of vocabulary. Use simple phrases to ask questions and clarify information.

Beginner Follow basic directions. Listen and respond to simple questions, using some vocabulary terms. Ask questions using longer phrases and short sentences.

Early Intermediate/Intermediate Demonstrate comprehension of oral questions that are based on academic content. Connect new information to background knowledge. Participate in limited discussions using adequate words and phrases.

Advanced/Transitioning Obtain information from a variety of sources. Increase detail and precision to improve writing.

Your Turn

Four families are planning a camping trip. A map of the campground is drawn on the coordinate plane. Help the families plan where to set up their four tents. Put each one in a different quadrant. Draw a point and write the ordered pair.
Answers will vary.

(___ , ___)   (___ , ___)

(___ , ___)   (___ , ___)

Talk and Write About It
Complete the sentences.

Vocabulary		
y-coordinate	x-axis	coordinate plane
y-axis	origin	ordered pair
x-coordinate	point	

1. An ordered pair gives the location of a point on the <u>coordinate plane</u> .

2. The second number in an ordered pair is the <u>y-coordinate</u> .

3. The origin is where the x-axis crosses the <u>y-axis</u> .

Produce Language
Write about how positive and negative integers can help you find places on the coordinate plane. Use as many vocabulary terms as you can. Share with a partner.

52   Lesson 13

Leveled Language Proficiency

Students at each proficiency level should be able to perform the following tasks.

Reading/Writing

Early Beginner Read for meaning when visual support or the assistance of others is provided. Copy lists of words and read them aloud.

Beginner Identify cognates in printed grade-level academic content vocabulary terms. Write lists of words and phrases needed to accomplish an assigned task.

Early Intermediate Apply knowledge of word context to gain meaning from text. Identify the purpose and audience for writing. Organize information for writing.

Intermediate Identify words, phrases, and sentences that determine meaning in text. Use words and phrases to make ideas clearer and more logical.

Advanced/Transitioning Read content area material with minimal support, including abstract concept. Increase detail and precision of language to improve writing.

⟳ Assess Understanding

Your Turn

Model Discuss camping in tents at a campground. Ask clarifying questions so that students understand the four quadrants. Ask: *Suppose I put a tent at (+6, −3).* Have students point to the quadrant that contains that point.

Talk and Write About It

On Their Own Have students work in pairs to complete the sentences about the coordinate plane.

Produce Language

On Their Own Have students work independently to write what they have learned about positive and negative numbers on the coordinate plane. Remind them to refer to Vocabulary in Context Picture It! for assistance, if needed. Encourage students to share their writing with others.

Wrap Up

Table Talk Have students look back at the lesson's objectives. Allow time for them to reflect on what they have learned and then answer the essential question.

☑ **Learned** and applied vocabulary related to the coordinate plane

☑ **Spoken** statements about the coordinate plane

☑ **Written** statements about the coordinate plane

Graphs of Equations

Vocabulary Variables, ordered pair, *x*-coordinate, *y*-coordinate, table of values, *x*-values, *y*-values, coordinate grid, *x*-axis, *y*-axis, origin, point, graph, linear equation, plot

Materials Index cards

Math Background

- The graph of a linear equation is a straight line.

- A variable represents any number.

Frontload the Lesson

Essential Question What vocabulary will help you understand and talk about graphs of equations?

Talk About It

Build Background Read each term aloud. Ask students to say what they might already know about these terms.

Content and Language

You Will

Model Read the objectives aloud and explain them in your own words. Use diagrams and symbols to support your explanations.

Your Turn

Guide Discussion Have students read the objectives. Discuss what these objectives mean. Invite partners to take turns discussing what the objectives mean to them.

Graphs of Equations

Essential Question What vocabulary will help you understand and talk about graphs of equations?

You Will
- Given an equation, complete a table of values and plot the ordered pairs.
- Describe how graphs represent the relationship between two variables.
- Use math vocabulary to discuss variables.

Talk About It

Copy each term from Vocabulary in Context on a card. As your teacher reads each term, create three piles of cards.

① Place terms that you know in **Pile 1.**

② Place terms you have heard but are not sure what they mean in **Pile 2.**

③ Place terms you do not know in **Pile 3.**

What do you know about each term? Explain, using the sentence starters for support.

I know … means …
I think … means …
I do not know what … means.

Your Turn
Look at the objectives under You Will at the top of the page. Working with a partner, predict what you are going to learn. Use the sentence starter for support.

I am going to learn about …

x-axis

ordered pair

coordinate grid

Leveled Instruction

Early Beginner Need longer response times to formulate their thoughts and words. Use words and gestures to complete activities. Benefit from working with partners of higher language proficiency.

Beginner Benefit from speaking slowly and conferring with other students for needed support. Use phrases and short sentences to complete activities.

Early Intermediate Often rely on sentence starters to speak in sentences. Need immediate feedback to self-correct.

Intermediate Speak in simple, complete sentences. Repeat sentences to build fluency.

Advanced/Transitioning Synthesize information and use elaborate sentences to complete activities. Model speaking for those students of low level language proficiency.

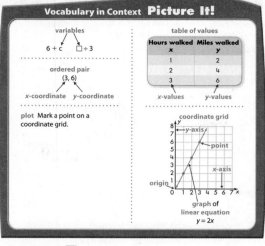

Vocabulary in Context **Picture It!**

variables

$6 + c$ $\square \div 3$

ordered pair

(3, 6)

x-coordinate   y-coordinate

plot Mark a point on a coordinate grid.

table of values

Hours walked **x**	Miles walked **y**
1	2
2	4
3	6

x-values   y-values

graph of
linear equation
$y = 2x$

Talk About It

Talk with a partner. Complete the sentences.

① In the table, 3 is an … *x-value.*
② The point (0, 0) is the … *origin.*
③ (3, 6) is an … *ordered pair.*
④ In the ordered pair (5, 10), 10 is the … *y-coordinate.*

Your Turn

Choose a term on this page. Write what it means to you. Share with a partner what you know about it. Use the sentence starter for help.

I think … means …

54   Lesson 14

Academic Vocabulary

- Point out and discuss the roots and suffixes for *vary, variable* and *linear, line.*

- Recall that the *coordinate plane* contains all four quadrants. Point out that a *coordinate grid* is part of the coordinate plane. The coordinate grid pictured on page 54 is only one quadrant of the coordinate plane.

- Point out that the term *graph* describes an action (verb) and names a picture (noun).

- Discuss everyday meanings of *plot,* such as a garden plot or the theme of a story. Then explain that in math, *plot* means to mark a point.

Additional resources for building and reinforcing vocabulary are provided on pages T37–T41.

↻ Comprehensible Input

Guide students to understanding

Vocabulary in Context Picture It!

1. **Say the Term** Have students repeat, stressing each syllable. Then combine syllables and have students repeat.

2. **Introduce Meaning** Connect the term to the visual that illustrates it.

3. **Demonstrate** Use symbols and visuals to demonstrate. For example, when teaching *variables,* write a question mark, other symbols, and letters and point to them.

4. **Apply** Have students demonstrate understanding with Talk About It.

Repeat the routine for each vocabulary term.

Talk About It

Guide Discussion Have pairs discuss the sentences with a partner. Encourage them to use examples to reinforce meaning. If time permits, provide this additional sentence completion:

A picture of a linear equation on a coordinate grid is a … **graph (or graph of the linear equation).**

Intervention

If students have difficulty with the word *linear* …

Then sweep your hand across, diagonally, or up and down (in a straight line) as you say *linear equations have graphs that are lines.*

Your Turn

Guide Discussion Ask volunteers to use their term in a sentence. Have others repeat each shared sentence.

Graphs of Equations

↻ Language Production

Comprehension Support Read aloud the problem for students. Emphasize that the table of values, the linear equation, and the graph all tell the same story about how the ages of Pete and Lynn are related. Use vocabulary terms as you discuss these ideas.

Model Help students understand the connection between the table of values and the linear equation. Provide an example. *When Pete is 1, x is equal to 1. Lynn is 3 years older, so y is equal to 4. If I write 1 for x and 4 for y in the equation* (demonstrate), *both sides are equal. Each pair of x- and y-values in the table makes the equation work.*

Next, be sure students understand the connection between the table of values and the graph. Explain that each row of the table provides an ordered pair marked on the coordinate grid. Work through Problem 1 with students. Show them the point marked at (1, 4). Have students work through the rest of the activity.

Talk About It

Guide Discussion Have students complete the Talk About It sentences on their own. Then have them work in pairs or small groups to discuss their answers. Encourage students to check one another by referring to the definitions in Vocabulary in Context Picture It!

Your Turn

Guide Discussion Have pairs read their explanations to a partner.

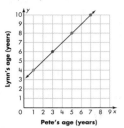
Leveled Language Proficiency

Students at each proficiency level should be able to perform the following tasks.

Listening/Speaking

Early Beginner Listen to and follow simple directions. Recognize a few vocabulary terms supported by visual cues. Repeat simple phrases, and use vocabulary terms to answer questions.

Beginner Follow basic directions. Listen and respond to simple questions, using some vocabulary terms. Say individual terms and simple phrases, and repeat longer phrases and short sentences.

Early Intermediate Demonstrate comprehension of oral questions that are based on academic content. Respond briefly to questions about content.

Intermediate Clarify meanings of unknown words, using context as well as other resources. Participate in limited discussions using words and phrases.

Advanced/Transitioning Clarify meanings of words both in and out of context. Summarize information that is heard during a class discussion or lesson.

Your Turn

Seth is 2 years older than Maria.
The linear equation that shows this is $y = x + 2$.

Write the missing values in the table below. Then graph the ordered pairs and draw a line through the points.

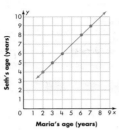

Maria x	Seth y
2	4
3	5
4	6
6	8
7	9

Points and line are shown on grid in red.

Talk and Write About It
Complete the sentences about the table and the grid.

Vocabulary:

variables	y-values	graph	table of values
coordinate grid	x-values	y-coordinate	ordered pair
linear equation	x-coordinate	origin	point

1. The graph is drawn on a ___coordinate grid___ .

2. x and y are ___variables___ .

3. The values in the column for Seth's age are ___y-values___ .

Produce Language
Write about what you have learned about graphing equations. You may include examples. Use as many vocabulary terms and symbols as you can.

Leveled Language Proficiency

Students at each proficiency level should be able to perform the following tasks.

Reading/Writing

Early Beginner Read a few short, common words and some vocabulary terms, with help from a partner. Copy words and phrases from the board; write a few vocabulary terms independently.

Beginner/Early Intermediate Read some vocabulary terms independently. Use sentence starters to write about vocabulary terms.

Intermediate Read and comprehend lesson vocabulary in context and read simple directions independently. Write complete sentences with some grammar, usage, mechanics, and spelling errors.

Advanced/Transitioning Read and carry out simple and complex written instructions; read sentences about lesson ideas and rephrase ideas and thoughts to express meaning. Write complete sentences with very few errors, using words and phrases to make ideas clearer and more logical.

↻ Assess Understanding

Your Turn

Model Read aloud the directions to students. Ask questions so that students connect the values in the table with the linear equation. Ask: *What do the table of values and the grid have in common? How do they both show $y = x + 2$?* Discuss these questions and then have students begin the activity.

Talk and Write About It

On Their Own Have students work independently to complete the sentences about the table and the graph.

Produce Language

On Their Own Have students work independently to write what they have learned about graphing equations. Remind them to refer to Vocabulary in Context Picture It! for assistance if needed. Encourage students to share their writing with the class.

Wrap Up

Table Talk Have students look back at the lesson's objectives. Allow time for them to reflect on what they have learned and then answer the essential question.

☑ **Learned** and applied vocabulary related to graphs of equations

☑ **Spoken** statements about graphs of equations

☑ **Written** statements about graphs of equations

Points, Lines, and Angles

Vocabulary Line, ray, line segment, horizontal line, vertical line, angle, vertex, intersecting lines, perpendicular lines, point of intersection, parallel lines

Math Background

- A *line* extends infinitely in both directions. A *line segment* is part of a line that stops at each end. A *ray* is part of a line that stops at one end.

- An *angle* is formed by two rays that have the same endpoint, the *vertex*.

⟳ Frontload the Lesson

Essential Question What vocabulary terms will help you describe points, lines, and angles?

Talk About It

Build Background Read each term above the chart. Explain the meaning of the chart columns and model how to place terms in first two columns of the chart using language such as *I know the term* … (See page T43 for additional copies of the chart.)

⟳ Content and Language

You Will

Model Read the objectives aloud and explain them in your own words. Use gestures and examples on the board to support your explanations.

Your Turn

Guide Discussion Have students read the objectives. Discuss what these objectives mean to them.

Points, Lines, and Angles

Essential Question What vocabulary terms will help you describe points, lines, and angles?

You Will
- Recognize the properties of points, lines, and angles.
- Understand the relationship among points, lines, and angles.
- Use math vocabulary to describe points, lines, and angles.

Talk About It

Look at the list of terms below. In the first two columns of the chart, write terms you **know** or **want** to know more about.

line	intersecting lines	angle
line segment	perpendicular lines	vertex
horizontal line	parallel lines	ray
vertical line	point of intersection	

Know	Want	Learned

What do you know about each term? Explain, using the sentence starters for support.

I know … means …
I want to know more about …

Your Turn
Look at the objectives under You Will at the top of the page. Working with a partner, predict what you are going to learn. Use the sentence starter for support.

I am going to learn about …

Leveled Instruction

Early Beginner Beginners should partner with students at higher language proficiency to complete the activities. Single words and gestures should be expected as answers.

Beginner Encourage students to use sentence starters to help them construct answers.

Early Intermediate Expect phrases and simple sentences from these students as answers to the activities.

Intermediate Students should produce complete sentences in tackling the activities with little assistance.

Advanced/Transitioning Students should produce detailed answers with minimal assistance and should partner with students at lower language proficiency levels to offer them assistance.

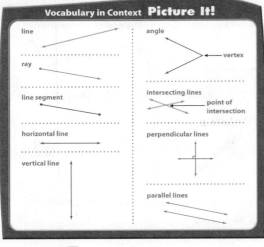

Vocabulary in Context **Picture It!**

line

angle ← vertex

ray

line segment

intersecting lines — point of intersection

horizontal line

perpendicular lines

vertical line

parallel lines

Talk About It 💬
Talk with a partner. Complete the sentences.

1. Part of a line that stops at each end is a ... line segment.
2. Part of a line that continues in only one direction is a ... ray.
3. The point where two or more lines meet is a ... point of intersection.
4. Lines that form square corners are ... perpendicular lines.

Your Turn ✏️
Choose three terms on this page. Draw an example of each. Share your drawings with a partner. Ask your partner to describe them.

↻ Comprehensible Input
Guide students to understanding

Vocabulary in Context Picture It!

1. **Say the Term** Have students repeat, stressing each syllable. Then combine syllables and have students repeat.

2. **Introduce Meaning** Connect the term to the visual that illustrates it.

3. **Demonstrate** Use gestures and visuals to demonstrate. As *angle* and *vertex* are discussed, form an angle using both index fingers and direct their attention to the vertex.

4. **Apply** Have students demonstrate understanding with Talk About It.

Repeat the routine for each vocabulary term.

Talk About It

Guide Discussion Have students discuss the sentences with a partner. Then point out examples of the geometric terms in the classroom. Model how to describe them. *The corner of my desk looks like the vertex of an angle.* Have partners look for and describe other examples of angles and vertices in the classroom. Then provide this additional sentence completion, if time permits:

The stripes on the flag look like ... **Sample answer: parallel lines.**

Intervention

If students confuse intersecting and perpendicular lines ...

Then explain that perpendicular lines are special intersecting lines that form square corners where they meet.

Your Turn

Guide Discussion Have pairs of students share their drawings and their discussions from Your Turn.

Academic Vocabulary

- Differentiate between the everyday use of the word *ray* (light) and *ray* as a math term. Point out that rays of light are similar to mathematical rays in math because they extend infinitely in one direction.

- Explain that the plural form of *vertex* is *vertices*, not *vertexes*.

- Point out the connection between the word *horizontal* and the word *horizon*.

Additional resources for building and reinforcing vocabulary are provided on pages T37–T41.

Cultural Consideration

If available, students might enjoy sharing street maps of the town where they were born or of the capital city of their native country. Point out streets that look like intersecting, perpendicular, or parallel lines. The map might also show curved streets. Explain that these do not represent lines.

Points, Lines, and Angles

⟳ Language Production

Comprehension Support Direct students' attention to the map of Kim's neighborhood. Point out the streets, home, and other features on the map. Read the names of the streets and point out the angles formed by the streets.

Model Help students locate Pine Road and Elm Drive. *Pine Road and Elm Drive cross at an intersection, so they are intersecting lines. Notice that the streets form square corners. Pine Road and Elm Drive look like perpendicular lines.*

Talk About It

Guide Discussion Have students complete the Talk About It sentences with a partner. Remind students that if they need help with the terms, they can check Vocabulary in Context Picture It!

Your Turn

Guide Discussion Have pairs of students join together to make groups of four. Have students share their drawings and describe them to other members of the group.

Look at the map of Kim's neighborhood. Use vocabulary terms to describe the map.

Kim's Neighborhood

1. The streets that cross at Kim's house look like ___intersecting lines___.
2. The path at Miller's Pond looks like an ___angle___.
3. The clubhouse at Miller's Pond is near the angle's ___vertex___.

Talk About It
Complete the sentences to help describe Kim's neighborhood.

4. Elm Drive and Main Street look like … Sample answer: parallel lines.
5. The streets that cross at the school look like … Sample answer: perpendicular lines.
6. Streets that cross each other and form square corners look like … perpendicular lines.
7. Oak Avenue and Maple Lane look like … intersecting lines.

Your Turn ✎
Draw a street that crosses Maple Lane. Describe the new street. Tell a partner using vocabulary terms.

Points, Lines, and Angles   59

Leveled Language Proficiency

Students at each proficiency level should be able to perform the following tasks.

Listening/Speaking

Early Beginner Follow oral directions that are supported by visual clues. Repeat simple phrases, and use single vocabulary terms to answer questions.

Beginner Follow simple directions; recognize some vocabulary terms. Say individual terms and simple phrases, and repeat longer phrases and short sentences.

Early Intermediate Show understanding of vocabulary terms through actions. Respond briefly to questions, showing an increasing understanding of lesson vocabulary.

Intermediate Recognize vocabulary as individual terms and in the context of spoken sentences. Participate in limited discussion using words and phrases.

Advanced/Transitioning Clarify meanings of words as needed by asking questions or using resources. Support responses with additional details and explanations.

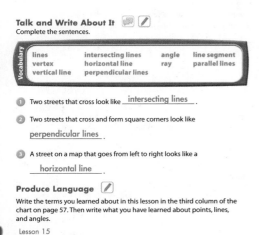

Think, Talk, and Write

Your Turn

Draw a neighborhood street map. Write a name on each street. Be sure your picture includes examples of at least five of the terms shown in the vocabulary box below.

Check students' drawings.

Talk and Write About It

Complete the sentences.

Vocabulary			
lines	intersecting lines	angle	line segment
vertex	horizontal line	ray	parallel lines
vertical line	perpendicular lines		

1. Two streets that cross look like __intersecting lines__ .

2. Two streets that cross and form square corners look like
   __perpendicular lines__ .

3. A street on a map that goes from left to right looks like a
   __horizontal line__ .

Produce Language

Write the terms you learned about in this lesson in the third column of the chart on page 57. Then write what you have learned about points, lines, and angles.

60   Lesson 15

Leveled Language Proficiency

Students at each proficiency level should be able to perform the following tasks.

Reading/Writing

Early Beginner Show willingness to read for meaning when visual support or the assistance of others is provided. Copy lists of words; write 1–2 vocabulary terms independently.

Beginner/Early Intermediate Read simple sentences with the help of a partner or an adult and visual support; read some vocabulary terms independently. Use sentence starters and other organizers to write individual words and phrases that use vocabulary terms.

Intermediate Show understanding of written material by ability to follow directions or summarize text. Write full sentences and complex phrases about lesson concepts, using vocabulary terms; sentences may contain some grammatical and spelling errors.

Advanced/Transitioning Read and carry out simple and complex written instructions; read sentences about lesson ideas that use lesson vocabulary. Write complete sentences with very few errors.

↻ Assess Understanding

Your Turn

Model Draw a pair of thick intersecting lines. Say: *Suppose these are streets on a map. They look like intersecting lines. They form four angles. The angles have the same vertex.* Point to the angles and the vertex. Then have students draw their own maps independently. Be sure that they understand that the map should show examples of at least five vocabulary terms. Remind students that *at least five* means *five or more than five.*

Talk and Write About It

On Their Own Have students work independently to complete the sentences. Then have students share their maps and sentences with a partner.

Produce Language

On Their Own Have students complete the Know-Want-Learn chart from the beginning of the lesson. Then have students write what they have learned about points, lines, and angles.

Wrap Up

Table Talk Have students look back at the lesson's objectives. Allow time for them to reflect on what they have learned and then answer the essential question.

☑ **Learned** and applied vocabulary related to points, lines, and angles

☑ **Spoken** statements about points, lines, and angles

☑ **Written** statements about points, lines, and angles

Lesson 16

Measuring Angles

Vocabulary Angle, vertex, side, protractor, measure, degrees, congruent, right angle, acute angle, obtuse angle, straight angle

Materials Protractors

Math Background

- Angles are classified by their measure: *Acute angles* measure less than 90°. *Right angles* measure exactly 90°. *Obtuse angles* measure between 90° and 180°. *Straight angles* measure exactly 180°.

↻ Frontload the Lesson

Essential Question

How can you use vocabulary terms to discuss measuring angles?

Talk About It

Build Background Ask students to say what they might already know about these terms.

↻ Content and Language

You Will

Model Read the objectives aloud and explain them in your own words. Use gestures and examples on the board to support your explanations. Display a protractor and point to the degree markings.

Your Turn

Guide Discussion Have students read the objectives. Discuss what the objectives mean to them.

Essential Question How can you use vocabulary terms to discuss measuring angles?

You Will
- Identify parts of an angle.
- Measure and classify angles.
- Use math vocabulary to discuss angles.

Talk About It

Rate these mathematical terms according to the following scale.

1. I have never heard this term.
2. I have heard this term, but I do not know how to use it in math.
3. I understand the meaning of this term and know how to use it in math.

_____ angle	_____ degrees
_____ straight angle	_____ congruent
_____ vertex	_____ right angle
_____ side	_____ acute angle
_____ protractor	_____ obtuse angle
_____ measure	

Explain what you know about each term, using the sentence starters.

I do not know what … means.
I think … means …
I know … means …

Your Turn
Look at the objectives under You Will at the top of the page. Working with a partner, predict what you are going to learn. Use the sentence starter for support.

I am going to learn about …

Leveled Instruction

Early Beginner Early beginners may need longer response times to formulate their thoughts and words. Encourage these students to use words and gestures to complete activities. If necessary, pair students with partners of higher language proficiency.

Beginner/Early Intermediate Remind students to speak slowly and confer with each other for needed support. Students will use phrases and simple sentences to complete activities. Provide immediate feedback so students can self-correct.

Intermediate Encourage students to express their ideas without sentence starters if possible. They should use complete sentences. Anticipate some grammatical errors.

Advanced/Transitioning Expect students to form sentences of increasing complexity. Have them try new sentence structures.

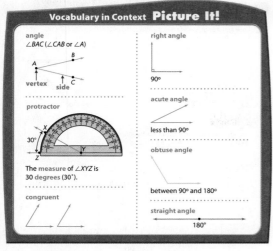

Vocabulary in Context Picture It!

angle
∠BAC (∠CAB or ∠A)

vertex   side

protractor

The measure of ∠XYZ is 30 degrees (30˚).

congruent

right angle
90°

acute angle
less than 90°

obtuse angle
between 90° and 180°

straight angle
180°

Talk About It
Talk with a partner. Complete the sentences.
1. The symbol ˚ means … degrees.
2. An angle with a measure of 90 degrees is a … right angle.
3. Two angles that are the same size are … congruent.
4. The point where two sides of an angle meet is a … vertex.
5. Angles are measured in … degrees.
6. Another name for ∠STU at the right is … ∠T (or ∠UTS).

Your Turn
Draw four different types of angles. Share your drawings with a partner.
Ask your partner to describe them.

Academic Vocabulary

- Differentiate between *degrees* that measure temperature vs. those that measure angles. Point out that the same symbol, °, is used in both contexts to indicate *degrees*.

- Explain that the plural form of *vertex* is *vertices*, not *vertexes*. Have students practice pronouncing both the singular and plural form.

- Point out that *congruent* angles have the same measure. In general, congruent figures have the same size and shape.

Additional resources for building and reinforcing vocabulary are provided on pages T37–T41.

↻ Comprehensible Input
Guide students to understanding

Vocabulary in Context Picture It!

1. **Say the Term** Have students repeat, stressing each syllable. Then combine syllables and have students repeat.

2. **Introduce Meaning** Connect the term to the visual that illustrates it.

3. **Demonstrate** Use gestures and visuals to demonstrate. As *angles* are discussed, point out angles such as the angle formed from the hands on the clock.

4. **Apply** Have students demonstrate understanding with Talk About It.

Repeat the routine for each vocabulary term.

Talk About It

Guide Discussion Have students discuss the sentences with a partner. Point out that when naming an angle with three letters, the center letter names the vertex. An angle may be named with just a single letter, the name of the vertex, but this should not be done when more than one angle is drawn with the same vertex as it will be unclear which angle is being named.

Intervention

If students confuse acute and obtuse angles …

Then point out that the number of letters in *acute* is less than the number of letters in *obtuse,* and an acute angle is less than 90°, while a obtuse angle is greater than 90°.

Your Turn

Guide Discussion Have pairs of students share their angles and their discussions from Your Turn.

↻ Language Production

Comprehension Support Point out the bicycle frame and the way that five angles are indicated with little curves, called *arcs*. Remind students of the differences between straight, obtuse, right, and acute angles.

Model Read the first question to students. *First I'll check out ∠ABC. That's one of the angles with vertex B. Points A and C help me find the sides of the angle.* Help students find ∠ABC in the diagram. *It makes sense that it's obtuse because I can see that it is greater than a right angle.*

As students measure the angles in Problem 2, offer assistance as needed. Be sure students place the center of the protractor at the vertex, line up one ray of the angle so that it passes through 0, and read the correct scale where the other ray intersects the protractor. Work through the remaining problems with students, using as many vocabulary terms as possible.

Talk About It

Guide Discussion Have students complete the Talk About It sentences with a partner. Help students notice that the angles in Problem 4 are not just obtuse, but also congruent. Remind students that if they need assistance they can refer to Vocabulary in Context Picture It! on page 62 or consult with students at higher language proficiency levels.

Your Turn

Guide Discussion Have students share their angles with a partner. Encourage them to show their angle measurements and discuss the classification.

Do You Understand?

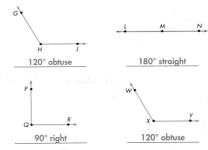

1. Look at the angles marked in the bicycle frame. Write whether the angles are acute or obtuse. The first angle is done for you.

∠ABC is obtuse.

∠ABE (or ∠EBA) is obtuse.

∠BED (or ∠DEB) is acute.

∠DEF (or ∠FED) is acute.

∠DCB (or ∠BCD) is acute.

2. Use your protractor to measure each angle below. Write the measure. Then write if the angle is right, acute, straight, or obtuse.

120° obtuse

180° straight

90° right

120° obtuse

Talk About It 💬

Complete the sentences to describe the angles.

3. In the bike frame, ∠BDE is an ... acute angle.

4. ∠GHJ and ∠WXY are ... congruent (or obtuse angles).

5. In ∠PQR, point Q is the ... vertex.

6. An angle with a measure of 180 degrees is a ... straight angle.

Your Turn ✏️

Draw an angle. Measure it with a protractor. Describe your angle to a partner. Use vocabulary terms to help you.

Measuring Angles 63

Leveled Language Proficiency

Students at each proficiency level should be able to perform the following tasks.

Listening/Speaking

Early Beginner Follow oral directions that are supported by visual clues. Repeat words or simple phrases to answer questions.

Beginner Demonstrate comprehension of simple sentences, including statements, questions, and commands, when spoken slowly; express confusion.

Early Intermediate Connect new information to prior knowledge; retell steps of a process in logical order.

Intermediate Demonstrate comprehension of classroom discussions and interactions when clarification is given; ask questions to clarify meaning in an academic context.

Advanced/Transitioning Understand classroom discussions and other academic interactions that include basic and complex sentence structures; use extended discourse to report information heard in lecture-style presentations.

Your Turn

Look at the frame of the house. Measure at least ten angles. Then draw a heart ♥ inside a right angle, a star ★ inside an acute angle, and a circle ● inside an obtuse angle.

Check students' angle classifications.

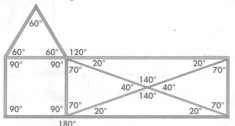

Talk and Write About It

Complete the sentences about measuring angles.

> **Vocabulary**
> vertex   degrees   measure   straight angle
> congruent   protractor   obtuse angle   acute angle
> right angle   side

1. When I measure angles, I use a _protractor_.

2. If two angles both measure 60°, the angles are _congruent_.

3. An angle with a measure between 90° and 180° is an _obtuse angle_.

4. Angles are classified as acute, right, obtuse, or _straight_.

Produce Language

Write how measuring angles helps you find out about different kinds of angles. Use as many vocabulary terms as you can.

64   Lesson 16

Assess Understanding

Your Turn

Model Discuss with students the process of building a house by starting with a frame. Draw a similar diagram on the board and model measuring the angles with a protractor, and then classifying the angles.

Talk and Write About It

On Their Own Have students work on their own for ten minutes to complete the sentences. Then have partners share and compare their responses.

Produce Language

On Their Own Have students review how they rated the terms on page 61. Encourage them to use as many terms as possible in their writing.

Wrap Up

Table Talk Have students look back at the lesson's objectives. Allow time for them to reflect on what they have learned and then answer the essential question.

☑ **Learned** and applied vocabulary related to measuring angles

☑ **Spoken** statements about measuring angles

☑ **Written** statements about measuring angles

Leveled Language Proficiency

Students at each proficiency level should be able to perform the following tasks.

Reading/Writing

Early Beginner Read a few short, common words and some vocabulary terms, with help from a partner. Copy words and phrases from the board; write a few vocabulary terms independently.

Beginner/Early Intermediate Read and understand previously learned essential vocabulary words. Apply knowledge of word context to gain meaning from text. Use sentence starters and other organizers to write individual words and phrases that use vocabulary terms.

Intermediate Identify words, phrases, and sentences that determine meaning in extended text. Write full sentences and complex phrases about lesson concepts, using vocabulary terms; sentences may contain some grammatical and spelling errors.

Advanced/Transitioning Obtain information from a variety of print and nonprint sources. Write complete sentences with very few errors.

Properties of Shapes

Vocabulary Shape, polygons, triangle, side, angle, quadrilateral, pentagon, hexagon, octagon, equilateral triangle, isosceles triangle, scalene triangle, right triangle, acute triangle, obtuse triangle, parallel, square, rectangle, rhombus, parallelogram, trapezoid

Materials Index cards

Math Background

- Triangles can be classified by their sides or their angles.

- Quadrilaterals with one or two pairs of parallel sides are given special names.

- The sum of the angles in a triangle is 180°. The sum of the angles in a quadrilateral is 360°.

Frontload the Lesson

Essential Question
What vocabulary terms should you use to talk about the properties of shapes?

Talk About It

Build Background Read each term aloud as students sort them into piles. Ask students to tell what they know about some of these terms.

Content and Language

You Will

Model Read the objectives aloud and explain them in your own words. Draw quadrilaterals and triangles to support your explanations.

Your Turn

Guide Discussion Have students read the objectives. Discuss what the objectives mean to them.

Essential Question What vocabulary terms should you use to talk about the properties of shapes?

You Will
- Identify the properties of shapes.
- Classify shapes.
- Use math vocabulary to discuss the properties of shapes.

Talk About It

Copy each term from Vocabulary in Context on a card. As your teacher reads each term, create three piles of cards.

1. Place terms that you know in **Pile 1**.
2. Place terms you have heard but are not sure what they mean in **Pile 2**.
3. Place terms you do not know in **Pile 3**.

square

What do you know about each term? Explain, using the sentence starters for support.

pentagon

I know … means …
I think … means …
I do not know what … means.

quadrilateral

Your Turn
Look at the objectives listed under You Will at the top of the page. Working with a partner, predict what you will learn. Use the sentence starter below.

I am going to learn about …

Leveled Instruction

Early Beginner Encourage students to use single words and gestures as well as pictures for their responses. Allow ample wait time so students can organize their thoughts.

Beginner/Early Intermediate Expect phrases and simple sentences from these students as answers to the activities. Encourage students to use sentence starters to help them construct answers.

Intermediate Students are able to speak about some abstract ideas. They often recognize vocabulary both as individual terms and in the context of spoken sentences.

Advanced/Transitioning Expect students to form sentences of increasing difficulty with minimal assistance. Have advanced students partner with students at lower language proficiency levels to offer them assistance.

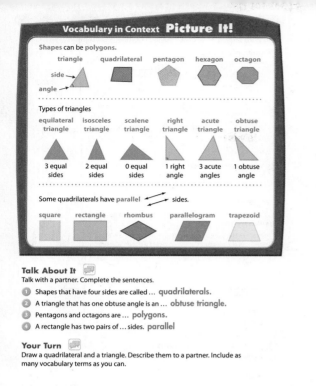

Vocabulary in Context Picture It!

Shapes can be polygons.

triangle quadrilateral pentagon hexagon octagon

side
angle

Types of triangles

equilateral triangle · isosceles triangle · scalene triangle · right triangle · acute triangle · obtuse triangle

3 equal sides · 2 equal sides · 0 equal sides · 1 right angle · 3 acute angles · 1 obtuse angle

Some quadrilaterals have *parallel* sides.

square · rectangle · rhombus · parallelogram · trapezoid

Talk About It
Talk with a partner. Complete the sentences.
1. Shapes that have four sides are called … quadrilaterals.
2. A triangle that has one obtuse angle is an … obtuse triangle.
3. Pentagons and octagons are … polygons.
4. A rectangle has two pairs of … sides. parallel

Your Turn
Draw a quadrilateral and a triangle. Describe them to a partner. Include as many vocabulary terms as you can.

66   Lesson 17

Academic Vocabulary

- Be sure students understand that a *shape* is a flat figure. *Polygons* are just those shapes that have straight sides. Circles and hearts are shapes, but they are not polygons. *Shape* is also an attribute of an object, as in the *shape of a garden*.

- Discuss the prefixes *tri-* and *quad-*, offering examples such as *tricycle/tripod/triplet* and *quadruple/quadrant/quadruplet*.

- Remind students that *parallel* lines are lines that never intersect. The sides of polygons can also be described as parallel if they are parts of parallel lines. Typically, students can recognize parallel sides as sides that are the "same distance apart" or look like they are "slanted" the same way.

Additional resources for building and reinforcing vocabulary are provided on pages T37–T42.

Cultural Consideration

Be aware that there are various definitions of *trapezoid*. Students schooled outside of the United States might have learned some properties of the trapezoid that are different from what they are learning in their math class here.

↻ Comprehensible Input
Guide students to understanding

Vocabulary in Context Picture It!

1. **Say the Term** Have students repeat, stressing each syllable. Then combine syllables and have students repeat.

2. **Introduce Meaning** Connect the term to the visual that illustrates it.

3. **Demonstrate** Use symbols and visuals to demonstrate. As *equilateral triangles* are discussed, write = on the board to remind students that the sides have the same length.

4. **Apply** Have students demonstrate understanding with Talk About It.

Repeat the routine for each vocabulary term.

Talk About It

Guide Discussion Have students discuss the sentences with a partner. Then point out examples of shapes and their properties in the classroom. Model how to describe them. *The chalkboard looks like a rectangle. It has four right angles and two pairs of equal and parallel sides.* Have partners look for and describe other quadrilaterals and triangles in the classroom. If your classroom floor is tiled, provide this additional sentence completion:

Each floor tile is shaped like a … **square.**

Intervention

If students are confused by the different pronunciations of *sc* in *isosceles* and *scalene* …

Then point out and model that *c* before *e* makes the sound /s/, and *c* before *a* makes the sound /k/.

Your Turn

Guide Discussion Have groups of four share their triangles and quadrilaterals and their discussions from Your Turn.

↻ Language Production

Comprehension Support Point out the triangles and quadrilaterals in the spider web, but do not classify their types.

Model Read the first question to students. *The red triangle has sides that are all the same length, so it must be an* equilateral triangle. *I can look at the angles, too. Since all of the angles are acute, I could also say that the red triangle is an* acute triangle. Have students complete Problems 2 and 3.

Next, discuss the properties about the sum of the angle measures in a triangle and in a quadrilateral. Show a few sample problems on the board and work through them with students. For example, draw a triangle with two angles labeled 45° and 70°. Have students find the measure of the third angle. Students should add 45 and 70 and subtract the sum from 180. 65°

Talk About It

Guide Discussion Have students complete the Talk About It sentences with a partner. Remind students that they can consult with students at higher language proficiency levels, if needed.

Your Turn

Guide Discussion Have two pairs join together to talk about the shapes in their designs.

Look at the angles, triangles, and quadrilaterals in the spider web below.

1 What type of triangle is shown in red?

    equilateral triangle
    (or acute triangle)

2 What type of quadrilateral is shown in green?

    trapezoid

3 What type of triangle is shown in blue?

    right triangle (or
    scalene triangle)

Take a look at the shapes below. Write the missing angle measures. Use these two properties:

- The sum of the measures of the angles in a triangle is 180°.
- The sum of the measures of the angles in a quadrilateral is 360°.

4 [triangle: 60°, ?, 60°]
5 [trapezoid: 120°, ?, 60°, 60°, 120°]
6 [triangle: ?, 60°, 30°]

Talk About It
Complete the sentences to describe the shapes.

7 An equilateral triangle is also an … acute triangle.
8 A trapezoid has one pair of … sides. parallel
9 A triangle with a right angle is a … right triangle.

Your Turn
Draw your own spider web design. Use vocabulary terms to tell your partner about some of the shapes in your design.

Properties of Shapes   **67**

Leveled Language Proficiency

Students at each proficiency level should be able to perform the following tasks.

Listening/Speaking

Early Beginner Use pictures, actions, and/or objects to show comprehension of vocabulary. Ask simple questions and respond to questions to clarify information.

Beginner/Early Intermediate Identify important information about academic content, using prior knowledge and/or visual cues as needed. Ask and respond to questions to clarify information.

Intermediate Demonstrate comprehension of oral, multiple-step directions. Demonstrate knowledge of spoken vocabulary, using specific, technical, and/or abstract vocabulary or grade-level academic content.

Advanced/Transitioning Understand words and phrases of grade-level academic content, including technical and abstract terms. Communicate using specific, technical, and abstract vocabulary.

Your Turn

Look at the quilt square shown below.

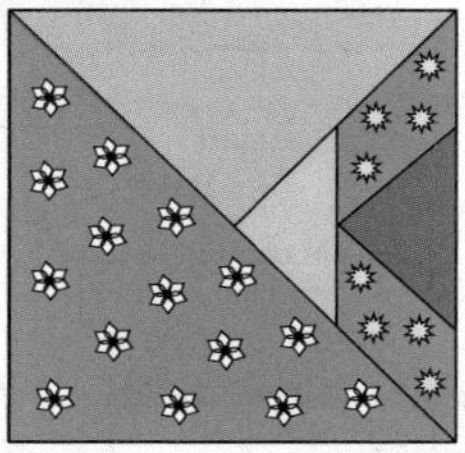

1. How many parallelograms are there? _____ **2** _____

2. What do the yellow triangle and bright blue triangle have in common?
   They have right angles; they are right triangles; they are isosceles triangles.

3. Are there any equilateral triangles in the quilt square? _____ **no** _____

4. Are there any obtuse triangles in the quilt square? _____ **no** _____

Talk and Write About It 🗨️ ✏️

Complete the sentences about shapes.

Vocabulary		
hexagon	quadrilaterals	isosceles triangle
trapezoid	rectangle	parallelogram
square	rhombus	equilateral triangle
right angle	right triangle	acute angle

5. A quadrilateral with four equal sides is a _____ rhombus (or square) _____ .

6. A polygon with six sides is a _____ hexagon _____ .

7. A triangle with two equal sides is an isosceles triangle (or equilateral triangle)

Produce Language ✏️

Use vocabulary terms to write about shapes that have one or more right angles. Then write about shapes that have parallel sides.

68 Lesson 17

Leveled Language Proficiency

Students at each proficiency level should be able to perform the following tasks.

Reading/Writing

Early Beginner Read and understand a few basic vocabulary words. Copy or write short lists of words.

Beginner/Early Intermediate Apply knowledge of word context to gain meaning from text. Organize information to be expressed in writing in a way that makes sense for the purpose and the audience.

Intermediate Identify words, phrases, and sentences that determine meaning in extended text. Identify and use words and phrases to make ideas clearer or more logical.

Advanced/Transitioning Obtain information from a variety of sources. Increase detail and precision of language to improve writing.

↻ Assess Understanding

Your Turn

Model Talk about quilts and that many of them are made with pieces of fabric in the shapes of different polygons. Sometimes smaller pieces of fabric are joined to make a *quilt square.* Then all of the quilt squares are sewn together to make the finished quilt. Discuss with students the shape of the quilt square. Say: *Each corner of the quilt square is a 90° angle.* Point out each angle and trace the sides with your finger. Explain that the sum of the measures of the four angles is 360°. Remind students that this is the rule for all quadrilaterals. Read the questions with students. Then have students answer the questions.

Talk and Write About It

On Their Own Have students work on their own to complete the sentences. Then have partners compare their responses.

Produce Language

On Their Own Have students write about what they learned using the support described.

Wrap Up

Table Talk Have students look back at the lesson's objectives. Allow time for them to reflect on what they have learned and then answer the essential question.

- ☑ **Learned** and applied vocabulary related to the properties of shapes

- ☑ **Spoken** statements about the properties of shapes

- ☑ **Written** statements about the properties of shapes

Converting Units
of Measure

Vocabulary Customary units, length, inch, foot, yard, mile, metric units, millimeter, centimeter, meter, kilometer, capacity, gallon, quart, pint, cup, fluid ounce, liter, milliliter, weight, ton, pound, ounce, mass, kilogram, gram, milligram, convert, unit of measure

Materials Index cards, Measurement Tables (page 95)

Math
Background

- To convert from larger units of measure to smaller units of measure, multiply.

- To convert from smaller units of measure to larger units of measure, divide.

- Weight is measured using customary units. Mass is measured using metric units.

Frontload the Lesson

How can you use vocabulary terms to talk about converting units of measure?

Talk About It

Build Background Have students create cards as described. Read each word aloud as students sort them into piles. Ask students to tell what they know about familiar terms.

Content and Language

You Will

Model Read the objectives aloud and explain them in your own words. Use classroom objects to support your explanations.

Your Turn

Guide Discussion Have students read the objectives. Discuss what the objectives mean to them.

Converting Units
of Measure

Essential Question How can you use vocabulary terms to talk about converting units of measure?

You Will
- Use customary and metric units of measure to solve problems.
- Convert measurements from one unit of measure to another.
- Use math vocabulary to discuss converting units of measure.

Talk About It

Make an index card for each vocabulary term below. Place each card in one of three piles.

Pile 1: I know what this term means.
Pile 2: I have heard of this term, but I am not sure how it is used in math.
Pile 3: I have not heard of this term.

customary units	capacity	gallon (gal)	quart (qt)
pint (pt)	kilometer (km)	ton (T)	pound (lb)
ounce (oz)	yard (yd)	foot (ft)	inch (in.)
metric units	liter (L)	milliliter (mL)	mass
kilogram (kg)	millimeter (mm)	milligram (mg)	meter (m)
centimeter (cm)	weight	fluid ounce (fl oz)	gram (g)
unit of measure	length	mile (mi)	cup (c)
convert			

unit of measure

What do you know about each term? Explain, using the sentence starters for support.

I know ... means ...
I think ... means ...
I do not know what ... means.

Your Turn
Look at the objectives under You Will at the top of the page. Working with a partner, predict what you are going to learn. Use the sentence starter for support.

I am going to learn about ...

Leveled Instruction

Early Beginner Early beginners may need longer response times to formulate their answers. Encourage these students to use both pictures and gestures to complete activities. If necessary, pair students with partners of higher language proficiency.

Beginner Encourage students to use sentence starters for support. Provide immediate feedback so they can self-correct.

Early Intermediate/Intermediate Encourage students to use sentence starters as support, and to repeat them to build fluency.

Advanced/Transitioning Classify previously learned vocabulary terms and phrases into concept-based categories. Encourage advanced students to work with those students of low-level language proficiency.

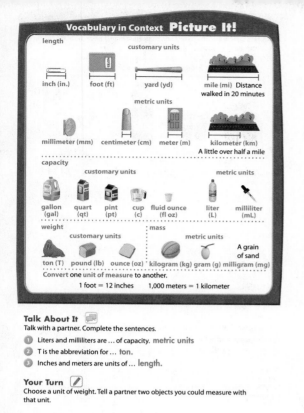

Vocabulary in Context **Picture It!**

length

inch (in.) foot (ft) yard (yd) mile (mi) Distance walked in 20 minutes

metric units

millimeter (mm) centimeter (cm) meter (m) kilometer (km)
A little over half a mile

capacity

customary units   metric units

gallon (gal) quart (qt) pint (pt) cup (c) fluid ounce (fl oz) liter (L) milliliter (mL)

weight   mass

customary units   metric units

A grain of sand

ton (T) pound (lb) ounce (oz) kilogram (kg) gram (g) milligram (mg)

Convert **one** unit of measure to another.

1 foot = 12 inches   1,000 meters = 1 kilometer

Talk About It
Talk with a partner. Complete the sentences.
1. Liters and milliliters are … of capacity. metric units
2. T is the abbreviation for … ton.
3. Inches and meters are units of … length.

Your Turn
Choose a unit of weight. Tell a partner two objects you could measure with that unit.

70   Lesson 18

Academic Vocabulary

- Be sure students understand that units of *length* are used to tell how *long* (or *tall*, *wide*, *thick*) an object is, units of *weight* are used to tell how *heavy* an object is, units of *mass* are used to tell how much *matter* is in an object, and units of *capacity* are used to tell how much (usually liquid) an object can *hold*.

- As you discuss the abbreviations for the units of measure, point out that the abbreviation for *inch* (*in.*) is the only one with a period.

- Discuss the irregular plural form of *foot/feet*, explaining that some nouns change completely in plural form. Offer other examples such as *person/ people* and *mouse/mice*.

- Point out the difference between the everyday context of *feet* and *yard* and their mathematical context as customary units of measurement.

Additional resources for building and reinforcing vocabulary are provided on pages T37–T41.

Cultural Consideration

Foreign-born students may be more familiar with metric measures than with customary ones.

↻ Comprehensible Input
Guide students to understanding

Vocabulary in Context Picture It!

1. **Say the Term** Have students repeat, stressing each syllable. Then combine syllables and have students repeat.

2. **Introduce Meaning** Connect the term to the visual that illustrates it.

3. **Demonstrate** Use gestures and visuals to demonstrate. As *capacity* is discussed, hold up or draw a picture of a cup and say: *a capacity of one cup.*

4. **Apply** Have students demonstrate understanding with Talk About It.

Repeat the routine for each vocabulary term.

Talk About It

Guide Discussion Ask students which terms they put in Pile 1 and their meanings. Model the sentence starters. Allow time for students to plan their answers. Provide this additional sentence completion, if time permits:

The customary unit you would use to measure the distance between cities is … mile.

Intervention

If students have difficulty differentiating a millimeter from a milliliter …

Then point out the root words meter and liter. Explain that people can run and jump meters, but never liters. Remind them that drinks come in 1- and 2-liter bottles, not meter bottles.

Your Turn

Guide Discussion Have volunteers offer their ideas for Your Turn.

Converting Units of Measure

⟳ Language Production

Comprehension Support Have students tear out the Measurement Tables on page 95.

Model Read the directions and the words in the box to students. Then point out the picture of the grapes on a scale. *These grapes are being measured on a scale, so we want a unit of weight or mass. The choices are tons or ounces. Tons are used to measure very large objects, and ounces are used for small objects, so I will choose ounces.* Work through the remaining problems with students, using the Measurement Tables for support.

Talk About It

Guide Discussion Have students complete the Talk About It sentences with a partner. Remind students that they can consult with students at higher language proficiency levels, if needed.

Your Turn

Guide Discussion Partners can record their work on copies of T44. Have them discuss and compare their ideas.

Match each picture with the correct unit of measure from the box. Write the unit underneath the picture.

| cups   tons   milliliters   feet   millimeters   ounces |

① _ounces_ ② cups or _milliliters_ ③ _feet_ ④ _millimeters_

Use the Measurement Table (page 95) to help you convert each measurement.

⑤ 7 yd = ___21___ ft

⑥ 20 kg = ___20,000___ g

⑦ 5 c = ___40___ fl oz

⑧ 300 m = ___30,000___ cm

⑨ 16 qt = ___4___ gal

⑩ 1.8 L = ___1,800___ mL

Talk About It 💬
Complete the sentences below.

⑪ Use gallons and liters to measure … capacity.

⑫ One yard equals 36 … inches.

⑬ Thirty-two ounces converts to 2 … pounds.

Your Turn 🖉
Write the units of measure given in the box at the top of the page. Write down an object you could measure using each unit. Share your ideas with a partner.

Leveled Language Proficiency

Students at each proficiency level should be able to perform the following tasks.

Listening/Speaking

Early Beginner Demonstrate comprehension of oral directions that include visual cues. Ask simple questions and respond to questions to clarify information.

Beginner/Early Intermediate Connect new information to prior knowledge. Use appropriate words, phrases, and expressions to interact with peers and adults.

Intermediate Understand specific information given in an academic context. Participate in limited discussions using appropriate and adequate words and phrases.

Advanced/Transitioning Demonstrate comprehension of specialized language structures from varied academic content. Use specialized language structures from multiple academic areas.

Your Turn

Use the Measurement Tables (page 95) to help you complete the following.

1. This building is 240 yards tall. How many feet is that? ____720____ ft

2. Macy bought 2 gallons of milk. How many pints of milk is this? ____16____ pt

3. How many inches is 12 feet of rope? __144__ in.

4. What is the diameter in centimeters of one U.S. quarter? __2.4__ cm

5. What is the diameter in millimeters of one U.S. quarter? __24__ mm

6. One U.S. quarter has a mass of 5.67 grams. What is the mass of a U.S. quarter in milligrams? __5,670__ mg

Talk and Write About It

Complete the sentences about the measurements.

Vocabulary			
customary units	capacity	milliliter	mass
metric units	weight	pounds	feet
yards	length	kilograms	gallons

7. Pounds and tons are units of ____weight____ .

8. Grams and kilograms are units of ____mass____ .

9. Yards and miles are __customary units__ of length.

10. Thirty-six inches converts to 3 ____feet____ .

Produce Language

Suppose you have a pet. Write about some things you could measure that are related to your pet and caring for your pet. Use your vocabulary cards for support.

72   Lesson 18

Leveled Language Proficiency

Students at each proficiency level should be able to perform the following tasks.

Reading/Writing

Early Beginner Read and understand a few basic vocabulary words. Write short lists of words to accomplish an assigned writing task.

Beginner/Early Intermediate Identify, compare, and provide examples of the linguistic features of English and other languages in print. Organize information to be expressed in writing in a way that makes sense for the purpose and the audience.

Intermediate Identify words, phrases, and sentences that determine meaning in extended text. Identify and use words and phrases to make ideas clearer or more logical.

Advanced/Transitioning Obtain information from a variety of sources. Increase detail and precision of language to improve writing.

↻ Assess Understanding

Your Turn

Model Revisit the Measurement Tables as you help students complete the first problem. *The Measurement Tables show that 1 yard is equal to 3 feet. Since the building is 240 yards tall, I need to multiply 240 by 3 to find how many feet that is.* Have students complete Problem 1. Then have students complete the other problems independently.

Talk and Write About It

On Their Own Have students work on their own to complete the sentences. Then have partners compare their responses.

Produce Language

On Their Own Have students use what they have learned in this lesson to write about what they could measure if they had a pet. If students have trouble getting started, have them work in pairs to share ideas. Some possibilities include measuring the animal itself, the animal's food, and the animal's dishes.

Wrap Up

Table Talk Have students look back at the lesson's objectives. Allow time for them to reflect on what they have learned and then answer the essential question.

☑ **Learned** and applied vocabulary related to converting units of measure

☑ **Spoken** statements about converting units of measure

☑ **Written** statements about converting units of measure

Perimeter and Area

Vocabulary Perimeter, distance, unit, area, square unit, square centimeter (cm^2), square inch (in^2), square foot (ft^2), square meter (m^2), dimensions, height (*h*), base (*b*), width (*w*), length (*l*), formulas

Materials Sari's Cloth (page 97)

Math Background

- The *perimeter* of a polygon can always be computed by adding all the lengths of the sides.

- The *height* of a triangle is not the same as its slant length.

↻ Frontload the Lesson

Essential Question

What words should you use to talk about area and perimeter?

Talk About It

Build Background Ask students to complete the first two columns of the Know-Want-Learn chart. (See page T43 for additional copies.) Have students tell what they already know about area, perimeter, and square units.

↻ Content and Language

You Will

Model Read the objectives aloud and explain them in your own words. Use visual examples to support your explanations.

Your Turn

Guide Discussion Have students read the objectives. Ask students to tell what the objectives mean to them.

Perimeter and Area

Essential Question What words should you use to talk about area and perimeter?

You Will
- Find the perimeter and area of triangles and rectangles.
- Use formulas to find the perimeter and area of triangles and rectangles.
- Use math vocabulary to discuss perimeter and area.

Talk About It

Look at the list of terms below. In the first two columns of the chart, write terms you **know** or **want** to know more about.

square inch	unit	square foot	formulas
square centimeter	square meter	area	square unit
dimensions	base	height	perimeter
length	width	distance	

Know	Want	Learned

What do you know about each term you wrote in the chart? Explain, using the sentence starters for support.

I know … means …
I want to know more about …

Your Turn
Look at the objectives under You Will at the top of the page. Working with a partner, predict what you are going to learn. Use the sentence starter for support.

I am going to learn about …

Leveled Instruction

Early Beginner Encourage students to use single words, pictures, and gestures. Allow ample time so students can organize their thoughts.

Beginner/Early Intermediate Expect phrases and simple sentences from these students as answers to the activities. Encourage them to use sentence starters to help them construct answers.

Intermediate Students are able to speak about some abstract ideas. They often recognize vocabulary as individual terms and in the context of spoken sentences.

Advanced/Transitioning Students can form sentences of increasing complexity. Have them try new sentence structures.

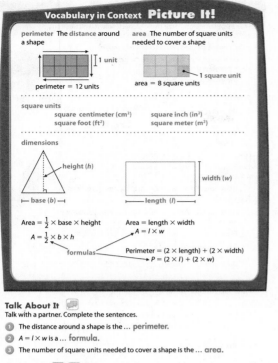

perimeter The distance around a shape

1 unit

perimeter = 12 units

area The number of square units needed to cover a shape

1 square unit

area = 8 square units

square units

square centimeter (cm²)   square inch (in²)
square foot (ft²)   square meter (m³)

dimensions

height (h)

base (b)

width (w)

length (l)

Area = $\frac{1}{2}$ × base × height
$A = \frac{1}{2} × b × h$

Area = length × width
$A = l × w$

formulas

Perimeter = (2 × length) + (2 × width)
$P = (2 × l) + (2 × w)$

Talk About It
Talk with a partner. Complete the sentences.

1 The distance around a shape is the … **perimeter.**
2 $A = l × w$ is a … **formula.**
3 The number of square units needed to cover a shape is the … **area.**

Your Turn
Draw a shape that has all straight sides. Explain to a partner how to find the perimeter. Use as many vocabulary terms as you can.

74   Lesson 19

Academic Vocabulary

- Differentiate between *base* in math (a specific side of certain polygons) and *base* in sports (baseball).

- Discuss the irregular plural ending of *foot/feet*, explaining that some nouns change completely in plural form. Offer other examples such as *person/people* and *mouse/mice*.

- Carefully discuss the abbreviations for various square units.

- Point out that the first letter of each dimension is used as a variable to represent that dimension. For example, the variable *h* represents the *height* of a triangle.

Additional resources for building and reinforcing vocabulary are provided on pages T37–T41.

Cultural Consideration

Many students will be more familiar with the metric system than the customary system of measurements. Be sure students understand the size of *inch* and *foot*.

⟳ Comprehensible Input
Guide students to understanding

Vocabulary in Context Picture It!

1. **Say the Term** Have students repeat, stressing each syllable. Then combine syllables and have students repeat.

2. **Introduce Meaning** Connect the term to the visual that illustrates it.

3. **Demonstrate** Use gestures and visuals to demonstrate. As *perimeter* is discussed, hold up a cup or jar and trace your finger around the rim. Say: *The word* rim *is part of the word* perimeter.

4. **Apply** Have students demonstrate understanding with Talk About It.

Repeat the routine for each vocabulary term.

Talk About It

Guide Discussion Be sure students understand the difference between perimeter and area. Then provide this additional sentence completion, if time permits:

You can use a formula to find the area of a triangle if you know the measures of the base and the … **height.**

Intervention

If students have difficulty pronouncing the long i in height …

Then remind them that the *gh* is silent. Explain that the letter combination *eight* normally sounds like *ate*, but in this case, it sounds like *ite*, as in kite. Write *eight, weight,* and *height* on the board. Take turns pointing at each word while students emphasize the proper long-a or long-i sound.

Your Turn

Guide Discussion Encourage pairs to discuss their drawings with others. They might recall that the shape they drew is a *polygon*. Encourage them to repeat their explanations to reinforce meaning and develop fluency.

⟳ Language Production

Comprehension Support Explain that the rectangle on page 97 represents Sari's cloth, and that each square shows one square centimeter of the cloth.

Model Have students cut out the rectangle on page 97. Guide students through the steps for the rectangle and then the triangle. Refer students to the formulas for area and perimeter on the previous page. Point out that the base and height of the triangle are the same as the length and width of the rectangle. Discuss the units that students need to write in their answers. *When I find* perimeter, *the answer should be labeled* centimeters. *But when I find* area, *the answer should be labeled* square centimeters.

Talk About It

Guide Discussion Have students complete the Talk About It sentences with a partner.

Your Turn

Guide Discussion Suggest that students add the label for length of the longest side to the triangle on page 75.

Do You Understand?

Sari has a small blue cloth in the shape of a rectangle. It is pictured on page 97. Tear out page 97 and cut out the rectangle.

Help Sari find the area and perimeter of the rectangle.

On the picture at the right, write the dimensions of the rectangle you cut out.

The length is 9 centimeters. The width is <u>12 centimeters</u>.

Area = length × <u>width</u>

The area of the rectangle is <u>108 square centimeters</u>.

Perimeter = (2 × <u>length</u>) + (2 × width)

The perimeter is <u>42 centimeters</u>.

Cut the rectangle in half from corner to corner.

Sari wants to know the area of each triangle. So she divides the area of the rectangle by 2.

108 square centimeters ÷ 2 = <u>54</u> square centimeters.

Sari's sister finds the area of the triangle by using the formula.

On the picture at the right, write the dimensions of one of the triangles.

The base is 9 centimeters. The height is <u>12 centimeters</u>.

Area = $\frac{1}{2}$ × base × <u>height</u>

The area of each triangle is <u>54 square centimeters</u>.

Talk About It 💬
Complete the sentences below.

1. An equation you use to find the area of a shape is called a … formula.
2. The dimensions of a rectangle are the length and the … width.
3. $P = (2 × l) + (2 × w)$ is the formula for the … of a rectangle. perimeter

Your Turn 💬
Look at one of the triangles you cut. The length of the longest side is 15 centimeters. Explain to your partner how you can find the perimeter of the triangle.

Leveled Language Proficiency

Students at each proficiency level should be able to perform the following tasks.

Listening/Speaking

Early Beginner Demonstrate comprehension of simple sentences, including statements, questions and commands. Follow conversations when spoken slowly. Use a few vocabulary terms and participate in simple conversations, supported by visual cues.

Beginner/Early Intermediate Demonstrate comprehension of oral directions that include visual cues and questions that are based on academic content. Express confusion and respond briefly to questions.

Intermediate Understands specific information given in an academic context. Participate in reaching consensus in groups.

Advanced/Transitioning Demonstrate comprehension of specialized language structures from varied academic content. Employ specialized language structures from varied academic areas.

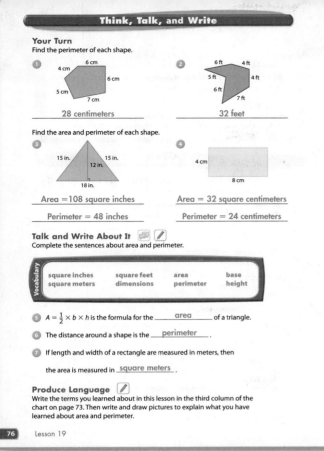

Your Turn

Find the perimeter of each shape.

① 28 centimeters

② 32 feet

Find the area and perimeter of each shape.

③ Area = 108 square inches

Perimeter = 48 inches

④ Area = 32 square centimeters

Perimeter = 24 centimeters

Talk and Write About It

Complete the sentences about area and perimeter.

Vocabulary

square inches	square feet	area	base
square meters	dimensions	perimeter	height

⑤ $A = \frac{1}{2} \times b \times h$ is the formula for the _____area_____ of a triangle.

⑥ The distance around a shape is the _____perimeter_____.

⑦ If length and width of a rectangle are measured in meters, then

the area is measured in _____square meters_____.

Produce Language

Write the terms you learned about in this lesson in the third column of the chart on page 73. Then write and draw pictures to explain what you have learned about area and perimeter.

76   Lesson 19

Leveled Language Proficiency

Students at each proficiency level should be able to perform the following tasks.

Reading/Writing

Early Beginner Read and understand previously learned sight words and phrases. Copy short lists of words independently.

Beginner/Early Intermediate Demonstrate understanding of the nature of language through comparisons between English and the student's first language. Write lists of words and phrases needed to accomplish an assigned writing task.

Intermediate Identify words, phrases, and sentences that determine meaning in extended text. Identify and use words and phrases to make ideas clearer or more logical

Advanced/Transitioning Students will obtain information from a variety of print and nonprint sources. Increase detail and precision of language to improve writing.

↻ Assess Understanding

Your Turn

Model Remind students that they don't need a formula to find the perimeter. Draw a figure on the board with 5 sides and label each with a length. *I know the length of each side. I can add up the lengths to find the distance around the figure.*

Talk and Write About It

On Their Own Have students work independently to complete the sentences. Then have partners compare their responses.

Produce Language

On Their Own Have student complete the Know-Want-Learn chart from the beginning of the lesson. Have students write what they know about the terms used in this lesson.

Wrap Up

Table Talk Have students look back at the lesson's objectives. Allow time for them to reflect on what they have learned and then answer the essential question.

☑ **Learned** and applied vocabulary related to perimeter and area

☑ **Spoken** statements about perimeter and area

☑ **Written** statements about perimeter and area

Lesson 20

Surface Area and Volume

Vocabulary Solid figures, cube, rectangular prism, vertex, face, edge, cubic unit, height, length, width, volume, surface area, square unit

Materials Solid Shape Patterns (page 99), scissors, tape

Math Background

- The volume of a rectangular prism is the number of cubic units needed to fill it: $V = l \times w \times h$.

- The surface area of a rectangular prism is the sum of the areas of the faces: $SA = 2\,(l \times w) + 2\,(w \times h) + 2\,(l \times h)$.

↻ Frontload the Lesson

Essential Question

How do you use vocabulary terms to discuss surface area and volume?

Talk About It

Build Background Have students tell what they already know about these terms related to surface area and volume.

↻ Content and Language

You Will

Model Read the objectives aloud and explain them in your own words. Use visual examples to support your explanations.

Your Turn

Guide Discussion Have students read the objectives. Invite volunteers to give examples of what the objectives mean to them.

Surface Area and Volume

Essential Question How do you use vocabulary terms to discuss surface area and volume?

You Will
- Find surface area and volume of rectangular prisms.
- Use math vocabulary to discuss surface area and volume.

Talk About It

Rate these mathematical terms according to the following scale.

1. I do not know this term.
2. I have heard this term, but I do not know how to use it in math.
3. I understand this term and I know how to use it in math.

_____ net	_____ volume
_____ cube	_____ cubic unit
_____ rectangular prism	_____ solid figure
_____ face	_____ area
_____ edge	_____ length
_____ square unit	_____ width
_____ vertex	_____ height
_____ surface area	

Explain what you know about each term, using the sentence starters.

I do not know what … means.
I think … means …
I know … means … in math.

Your Turn
Look at the objectives under You Will at the top of the page. Working with a partner, predict what you are going to learn. Use the sentence starter for support.

I am going to learn about …

Leveled Instruction

Early Beginner Have students work with partners of higher language proficiency. Expect these students to need more time to organize their thoughts. Encourage them to use words and gestures to complete activities.

Beginner/Early Intermediate Expect students to use phrases and short sentences to complete activities. Encourage students to use sentence starters and to practice self-correction.

Intermediate Have students demonstrate comprehension of many words and phrases. Expect students to be able to speak about some abstract ideas. Have them repeat their sentences to build fluency.

Advanced/Transitioning Expect students to form sentences of increasing complexity. Encourage them to model language for students of lower language proficiency.

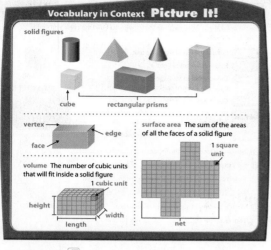

Vocabulary in Context **Picture It!**

solid figures

cube   rectangular prisms

vertex — edge
face

surface area The sum of the areas of all the faces of a solid figure

1 square unit

volume The number of cubic units that will fit inside a solid figure

1 cubic unit

height   length   width

net

Talk About It
Talk with a partner. Complete the sentences.
1. Rectangular prisms are … **solid figures.**
2. A rectangular prism has six … **faces.**
3. The area of a surface is measured in … **square units.**
4. The volume of a solid figure is measured in … **cubic units.**
5. When folded, a … makes a solid figure. **net**

Your Turn
Choose a solid figure in your classroom to describe. Use vocabulary terms. Share your description with your partner.

78   Lesson 20

Academic Vocabulary

- Differentiate between *face* in math (a flat surface) and a person's face.

- Point out that the plural form of *vertex* is *vertices*.

- Differentiate between *net* in math (unfolded solid figure) and a *net* used to catch things.

- Discuss the relationship between *cube* and *cubic*. Give examples of other words that end with the suffix *-ic*, such as *poet/poetic, allergy/allergic,* and *microscope/microscopic.*

- As you discuss *cubic unit,* point out that if the length of an edge of the cubic unit is 1 centimeter, then the cubic unit is 1 *cubic centimeter.* Similarly, if the length of an edge is 1 inch, the cubic unit is 1 *cubic inch.* Discuss *cubic foot* and *cubic meter.*

Additional resources for building and reinforcing vocabulary are provided on pages T37–T42.

↻ Comprehensible Input
Guide students to understanding

Vocabulary in Context Picture It!

1. **Say the Term** Have students repeat, stressing each syllable. Then combine syllables and have students repeat.

2. **Introduce Meaning** Connect the term to the visual that illustrates it.

3. **Demonstrate** Use gestures and visuals to demonstrate. As *surface* is discussed, mimic holding your breath and swimming to the surface of the water. Say *I am underwater and must swim to the surface.*

4. **Apply** Have students demonstrate understanding with Talk About It.

Repeat the routine for each vocabulary term.

Talk About It

Guide Discussion Have students discuss the sentences with a partner. Then provide this additional sentence completion, if time permits:

The total area of all the faces of a rectangular prism is its … **surface area.**

Intervention

If students have difficulty differentiating between volume and surface area …

Then point out that volume is like the water in a full fish tank, while the glass walls and cover of the tank are the surface area.

Your Turn

Guide Discussion Have volunteers offer their description of solid figures. Encourage students to provide examples to help explain their understanding of the vocabulary.

↻ Language Production

Comprehension Support Have students tear out page 99, Solid Shape Patterns. Read the directions and monitor the construction of the cube and the rectangular prism. Remind students to fold the prism in such a way that the grid lines are visible.

Model Have students examine the cube. Point out that it has a volume of 1 cubic unit. Have students assemble the rectangular prism. Refer to Problem 1. Say: *I need to count all of the faces of the rectangular prism. I don't want to count any faces more than once, so I make a pencil mark on each face as I count.* Repeat the process with edges. For Problem 3, say: *I need to count units to find the length of each edge. How many units long is the length?* Clarify for students that when they find how *long* something is, they are finding its *length*. The term, *length,* also refers to a dimension. Guide students as they complete this and the other problems.

Talk About It

Guide Discussion Have students complete the Talk About It sentences with a partner. Remind them to check the Vocabulary in Context Picture It! if they need help with the terms.

Your Turn

Guide Discussion Have students use vocabulary terms to compare and contrast the cube and rectangular prism they made.

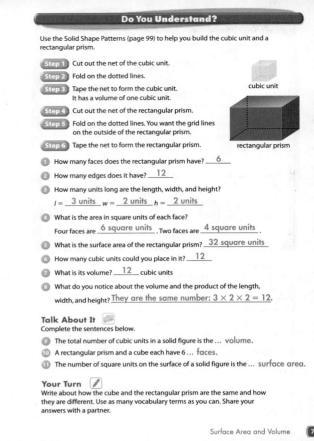

Do You Understand?

Use the Solid Shape Patterns (page 99) to help you build the cubic unit and a rectangular prism.

Step 1 Cut out the net of the cubic unit.
Step 2 Fold on the dotted lines.
Step 3 Tape the net to form the cubic unit. It has a volume of one cubic unit.
Step 4 Cut out the net of the rectangular prism.
Step 5 Fold on the dotted lines. You want the grid lines on the outside of the rectangular prism.
Step 6 Tape the net to form the rectangular prism.

cubic unit

rectangular prism

1. How many faces does the rectangular prism have? __6__
2. How many edges does it have? __12__
3. How many units long are the length, width, and height?
   $l =$ __3 units__ $w =$ __2 units__ $h =$ __2 units__
4. What is the area in square units of each face?
   Four faces are __6 square units__. Two faces are __4 square units__.
5. What is the surface area of the rectangular prism? __32 square units__
6. How many cubic units could you place in it? __12__
7. What is its volume? __12__ cubic units
8. What do you notice about the volume and the product of the length, width, and height? They are the same number: $3 \times 2 \times 2 = 12$.

Talk About It
Complete the sentences below.

9. The total number of cubic units in a solid figure is the ... volume.
10. A rectangular prism and a cube each have 6 ... faces.
11. The number of square units on the surface of a solid figure is the ... surface area.

Your Turn
Write about how the cube and the rectangular prism are the same and how they are different. Use as many vocabulary terms as you can. Share your answers with a partner.

Surface Area and Volume **79**

Leveled Language Proficiency

Students at each proficiency level should be able to perform the following tasks.

Listening/Speaking

Early Beginner Demonstrate comprehension of simple sentences. Follow conversations when spoken slowly. Ask and respond to simple questions.

Beginner/Early Intermediate Identify important information about academic content, using prior knowledge and/or visual cues as needed. Retell steps of a process in logical order.

Intermediate Demonstrate comprehension of oral, multiple-step directions. Participate in classroom discussions and activities, when frequent clarification is given.

Advanced/Transitioning Understand words and phrases of grade-level academic content, including technical and abstract terms. Communicate academic language orally, using specific, technical, and abstract vocabulary of grade-level, academic content.

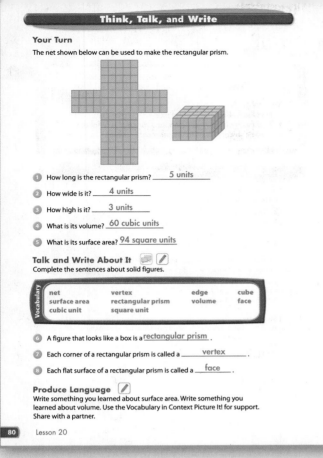

Your Turn

The net shown below can be used to make the rectangular prism.

1. How long is the rectangular prism? **5 units**
2. How wide is it? **4 units**
3. How high is it? **3 units**
4. What is its volume? **60 cubic units**
5. What is its surface area? **94 square units**

Talk and Write About It

Complete the sentences about solid figures.

Vocabulary			
net	vertex	edge	cube
surface area	rectangular prism	volume	face
cubic unit	square unit		

6. A figure that looks like a box is a **rectangular prism**.
7. Each corner of a rectangular prism is called a **vertex**.
8. Each flat surface of a rectangular prism is called a **face**.

Produce Language

Write something you learned about surface area. Write something you learned about volume. Use the Vocabulary in Context Picture It! for support. Share with a partner.

80   Lesson 20

Leveled Language Proficiency

Students at each proficiency level should be able to perform the following tasks.

Reading/Writing

Early Beginner Read and understand previously learned sight words and phrases. Copy short lists of words independently.

Beginner/Early Intermediate Apply knowledge of word context to gain meaning from text. Write lists of words and phrases needed to accomplish an assigned writing task.

Intermediate Identify words, phrases, and sentences that determine meaning in extended text. Identify and use words and phrases to make ideas clearer or more logical.

Advanced/Transitioning Students will obtain information from a variety of print and nonprint sources. Increase detail and precision of language to improve writing.

↻ Assess Understanding

Your Turn

Model Read the problems to students. *When I'm asked how* long *something is, I need to find the* length. *When I'm asked how* wide *something is, I need to find the* width. *And when I'm asked how* high *something is, I need to find the* height. Have students work together to complete the problems.

Talk and Write About It

On Their Own Have students work independently to complete the sentences. Then have partners compare their responses.

Produce Language

On Their Own Have students use the support described to write about what they have learned in this lesson.

Wrap Up

Table Talk Have students look back at the lesson's objectives. Allow time for them to reflect on what they have learned and then answer the essential question.

☑ **Learned** and applied vocabulary related to surface area and volume

☑ **Spoken** statements about surface area and volume

☑ **Written** statements about surface area and volume

Mean, Median, and Mode

Vocabulary Data, value, data set (set of data), minimum, maximum, range, mean (average), median, mode

Materials Index cards

Math Background

- The *mean* is also called the *average*.

- The *mode* is the most frequently occurring value in a *set of data*.

- The *median* is the middle value in an ordered set of data with an odd number of values. If the set has an even number of values, the median is the mean of the two middle values.

Mean, Median, and Mode

Essential Question What vocabulary terms will help you understand mean, median, and mode?

You Will
- Find the median, mean, and mode of a set of data.
- Find the minimum, maximum, and range of a set of data.
- Use vocabulary terms to discuss mean, median, and mode.

Talk About It

Copy each term from Vocabulary in Context on a card. As your teacher reads each term, create three piles of cards.

1. Place terms that you know in **Pile 1.**
2. Place terms you have heard but are not sure what they mean in **Pile 2.**
3. Place terms you do not know in **Pile 3.**

average

median

What do you know about each term? Explain, using the sentence starters for support.

I know … means …
I think … means …
I do not know what … means.

mode

Your Turn
Look at the objectives under You Will at the top of the page. Working with a partner, predict what you are going to learn. Use the sentence starter for support.

I am going to learn about …

 Frontload the Lesson

What vocabulary terms will help you understand mean, median, and mode?

Essential Question

Talk About It

Build Background Ask students to say what they might already know about these terms.

Content and Language

You Will

Model Read the objectives aloud and explain them in your own words. Use diagrams and data displays to support your explanations.

Your Turn

Guide Discussion Have students read the objectives. Discuss what these objectives mean to them.

Leveled Instruction

Early Beginner Students benefit from working with partners of higher language proficiency. Encourage these students to use words and gestures to complete activities.

Beginner Students benefit from gestures, drawings, and simple phrases to help them understand vocabulary terms and concepts.

Early Intermediate Expect phrases and simple sentences from these students as they participate in the activities.

Intermediate These students need minimal assistance to complete activities. Help students include details in their written and oral responses.

Advanced/Transitioning Expect students to form sentences of increasing difficulty. Have them use more sophisticated terms, and encourage them to express themselves using more complex sentence structures.

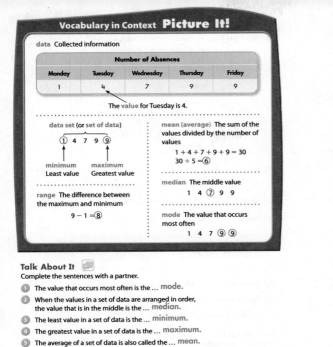

Vocabulary in Context **Picture It!**

data Collected information

Number of Absences				
Monday	Tuesday	Wednesday	Thursday	Friday
1	4	7	9	9

The **value** for Tuesday is 4.

data set (or set of data)

① 4 7 9 ⑨

minimum
Least value

maximum
Greatest value

range The difference between the maximum and minimum

$9 - 1 = ⑧$

mean (average) The sum of the values divided by the number of values

$1 + 4 + 7 + 9 + 9 = 30$

$30 \div 5 = ⑥$

median The middle value

1 4 ⑦ 9 9

mode The value that occurs most often

1 4 7 ⑨ ⑨

Talk About It
Complete the sentences with a partner.

1. The value that occurs most often is the … mode.
2. When the values in a set of data are arranged in order, the value that is in the middle is the … median.
3. The least value in a set of data is the … minimum.
4. The greatest value in a set of data is the … maximum.
5. The average of a set of data is also called the … mean.

Your Turn
Choose a term on this page. Think about what it means to you. Share with a partner. Use the sentence starter for support.

I think … means …

82 Lesson 21

Academic Vocabulary

- Differentiate between *mean* in math (the average number in a set of data) and the common meaning of *mean* (unfriendly, angry, spiteful).

- Help students understand the concept of a *set of data* by naming sets of things, such as dishes, a matching set of furniture, and a paint set.

Additional resources for building and reinforcing vocabulary are provided on pages T37–T41.

Cultural Consideration

The word *mode* means *most popular*. Ask students to share popular items or trends in their countries.

↻ Comprehensible Input
Guide students to understanding

Vocabulary in Context Picture It!

1. **Say the Term** Have students repeat, stressing each syllable. Then combine syllables and have students repeat.

2. **Introduce Meaning** Connect the term to the visual that illustrates it.

3. **Demonstrate** Use gestures and visuals to demonstrate. As *mode* is discussed write 1, 2, 2, 2, 3, 4 and say *2 is the mode because 2 appears most often.* Point out that some sets of data have no mode, such as 3, 6, 2, 9, 10. Others might have more than one mode, such as 3, 1, 3, 7, 5, 7, 2.

4. **Apply** Have students demonstrate understanding with Talk About It.

Repeat the routine for each vocabulary term.

Talk About It

Guide Discussion Encourage students to discuss their responses. Then provide this additional sentence completion, if time permits:

The difference between the maximum and the minimum is the … range.

Intervention

If students have difficulty remembering the meaning of *median* …

Then compare it to the median on a highway, which runs down the middle of the road.

Your Turn

Guide Discussion Ask volunteers to use their term in a sentence. Have others repeat the sentence.

Mean, Median, and Mode

↻ Language Production

Comprehension Support Read the title of the chart and the column heads to students. Explain that the set of data tells how many minutes Arturo swam each day.

Model Read the first problem to students and model finding the answer. *The first question asks me to write the data in order. That's generally a good idea, especially because it makes it easier to find the* minimum, maximum, range, median, *and* mode. Guide students as they complete the remaining problems.

Some students might wonder how they find the median when there is an even number of data values. In that case, you find the average of the two middle numbers. Students will work with that situation in their math class.

Talk About It

Guide Discussion Have students complete the Talk About It sentences with a partner. Remind students that if they need help with the terms, they can check the Vocabulary in Context Picture It!

Your Turn

Guide Discussion Students might want to use an example in their written response. Have students share their explanation and example with a partner.

The table below shows the number of minutes Arturo swam each day for 5 days.

Minutes Arturo Swam

Day	Number of Minutes
Monday	20
Tuesday	25
Wednesday	14
Thursday	25
Friday	11

1. Write the data in order from least to greatest.
   <u>11</u>   <u>14</u>   <u>20</u>   <u>25</u>   <u>25</u>

2. What is the minimum number of minutes Arturo swam? <u>11</u>

3. What is the maximum number of minutes Arturo swam? <u>25</u>

4. What is the difference between the maximum and the minimum? That number is the range. <u>14</u>

5. What value occurs most often? That number is the mode. <u>25</u>

6. What value is in the middle? That number is the median. <u>20</u>

7. Add all the values. Then divide the sum by the number of values. The result is the mean. <u>19</u>

Talk About It
Complete the sentences.

8. The mean of a set of data is also called the … average.

9. If a data set has all different values, there is no … mode.

10. To find the range, subtract the maximum minus the … minimum.

Your Turn
Write what you know about finding the mean of a set of data. Then tell a partner what you know about the mean.

Mean, Median, and Mode   **83**

Leveled Language Proficiency

Students at each proficiency level should be able to perform the following tasks.

Listening/Speaking

Early Beginner Demonstrate comprehension of simple sentences, including statements, questions, and commands. Follow conversations when spoken slowly. Use a few vocabulary terms and participate in simple conversations, supported by visual cues.

Beginner/Early Intermediate Demonstrate comprehension of oral directions that include visual cues and questions that are based on academic content. Express confusion and respond briefly to questions.

Intermediate Demonstrate understanding of academic content words and phrases. Explain the thinking process used in academic content areas.

Advanced/Transitioning Compare and contrast features of English words with words in students' first language. Summarize information that is heard during a class or lesson.

Your Turn

The table below shows the number of books some students read.

Books Read	
Name	**Number of Books**
Olivia	8
Jamie	5
Adam	1
Enrique	5
Leah	10
Josh	5
Isabella	8

1. What is the minimum number of books read? ___1___
2. What is the maximum number of books read? ___10___
3. What is the range of the data? ___9___
4. What is the mean number of books read? ___6___
5. What is the median number of books read? ___5___
6. What is the mode? ___5___

Talk and Write About It

Complete the sentences.

Vocabulary			
mean	median	mode	minimum
maximum	range	average	data
data set	value		

7. The value that occurs most often is the ___mode___ .
8. The mean is also called the ___average___ .
9. The difference between the minimum and maximum is the ___range___ .
10. The value that is in the middle of the data is the ___median___ .

Produce Language

Write directions for how to solve Problem 5.

Leveled Language Proficiency

Students at each proficiency level should be able to perform the following tasks.

Reading/Writing

Early Beginner Read and understand previously learned sight words and phrases. Copy short lists of words independently.

Beginner/Early Intermediate Identify, compare, and provide some examples of the linguistic features of English and other languages in print. Organize information about a topic into a paragraph.

Intermediate Apply knowledge of word analysis to expand comprehension of vocabulary found in text. Select and use words to increase detail in writing.

Advanced/Transitioning Obtain information from a variety of print and nonprint sources. Revise writing to improve organization of ideas.

↻ Assess Understanding

Your Turn

Model Read the directions to students. Suggest that students write the values in order before they answer the questions. Get students started by saying: *The minimum is the least, or smallest value. In this set of data, 1 is the least value.* Assist students as needed as they work on the problems.

Talk and Write About It

On Their Own Have students work on their own to complete the sentences. Then have partners compare their responses.

Produce Language

On Their Own Have students write directions for solving Problem 5. Provide these sentence starters for support:

First, I …
Then, I …
Next, I …
Finally, I …

Wrap Up

Table Talk Have students look back at the lesson's objectives. Allow time for them to reflect on what they have learned and then answer the essential question.

☑ **Learned** and applied vocabulary related to mean, median, and mode, as well as other descriptions of data

☑ **Spoken** statements about mean, median, and mode, as well as other descriptions of data

☑ **Written** statements about mean, median, and mode, as well as other descriptions of data

Lesson 22

Graphs

Vocabulary Frequency table, data, plot, frequency, picture graph, key, line graph, trend, bar graph, circle graph

Materials Graph Matching Activity (pages 101–104), scissors

Math Background

- The general direction of data is called a *trend*. A trend in a line graph might be that the data are increasing (or decreasing) over time.

- A *line plot* is always graphed above a number line, and always represents numeric data.

Frontload the Lesson

Essential Question How can you talk about different types of graphs?

Talk About It

Build Background Have students complete the first two columns of the Know-Want-Learned chart and tell what they already know about these terms. (See page T43 for additional copies of the chart.)

Content and Language

You Will

Model Read the objectives aloud and explain them in your own words. Use visual examples to support your explanations.

Your Turn

Guide Discussion Have students read the objectives. Discuss what the objectives mean to them.

Graphs

Essential Question How can you talk about different types of graphs?

You Will
- Interpret and label circle graphs.
- Construct and interpret line plots, line graphs, and bar graphs.
- Use math vocabulary to discuss different types of graphs.

Talk About It

Look at the list of terms below. In the first two columns of the chart, write terms you **know** or **want** to know more about.

data	frequency	frequency table	line plot
picture graph	key	bar graph	line graph
trend	circle graph		

Know	Want	Learned

What do you know about each term? Explain, using the sentence starters for support.

I know … means …
I want to know more about …

Your Turn
Look at the objectives under You Will at the top of the page. Working with a partner, predict what you are going to learn. Use the sentence starter for support.

I am going to learn about …

Graphs 85

Leveled Instruction

Early Beginner Early beginners may not use many English words in their responses. Encourage them to use gestures, pictures, and yes/no responses to communicate.

Beginner Have students partner with students of higher English language proficiency to complete activities. Expect short, simple sentences as responses.

Early Intermediate Expect phrases and simple sentences from these students as they participate in the activities. Encourage students to use sentence starters for support.

Intermediate Encourage students to express their ideas without sentence starters, if possible. They should use complete sentences. Anticipate some grammatical errors.

Advanced/Transitioning Expect students to form sentences of increasing complexity. Have them use more advanced terms and encourage them to try new sentence structures.

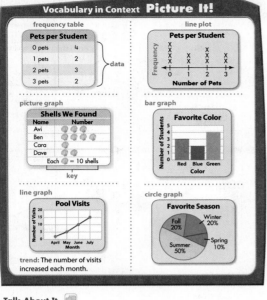

Vocabulary in Context Picture It!

frequency table

Pets per Student

0 pets	4
1 pets	2
2 pets	3
3 pets	2

data

line plot

Pets per Student

Number of Pets

picture graph

Shells We Found

Name	Number
Avi	
Ben	
Cara	
Dave	

Each = 10 shells

key

bar graph

Favorite Color

Red Blue Green
Color

line graph

Pool Visits

April May June July
Month

trend: The number of visits increased each month.

circle graph

Favorite Season

Fall 20% Winter 20% Spring 10% Summer 50%

Talk About It
Talk with a partner. Complete the sentences.
1. In a line plot, the Xs above a number show the … frequency.
2. A graph that uses pictures to show data is a … picture graph.
3. A graph of points connected by line segments is a … line graph.

Your Turn
Choose three of the graphs above. Write a sentence about how each graph shows data. Talk about your ideas in a small group.

Academic Vocabulary

- Clarify that *data* can be pronounced dā′ tə or dat′ ə. Note that *data* is plural, so one says *the data are*, not *the data is*. However, it is not necessary to emphasize the point at this time.

- Point out that *tables* and *graphs* are ways to display data. As you go through the lesson, help students understand *display* as both a noun and a verb.

- Distinguish the common meanings of these terms: *bar* (counter; piece of rigid material; solid piece of soap); *key* (device for opening a lock; system of related notes in music; a button to press on a keyboard); *plot* (secret plan; events that form the main story in fiction; small piece of land) from the mathematical meanings.

- Students may already be familiar with the terms *trend* and *frequency*. Explain that their math meaning is similar.

Additional resources for building and reinforcing vocabulary are provided on pages T37–T41.

↻ Comprehensible Input
Guide students to understanding

Vocabulary in Context Picture It!

1. **Say the Term** Have students repeat, stressing each syllable. Then combine syllables and have students repeat.

2. **Introduce Meaning** Connect the term to the visual that illustrates it.

3. **Demonstrate** Use gestures and visuals to demonstrate. Help students to see how the name of each graph describes it. For example, as you discuss *bar graphs,* point to the bars on the graph.

4. **Apply** Have students demonstrate understanding with Talk About It.

Repeat the routine for each vocabulary term.

Talk About It

Guide Discussion Encourage students to discuss their responses. Then provide this additional sentence completion, if time permits:

A circle is divided into sections in a … circle graph.

Intervention

If students confuse line graph and line plot …

Then point out that a line graph is often drawn on what is commonly known as *graph* paper. If you have samples of line graphs and line plots, take turns holding them up, and have students repeat *graph* and *plot*.

Your Turn

Guide Discussion Have students work in a small group for Your Turn. Then ask students to share their discussions. Touch upon each type of graph. Students may include the frequency table if they wish. A frequency table is not a graph, but, like a graph, it is often used to display data.

↻ Language Production

Comprehension Support Help students understand the context of each graph. Read the titles and labels, and investigate the nature of the data being displayed.

Model Examine and identify the first graph. *This graph uses pictures of books to display the data. This looks like a picture graph.* Then read the question above the graph aloud and model the solution. *I need to find the number of books donated by Grade 4. I look at Grade 4 on the graph. I see 2 pictures next to it. The key tells me each picture is 50 books. Two times 50 equals 100. So, Grade 4 donated 100 books.*

Talk About It

Guide Discussion Have students complete the Talk About It sentences with a partner. Remind them to look at the Vocabulary in Context Picture It! if they need help identifying the graphs.

Your Turn

Guide Discussion Have students work in pairs to complete Your Turn. Have them begin their explanation by identifying the graphs they will be talking about.

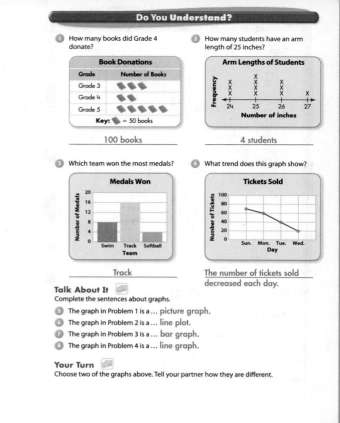

Do You Understand?

1. How many books did Grade 4 donate?

Book Donations

Grade	Number of Books
Grade 3	
Grade 4	
Grade 5	

Key: = 50 books

100 books

2. How many students have an arm length of 25 inches?

Arm Lengths of Students

4 students

3. Which team won the most medals?

Medals Won

Track

4. What trend does this graph show?

Tickets Sold

The number of tickets sold decreased each day.

Talk About It
Complete the sentences about graphs.

5. The graph in Problem 1 is a … picture graph.
6. The graph in Problem 2 is a … line plot.
7. The graph in Problem 3 is a … bar graph.
8. The graph in Problem 4 is a … line graph.

Your Turn
Choose two of the graphs above. Tell your partner how they are different.

Graphs **87**

Leveled Language Proficiency

Students at each proficiency level should be able to perform the following tasks.

Listening/Speaking

Early Beginner Recognize a few vocabulary terms and follow very simple conversations with support. Repeat simple phrases, and use vocabulary terms to answer questions.

Beginner Follow simple directions. Recognize and use some vocabulary terms. Say individual terms and simple phrases, and repeat longer phrases and short sentences.

Early Intermediate Begin to follow more abstract discussions about vocabulary terms. Speak in phrases and simple sentences, showing an increasing understanding of lesson vocabulary.

Intermediate Understand abstract ideas; recognize vocabulary as individual terms and in the context of spoken sentences. Show an ability to express abstract ideas about vocabulary.

Advanced/Transitioning Understand complex sentence structures; follow abstract conversation involving lesson vocabulary. Speak on abstract topics, including those that involve lesson vocabulary, with few if any grammatical and syntactical errors.

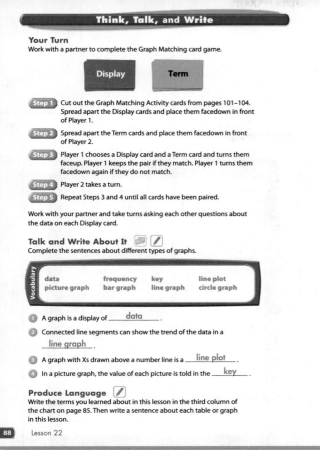

Leveled Language Proficiency

Students at each proficiency level should be able to perform the following tasks.

Reading/Writing

Early Beginner Read some short, common words and easier vocabulary terms, if given visual support or help from a partner or adult. Copy terms and phrases from the board; write a few vocabulary terms independently.

Beginner Read a growing number of commonly used words and some lesson vocabulary terms. Use sentence starters and visual supports to write individual terms and phrases.

Early Intermediate/Intermediate Read most lesson vocabulary in isolation and in context; read sentences composed of phonetically regular words and sight words, including directions. Write full sentences with support to describe ideas and explain vocabulary with some spelling and grammatical errors. Read and understand some abstract ideas.

Advanced/Transitioning With minimal support, read and write complete sentences, with few errors, that contain concrete and abstract ideas related to lesson vocabulary.

↻ Assess Understanding

Your Turn

Model Read the directions and the steps of the activity to students. Model finding a match. *The Term card I chose says "Bar Graph." The Display card I chose is a graph with bars on it. This is a correct match.*

Talk and Write About It

On Their Own Have students work on their own to complete the sentences. Then have partners compare their responses.

Produce Language

On Their Own Have students complete the Know-Want-Learn chart from the beginning of the lesson. Have students write what they have learned about the table and graphs in this lesson.

Wrap Up

Table Talk Have students look back at the lesson's objectives. Allow time for them to reflect on what they have learned and then answer the essential question.

☑ **Learned** and applied vocabulary related to graphs

☑ **Spoken** statements about graphs

☑ **Written** statements about graphs

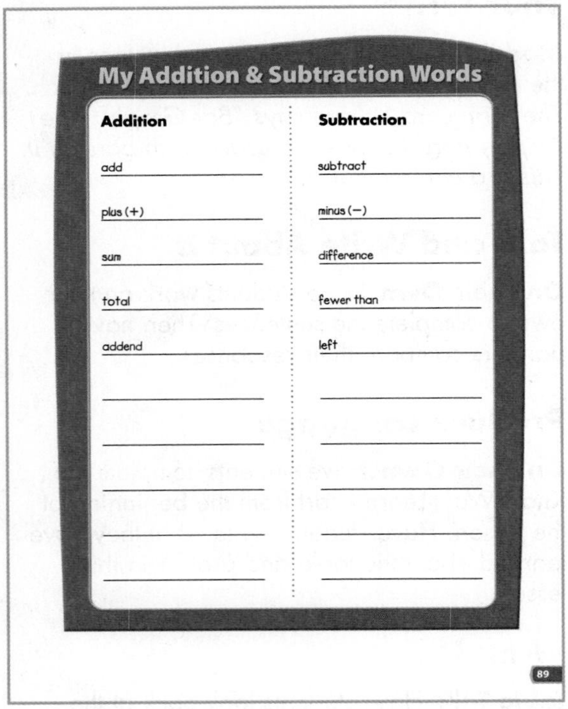

STUDENT BOOK RESOURCES

My Addition & Subtraction Words

Addition	Subtraction
add	subtract
plus (+)	minus (−)
sum	difference
total	fewer than
addend	left

89

page 89

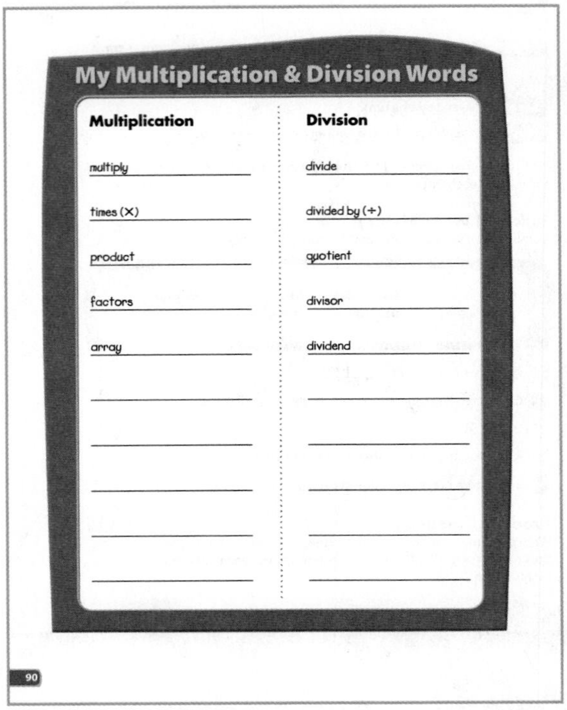

My Multiplication & Division Words

Multiplication	Division
multiply	divide
times (×)	divided by (÷)
product	quotient
factors	divisor
array	dividend

90

page 90

School Shopping
Four Corners Activity

Corner 1

Paste your card(s) here:

What is the total cost of 4?
(HINT: Multiply the cost by 4.)

Corner 2

Paste your card(s) here:

What is the sum?

92

Use with Lesson 3.   91

pages 91–92

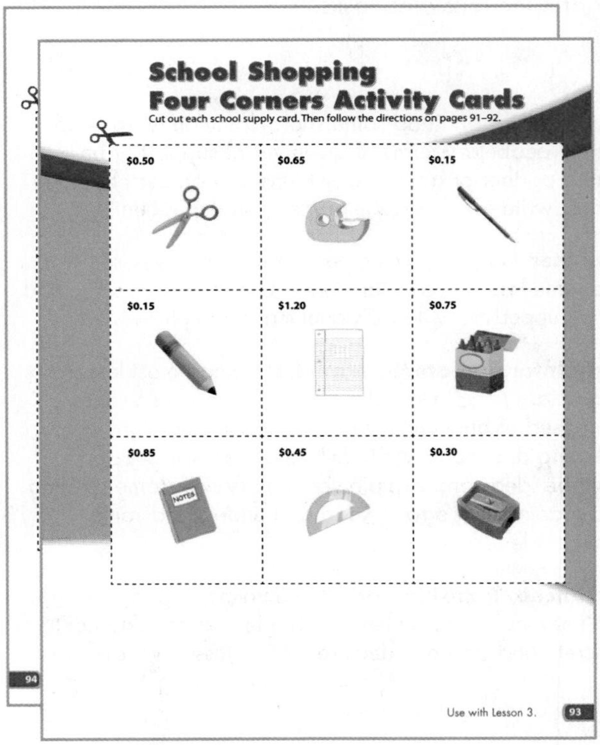

School Shopping
Four Corners Activity Cards

Cut out each school supply card. Then follow the directions on pages 91–92.

$0.50	$0.65	$0.15
$0.15	$1.20	$0.75
$0.85	$0.45	$0.30

94

Use with Lesson 3.   93

pages 93–94

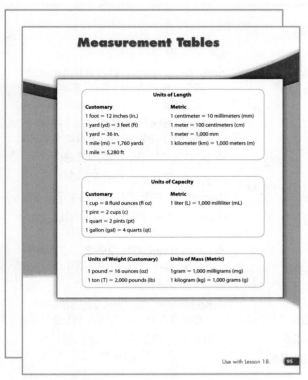

pages 95–96

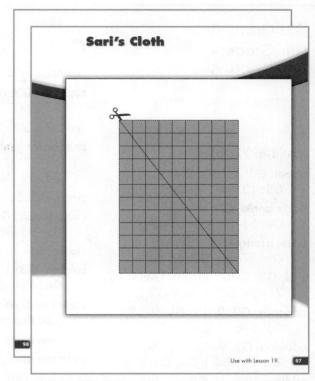

pages 97–98

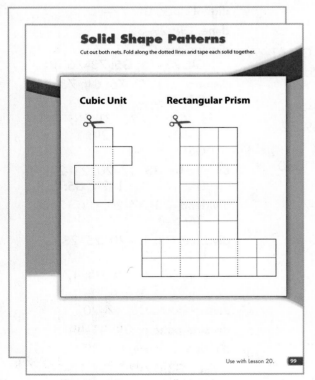

pages 99–100

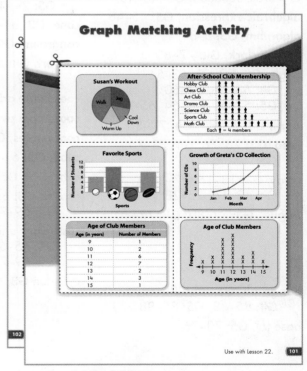

pages 101–102

INDEX

G3: Grade 3
G4: Grade 4
G5: Grade 5

INDEX, *cont.*

INDEX, *cont.*